D1600809

Construction Guide
for
Soils and Foundations

Construction Guide
for
Soils and Foundations

Gordon A. Fletcher, P.E.

Raymond International Inc., Houston, Texas (retired)

Vernon A. Smoots, P.E.

Partner, Dames and Moore, Consulting Engineers
Los Angeles, California

A Wiley-Interscience Publication

JOHN WILEY & SONS, New York • London • Sydney • Toronto

Library of Congress Cataloging in Publication Data:

Fletcher, Gordon A   1900–
   Construction guide for soils and foundations.

   (Wiley series of practical construction guides)
   "A Wiley-Interscience publication."
   Includes bibliographical references.
   1. Foundations—Contracts and specifications.
I. Smoots, Vernon A., joint author.   II. Title.

TA775.F55   624'.15   73–21789
ISBN 0–471–26400–8

Printed in the United States of America

10 9 8 7 6 5 4 3 2 1

Series Preface

The construction industry in the United States and other advanced nations continues to grow at a phenomenal rate. In the United States alone construction in the near future will exceed ninety billion dollars a year. With the population explosion and continued demand for new building of all kinds, the need will be for more professional practitioners.

In the past, before science and technology seriously affected the concepts, approaches, methods, and financing of structures, most practitioners developed their know-how by direct experience in the field. Now that the construction industry has become more complex there is a clear need for a more professional approach to new tools for learning and practice.

This series is intended to provide the construction practitioner with up-to-date guides which cover theory, design, and practice to help him approach his problems with more confidence. These books should be useful to all people working in construction: engineers, architects, specification experts, materials and equipment manufacturers, project superintendents, and all who contribute to the construction or engineering firm's success.

Although these books will offer a fuller explanation of the practical problems which face the construction industry, they will also serve the professional educator and student.

M.D. MORRIS, P.E.

Preface

This book is one of the Wiley Series of Practical Construction Guides. Its aim is to provide practical and useful information in an easy to understand form. Presently available books on soils and foundations have been written by professors as college textbooks. Such textbooks serve to train engineers and other professionals, but do not supply the information needed by the men who will physically construct the foundations.

The book discusses soils, soil behavior, and the construction of foundations. It emphasizes that soil is as much a part of the overall structure as is the concrete, steel, and wood superstructure.

Many of the ideas in the book are based on experience, including descriptions of job problems and their solutions. The things to watch out for on the job are briefly summarized. This book will hit its mark if it helps field construction personnel to avoid a few of the many possible subsurface problems or delays.

Such a book seems especially needed in today's changing and increasingly complex construction environment. Efforts to protect and maintain the existing environment have made many construction sites unavailable. Projects are therefore moved onto sites that are less desirable for subsurface construction. Greater construction effort and ingenuity are required on the part of the contractor. Deeper excavations and more buried structures and underground parking lots are needed to reduce visual impact. The result is more complicated construction procedures and higher construction costs.

We thank those who helped us in the preparation of the book. The Series Editor, M. D. Morris, encouraged us to write it. Steve Olko, George Flay, and Andrew Reti reviewed it.

Many contractors, industry sources, and other individuals provided information: Armco, American Wood Preservers Institute, George F. Casey Company, Intrusion Prepact, Inc., Franki Foundation Company, Raymond International, Soil Test, Inc., Vibro Plus Products, and other individuals who contributed information, including, Robert Lenihan, Joe Lipow, B. J. Prugh, William Spencer, and G. M. Reynolds.

VERNON A. SMOOTS

GORDON A. FLETCHER

Los Angeles, California
Bronxville, New York
November 1973

Contents

Construction Guide
for
Soils and Foundations

1

Introduction

1.1 Purpose of the Book

Most construction contractors have little trouble in forming and pouring concrete, setting steel, and conducting carpentry, plastering, and other work above ground. However, the first stage of construction involves underground work such as excavation, shoring up the slopes, dewatering, and constructing foundations. The underground stage frequently includes many problems. This stage is the source of more financial loss, delays, and claims for extras than any other phase of construction. Contractors seem to have a fatalistic philosophy that the "hard way" is the only way to learn about underground construction.

The literature on soil mechanics and foundation engineering is written for engineering students and is very technical. We feel that a book that avoids theory and emphasizes the practical aspects would be helpful to the contractor. The purpose of this book is to emphasize the contractor's viewpoint and obligations in underground work, and to provide contractors with a more specific approach to bidding and performing subsurface construction. It is hoped that this book will do the following.

1. Provide an understanding of soil investigations and a guide for the interpretation of boring logs and data from laboratory tests on soil samples. Soil investigations must have real value—because so

1

many are run. Why shouldn't contractors turn some of these data to their own use?

2. Aid contractors in looking for and recognizing potential soil problems. Cost allowances should be made for them during bidding.

3. Offer suggestions, based on experience, for coping with the difficulties most frequently encountered in foundation construction.

4. Suggest the kind of questions contractors should put to the soils engineers during bidding.

1.2   Planning Subsurface Work

1.2.1   Contract Documents

The contract documents (plans and specifications) direct the contractor as to what to build. It is generally up to the contractor to select his own methods of site preparation and protection, and to be responsible for them. If unanticipated difficulties arise, such as "quick sand," unstable ground, rupture of utilities, or slipping of excavation bracing systems, substantial changes in the method of construction may be necessary. These changes also may change the substructure itself. As a result, the structure may not perform according to the original plans.

While many contracts provide for "supervision of construction" by the architect or engineer, such supervision is usually intermittent and confined to the structure. It is only after serious problems have developed that the engineer becomes involved with the construction methods.

1.2.2   Deep Excavations

Deep excavations, by their very nature, "ask" for trouble. The flat, uniform, normal ground situation is interrupted by abrupt new changes. Unloading of the ground results in rebound. Undermining of adjacent streets causes lateral movements. Such small movements can break water mains, softening the ground and causing more movement.

The process of excavation, shoring, prestressing of shoring, installation of permanent foundations and walls, and backfilling requires as much planning as a military offensive. The steps above must be fitted into a general plan, with alternatives if problems develop and cause time delays in certain phases of the work.

Safe side slope angles for excavations may encroach on streets or adjacent property. Where soils are to be shored, the excavation must be done in steps to provide time and working space to install bracing or tiebacks.

1.2.3   Dewatering

Where the soil information reveals a water level above the subgrade, the decision about dewatering methods should take into account the draining characteristics of the soil and whether pumping may be performed from within or outside the excavation. The effect of dewatering in the area is equally important. Dewatering may cause settlement of nearby structures—particularly if the structures show signs of structural strain, as evidenced by settlement cracks, no matter how thin. Furthermore, buildings on wood piles may be endangered if the lowering of the ground water will expose the tops of the piles to dry rot. If site dewatering continues for several months, a process of recharging to maintain the water level may be needed.

1.2.4   Underpinning

Where underpinning of adjacent structures is required, the methods to be used and the time required have to be settled before any progress schedule can be made. Decisions must be reached concerning step by step excavation, sheeting, and bracing procedures. The job must be built "mentally" and "on paper" as carefully as the real job.

1.3   Position of the Contractor

As long as the contractor installs the subsurface construction in accordance with the contract documents, his position for this part of foundation work imposes no greater responsibility on him than the superstructure work does. However, the scope of the work involved in preparing the site for the permanent substructure becomes the complete responsibility of the contractor for that part of the work. Engineers generally refrain from specifying the methods or design of temporary construction. There are good reasons for this general practice. There are some exceptions. Frequently, specialist subcontractors are brought in to handle the subsurface work. Several such contractors may be asked to bid. Their inventiveness, special equipment, and knowledge are brought into competition, which may result in the best method and also the lowest price.

Accordingly, the general contractor will select subcontractors to perform the subsurface construction. The subcontractors will do their work in accordance with designs for the excavation of safe slopes, sheeting and bracing of banks, and other temporary work. These designs are developed by registered professional engineers working for or retained by the subcontractor. When making designs for site preparation, engineers must consider that the subcontractor is responsible for protecting streets, utilities, and nearby buildings from damage. Occasionally the owner will prepare the design for site preparation, in which case he retains responsibility for protecting adjacent facilities.

1.4 Available Information

Usually when a contractor has trouble with the soil, rock, or underground, there was information available somewhere which could have helped the contractor to anticipate the problem. Where can this information be found? It is hard work to track it down—and sometimes it is not there. However, it is worth looking for. This book outlines some places to look and gives a checklist to serve as a reminder.

1.5 Method of Presentation

Soils engineering—like most engineering—is partly scientific. The simple and understandable ideas of science can be applied to the solution of everyday problems. The rest (hopefully) is common sense and experience. Engineering also is restrained by economics, building codes, and politics. Therefore, engineering is not infallible and should be questioned. The man who is going to risk his dollars in constructing the project should question the soils and the design engineers.

The practice of soils engineering is developing rapidly and changes with new findings. The answer given last year may be somewhat different today. Such progress can be confusing. However, engineering reports should attempt to give as much guidance as possible. A report should also describe enough of the problems (and possible solutions) to suggest to the reader some of his own ways to do the job.

Regarding presentation within this book, the following is true.

1. Many of the chapter titles were selected to match paragraph titles common in bidding documents and specifications. For this reason, there is some duplication between chapters and referral from one chapter to another.

2. The words and methods of description are designed for readability. Complex textbook treatises are omitted.

3. Formulas and mathematics are almost eliminated.

4. References are given to books and other sources which treat this subject in more depth and detail.

2

Available General Information

At most construction sites, some general information is available. This information may already have been researched by the engineer who designed the project. However, the contractor is obligated to research all the available data himself. He must attempt to unearth all history of construction at the site. Review of such data may warn of a problem which is not discussed in the design specifications. Specification writers "cut and paste" and copy from previous jobs. They do not always rewrite the specifications to fit exactly the new project.

If there should be a lawsuit or extra costs, it is to the contractor's advantage to demonstrate that he did consult the available data. Some sources of data are presented in the following sections.

2.1 Topographic Maps

The United States Geological Survey (USGS) prints maps at various scales. These indicate elevation contours, marshy areas, man-made construction, mines, quarries, borrow pits, and other similar information. These maps are available at most map stores and at offices of the USGS in most major cities.

2.2 Geologic Maps

Geological maps are published by the USGS. These maps usually are part of a report of the USGS.

Usually, the easiest method of finding geological data is to contact the nearest regional office of the USGS. Also, one can contact the USGS to see if they have made independent maps of the area desired. Occasionally university libraries will contain unpublished geological mapping. The Geological Society of America, Boulder, Colorado, publishes a "Glacial Map" of the United States.

2.3 Soil Maps

The Soil Conservation Service, a division of the U.S. Department of Agriculture, has prepared county maps of many of the agricultural counties. While these maps are slanted toward agricultural use, the classifications of various types of soils in a particular area may be helpful.

2.4 Fill and Unsuitable Ground Maps

In many urban areas, maps are prepared by city agencies or sometimes by real estate groups which show portions of the city in which fills have been placed or soil conditions are generally considered to be unsuitable for construction.

For instance, maps have been prepared which show the zone of fill materials placed around the perimeter of Lower Manhattan Island. Also, there is a map of San Francisco showing the original shoreline and the fill placed beyond this shoreline. In Los Angeles, many areas in the harbor area have been filled. These areas are depicted on available maps. Generally, this information can be most readily obtained from the City Engineer's office.

2.5 Hillside Maps

In cities having hilly areas, the building department frequently requires more stringent building standards. Therefore, maps are prepared showing hillside areas. Frequently these maps also show areas of previous landslides. Also, some special maps, such as USGS maps, show areas of previous landslides.

2.6 Subsidence Maps

In several areas of the United States, land subsidence has occurred. Usually the subsidence is attributed to overdrafts of the natural ground water supply or to removal of oil and gas or to underground mines. Maps of subsidence can be obtained for these areas. Generally, the best contact is the City or County Engineer. Some areas of known subsidence due to removal of oil or water include Long Beach-Terminal Island, California; Houston Ship Canal, Texas; San Jose-Santa Clara, California; and Lake Maracaibo, Venezuela. Subsidence due to coal mining has occurred in eastern Pennsylvania and West Virginia.

2.7 Flooding Maps

Many areas of the United States have been flooded in the past. Some such areas continue to be flooded in each season of heavy rainfall, or heavy stream flow due to snow melt. The best source of such information is the office of the local City Engineer, County Engineer, or United States Corps of Engineers. In some counties, a flood control agency is set up, and this is the best source of such information.

2.8 Frost Depth Maps

The depth of freezing is important in establishing depths of foundations and of utility lines. Maps of the United States showing, in gen-

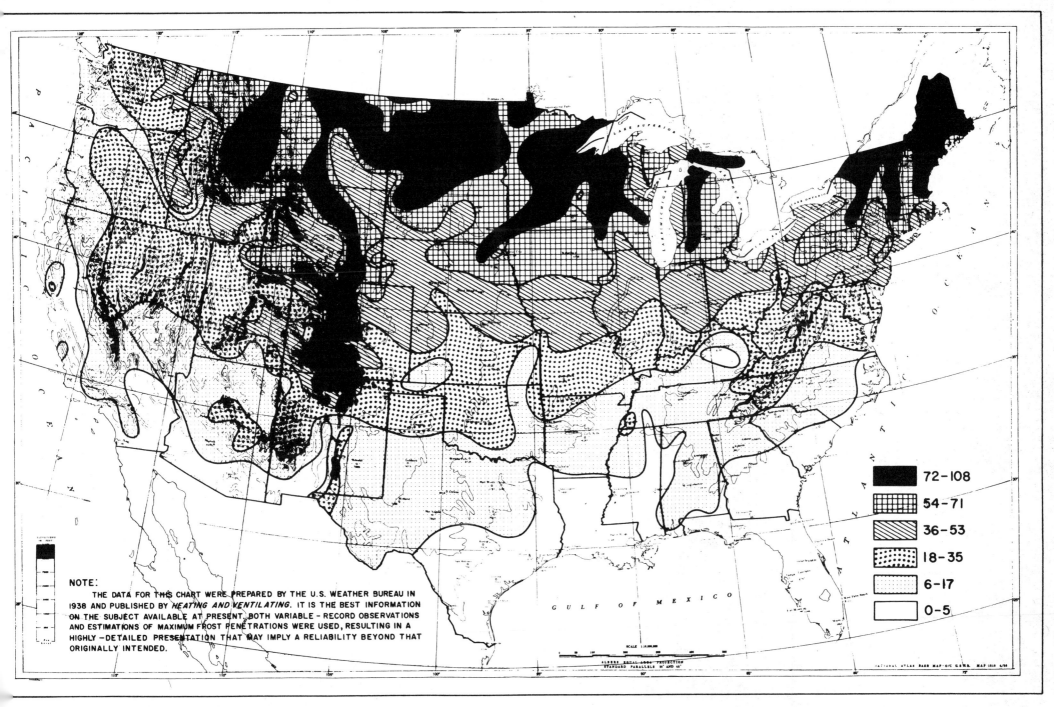

NOTE:
THE DATA FOR THIS CHART WERE PREPARED BY THE U.S. WEATHER BUREAU IN
1938 AND PUBLISHED BY *HEATING AND VENTILATING*. IT IS THE BEST INFORMATION
ON THE SUBJECT AVAILABLE AT PRESENT. BOTH VARIABLE - RECORD OBSERVATIONS
AND ESTIMATIONS OF MAXIMUM FROST PENETRATIONS WERE USED, RESULTING IN A
HIGHLY - DETAILED PRESENTATION THAT MAY IMPLY A RELIABILITY BEYOND THAT
ORIGINALLY INTENDED.

■	72-108
▦	54-71
▨	36-53
⣿	18-35
⠂	6-17
□	0-5

2.1 Typical frost depth map.

eral, the depths of frost penetration are available. In addition, required foundation depths for protection against frost are specified by building departments of the respective cities and counties. A typical frost depth map is shown in Fig. 2.1.

2.9   Aerial Photographs

Aerial photographs have been taken of most of the United States. The Soil Conservation Service of the U.S. Department of Agriculture obtains such aerial photography on contract and keeps a library of such photographs. The Forest Service of the U.S. Department of the Interior maintains aerial photographs of many mountain areas.

The USGS also obtains aerial photographs of many areas. These are used as a basis for mapping and plotting elevation contours. These generally are vertical photographs and can be obtained in pairs for three-dimensional viewing through a stereoscope.

Inquiries regarding available photography may be made to:

    U.S. Geological Survey
    Map Information Office
    Washington, D.C. 20242

Many aerial survey firms throughout the United States maintain libraries of photographs. In some cases, it is possible to obtain photographs from flights on two, three, or more dates. These sometimes show steps in previous site development. Changes that have occurred on a site over the past 20 or 30 years may show up. Aerial survey firms are shown in the telephone book yellow pages under "Photographers—Aerial."

Numerous aerial photographers in or near most cities do photogrammatic work, mainly for engineering firms, architects, and planning departments. Most of them do not have blanket coverage over wide areas. Their activity is usually limited to flying route strips, urban districts, and proposed development tracts.

Many "Photographer—Aerial" companies had as recently as 1966 housed a substantial library of stereo negatives and mosaics. For more information, see Ref. 1.

2.10   Adjacent Construction Data

Information may have been developed for construction of an adjacent structure. This includes boring logs and soil tests. More important, the construction contractor has already pioneered the area. What problems did he have? Is he bidding this job? If not, why not? Did he have trouble with City Hall? Take a tour of all nearby buildings. Are they in good shape, or are they cracked or damaged? Look at vacant lots. Is the soil dry and cracked? Is it muddy after a rain?

Check the Street Maintenance Department, the Water Department, and the Sewer Department regarding rebuilding of streets, water line breaks, sewer line breaks, and other maintenance problems. There may be a pattern of frequent repairs around the proposed job site. Check the local library and local newspaper files for old and current photographs. Historical museums sometimes keep files of old road maps, and maps showing old shorelines, old bulkhead lines, and old railroad embankments.

A checklist which can serve as a reminder in running a "site check" is presented in Chapter 3, Section 3.7.

3

Available Subsurface Information

On most major construction projects, the owner or design engineer has acquired subsurface soil and rock information to serve as a basis for design. This information generally is reproduced on the drawings or described in the specifications or made available by reference. It is believed very desirable to have a prebid conference at which various information can be exchanged, including a discussion of the available soils information.

On some projects, subsurface information may be lacking. In addition, it is to the advantage of the contractor to check possible sources of existing available information.

3.1 Investigations by Federal and State Agencies

The Corps of Engineers and other federal agencies drill test borings and obtain other subsurface information on various projects. The state highway department and other state agencies require subsurface information for highway bridges, school houses, and other state structures. Generally, these agencies are willing to let contractors review their report of test drilling.

3.2   Existing Structures

If existing major structures are near the proposed site of construction, information may be obtained regarding the conditions at the site of the existing structure. It is particularly interesting to tour existing structures to examine performance. Generally, the maintenance engineer or building manager is willing to let a contractor tour the buildings. Items to look for include:

Cracking of walls due to differential settlements.
Indications of water seepage through basement walls or floor slab.
Tilting of retaining walls.
Settlement of sidewalks through irrigated lawn areas.

These various problems can point to soil conditions which should be considered in design.

3.3   Other Contractors

Frequently information regarding construction difficulties can be obtained from other contractors in the area. This might include:

High ground water level, particularly in rainy seasons or artesian flow of water above general grade.
Difficulty in excavation.
Caving of the walls of excavations.
Difficulty in compacting on-site soil behind basement walls.
Shrinkage and cracking of soils when opened up in excavations.
Unstable soils due to high moisture content or loose soils.

3.4   Engineers Experienced in the Area

The contractor should make a special effort to discuss with the design engineer and the soils engineer the soils and water conditions likely to be found at the site.

Prebid conferences with the engineer and with the soils engineer should be a *must* on the contractor's checklist of information that may be available for the asking. If other structures have been built in the area, other engineers and soils engineers may have some experience history in the area. Generally, they are willing to make the data available.

3.5 Building Departments

Building plans with accompanying soils reports are filed with the building department for all major buildings. These generally are considered to be public records and are available. Many building departments permit contractors, or others with a legitimate purpose, to review or copy soil information from nearby projects. In addition, building departments know what kind of foundations generally have been used for other nearby buildings.

3.6 Water Agencies

In many parts of the country, water agencies regularly print reports and prepare maps indicating the depth to ground water at various locations. Such information frequently can be applied to a proposed construction site to indicate ground water levels and historic fluctuations in the water level.

3.7 Checklist

3.7.1 Available Data and Inspection Data

1. Topo. maps.
2. Geologic maps.
3. Soils maps.
4. Fill and unsuitable ground maps.
5. Hillside maps.
6. Subsidence maps.
7. Flooding maps.
8. Aerial photos.
9. Frost depths.
10. Federal and state agency reports.
11. Inspection of existing structures.

Height.
Structural frame.
Foundation type.

> Depth.
> Foundation total load.
> Bearing pressure.

Structural damage.

> Cracks (should be measured and photographed).
> Basement floor seepage.
> Retaining walls tilted.
> Sidewalk settlement.
> Street condition (should be measured and photographed).

>> Settlement.
>> Cracking of pavement or of curbs.
>> Pavement repairs.

Distance to adjacent structures.

> All structures close enough to be influenced:
>> By proposed excavation.
>> By proposed dewatering.

12. Other contractors.

> Water level.
> Difficulty in excavation.
> Caving.
> Compaction of fills.
> Shrinkage and cracking of soil.
> Unstable soils or loose soils.

13. Engineers experienced in the area.
14. Local building department.
15. Local water agencies, sewer department, utility companies.

> Utilities in the street.
> Utilities near the site.
> Record of breakage and leaks.

4

Subsurface Exploration

4.1 Surface Examination

Walking over and examining a site can indicate several characteristics. These may include:

1. Existence of old landslides.
2. Previous fills placed on the site.
3. Previous excavations or cuts.
4. Previous agricultural use.
5. Cracking of the upper soils, if they are dry. This would indicate
shrinkage of the soils. Usually such soils are expansive and could be
a problem during construction, and also could be a problem to performance of the completed structures. Leaning trees are evidence of
past instability of a slope.

4.2 Aerial Photographs

Aerial photographs were discussed under Chapter 3. An aerial photograph in hand while on the site may help indicate points to be
examined on the ground. This might include:

1. Sharp changes in darkness of tone of the surface soils.
2. Areas of possible outcropping of rock.
3. Areas of heavy growth of plants indicating shallow water table.

4.3   Probings

A ½-in. steel rod, 4 ft long, pointed on one end, and with a handle on the other end, can be helpful for probing the firmness and characteristics of the upper site soils. Tight clay soils can be distinguished from loose sandy soils. The presence of gravel and cobbles can be detected. Also, soft areas and wet areas can be found.

A much more sophisticated method of probing is the "dutch cone." This device is pushed into the ground with hydraulic jacks which measure resistance at a constant rate of penetration. The cone can be operated separately from a "sleeve" above the cone, so that both end bearing and side friction can be measured.

4.4   Excavations

Excavations and cuts may have been made in the area for highway construction, for general grading in the area, or for installation of underground utilities. Inspection of excavations is important for assessing problems in excavation and stability.

4.5   Test Pits

A Gradall, front-end loader, or bulldozer can excavate several test pits in a day. Such pits, dug to depths of 5 or 10 ft below grade, are an economical way to develop information regarding excavation procedures.

4.6   Borings

Soil information can be obtained to greater depths in borings than in test pits. In many areas of the country, borings can be drilled using auger rigs or truck-mounted bucket-auger rigs. This type of boring permits examination of the soil removed from the boring on a foot-by-foot basis, and permits a relatively good classification of the various soils encountered. Several borings can be drilled to depths of 20 to 30 ft in one day using such drilling equipment.

4.6.1   Auger Rigs

There are three common types of augers: the flight auger, the bucket auger, and the Iwan auger. The first two types are used on large power rigs. A bucket auger is shown on Fig. 4.1.

The drill rig twists the auger, cutting loose the soil. At intervals the auger is pulled out of the hole and emptied or "spun." The soil is piled beside the hole. Typical power auger sizes are 12 to 30-in. in diameter.

The Iwan auger is usually employed for hand-turned augering. These augers can be bought in hardware stores. Test holes 10 to 15 ft deep are commonly drilled this way; sometimes holes 20 to 30 ft deep are drilled by hand. These holes are usually 4, 6, or 8 in. in diameter.

Auger rigs can be used where the ground water is low and the soil stands without caving. Drilling below the water level is possible in clay soils, but in other soils—such as sandy soils—caving occurs and drilling cannot continue. Sometimes casing is placed in an augered hole temporarily to hold caving soils, or to prevent boulders from binding the auger.

4.6.2   Churn Drills

The hole is advanced by driving a steel casing into the soil, pouring water into the casing, chopping the soil with a chisel-shaped tool weighing 1000 lb or more, and then bailing out the mud. This usually advances the hole 2 or 3 ft. Then the casing is driven again and the process above is repeated (see Fig. 4.2).

4.6.3   Wash-Boring Drill Rigs

The hole is drilled by chopping with a fishtail bit on $1\frac{1}{2}$-in.-diameter water pipe. Usually a casing is set, and water is circulated through the water pipe, through the bit, and comes back up outside of the water pipe. At the ground surface the water is sieved to remove soil cuttings and then pumped back down the hole through the water pipe (see Fig. 4.3).

Fig. 4.1 Bucket auger rig.

Fig. 4.2 Churn drills.

Fig. 4.3 Wash-boring drill rig.

Fig. 4.4 Meyhew rig, Baltimore.

4.6.4 Rotary Rigs

A drill stem and bit are rotated by a turntable to cut the soil. Water or driller's mud is pumped down through a center hole in the drill stem and comes up outside the drill stem to wash away the soil cuttings. The bit can be a fishtail or chisel shape, or can be a roller bit to cut boulders or rock. The drilling fluid or mud is returned to a pit or tank, sieved, and pumped back down the boring (see Fig. 4.4).

4.6.5 Percussion Rigs

Percussion rigs can be jack hammers and drill steel, or wagon drills, which are used primarily in hard soil or rock. The drill stem is hollow, and air is blown down and returns up outside the drill stem to remove cuttings. The cutting operation is from a jack hammer chopping action on the bit.

Another variation used in boulder soil is called a percussion casing drill. An example is the "Becker" rig. This rig is much larger, using a pile driving hammer as the energy to chop on the soil and rock and break it up. This type of rig is shown in Fig. 4.5.

With the wash-boring, rotary, and churn-type drill rigs, the soil is mixed with water and brought to the surface as a mud slurry. It is difficult to classify the soils. However, the drilling rates indicate the firmness of the soil. Drive samples of soil should be obtained for examination and testing. With the auger drill rig, the soils can be examined foot by foot, resulting in a much more accurate log of the boring.

Drilling contractors are listed in the yellow pages of the telephone directory in any area, usually under one of the following listings: drilling companies, contractors, cesspools, septic tanks, and water well drilling.

4.6.6 Water Level

During and after drilling, the ground water level should be carefully measured. For borings drilled with mud, it is necessary to flush out the boring to get satisfactory water level measurements. The borings should be covered and protected, or cased if necessary. Measurements

Fig. 4.5 Becker rig.

should be taken for a period of time sufficient to indicate the true ground water level. There may be fluctuations in the water level, a perched ground water level, or zones of seepage. In many cases, a temporary perched ground water level will exist for several months after a heavy rainy season, but gradually drain away and not exist during the dry season of the year.

If the ground water level fluctuates substantially, a long-term series of measurements may be necessary to aid in construction planning (see Chapter 9, Section 9.5 and Chapter 10, Section 10.11).

Water level measurements also may indicate artesian water at depth, and the water pressure or pressure head can be measured.

4.6.7   Depth of Borings

If there will be a deep excavation, make sure that the borings were deep enough and that the water level was measured.

For instance, assume an excavation 50 ft deep. Borings drilled to 70 feet. All firm soil. Firm clay at the bottom of boring. No indication of water problem. Everything sounds good. But also consider that a sand layer is at 75 ft; it contains water with a hydrostatic pressure such that the water level (WL) would stand at a depth of 10 ft if a boring had been drilled to 75 feet. In that case, when the excavation was opened up, the water uplift pressure down at elevation 75 ft would be 65 ft by 62.4 lb which equals 4000 psf. The weight of soil overlying the sand is 25 ft by 130 lb which equals 3250 psf. This calculation says that the bottom of the excavation would uplift, or boil, or "blow out." As a rule of thumb, at least one or two of the borings drilled where deep excavations are planned should go twice as deep as the planned excavation. Water levels should be measured in the boring for several days after it is completed.

4.7   Geophysical Methods

Several soils engineering and geology firms have the equipment and qualified people to run geophysical surveys. Such surveys are described in detail in Chapter 6.

Geophysical explorations can be used to obtain a rough profile of the subsurface materials along lines crossing a site. The method moves quickly, so long lengths of profile can be obtained at a low cost. Profiles of short length, such as on a building site, also are moderate in cost, perhaps in the range of $2000. The information obtained may include:

1. Depth of soil underlying the site.
2. Surface of bedrock.
3. Depth of ground water level.
4. Substantial changes in subsurface conditions from one area to the next.
5. Relative hardness of the soils.
6. Relative hardness of the rock. (This information can be helpful in estimating the difficulty in excavating rock and whether blasting may be necessary.)

4.8   Geologic Examination

Rock may be exposed at the surface of the site. It should be examined carefully to determine whether it is a boulder or an outcrop of bedrock. This situation should be discussed immediately with the design engineer.

Excavations for basements, foundations, or utility trenches could be affected seriously.

The site may be covered with soil and have no sign of rock. However, if rock outcrops exist in nearby areas, this may be an indication of rock located only a few feet below ground surface.

If it is known that rock underlies the site and will have an influence on the construction, the contractor should find out as much as possible about the rock.

Frequently, bedrock underlying a site will outcrop some distance away. The surface outcrops can be examined to determine the characteristics of the rock underlying the site.

Bedrock at the site may be bedded, jointed, or fractured. These weak zones may be at steep angles. If deep excavations are made into the rock, it is likely to be unstable in steep slopes. Blocks of rock could slide into the excavation. Geologic examination would help to show in which direction instability could be a problem.

4.9 Offshore

It is more difficult to obtain subsurface information on offshore sites being considered for proposed piers, docks, bridges, oil drilling platforms, new man-made fills, or outfall sewers. Usually such information is obtained by soils engineers experienced in obtaining such information. This work generally is obtained prior to bidding. More detailed information regarding offshore exploration can be found in Ref. 2.

Some information can be obtained at offshore locations by bottom sampling. Divers can obtain bottom samples or force tubes into the soil to depths of as much as 5 to 10 ft below mudline.

Deeper cores can be obtained by using a pile hammer to drive pipes into the bottom, or by vibrating pipes or soil samplers into the bottom. Such sampling can obtain penetrations of 10 to 30 ft or more below mudline. Such sampling provides information to be used in estimating problems of stability of the upper soils, in determining pile supporting capacity, and in searching for suitable materials to be used as hydraulic fill. A photo of a "vibracore" device is shown on Fig. 5.7.

Deeper exploration can be made with drill rigs mounted on barges or on drill ships. The drilling methods must be modified somewhat to account for motion back and forth and up and down. A drill rig mounted on a barge is shown in Fig. 4.4. Stable drilling operations can be obtained by the use of self-elevating barges (see Fig. 4.6).

Also underwater drill rigs can be placed on the ocean bottom, where they are operated by divers.

Fig. 4.6 Self-elevating barge.

5

Subsurface Sampling

5.1 Sampling of Soil

5.1.1 Penetration

The standard penetration soil sampler was developed many years ago as a means of obtaining small samples of soils in test borings.

Samples of the soils encountered are secured by driving a sample spoon or tube into the formation and removing a representative section of soil for visual examination, classification, and preservation (usually a screw-top glass jar). Since the sample spoon has a wall thickness of 1/4 to 5/16 in., the soil is remoulded from its natural state. Such samples are called "drive" or "disturbed" to distinguish them from "undisturbed" soil samples.

Based on the theory that the denser or stiffer the soil, the greater the total energy needed to drive the sample spoon a uniform distance with the same driving force, the "standard penetration test" was developed to provide an index of soil density or stiffness.

The sample spoon used for the test has an outside diameter (OD) of 2 in. and an inside diameter (ID) not less than 1⅜ in. It is split longitudinally and held together at the bottom by a shoe shaped as a cutting edge and a fitting at the top containing a ball check valve. It is a minimum of 24 in. long. The ball valve functions to permit the fluid in the spoon to escape vertically as the sampler is driven, and to relieve the soil in the tube from water pressure in the drill rods as the sampler is withdrawn. The spoon is shown in Fig. 5.1*a*. The sample spoon is attached to size A drill rods, A shot drill rods, or 1-in. extra heavy pipe. Other sizes of rods must not be used. A driving head is attached to the top of the drill rods to protect the threads. The drop weight weighs 140 lb and is fitted with a $\frac{3}{4}$-in. rod which guides the weight in its fall (see Fig. 5.1*b*).

The standard penetration test (symbol N) is the number of blows of a 140-lb weight falling 30 in. required to drive the sample spoon 12 in. into undisturbed soil. Usual practice is to drive the spoon 18 in. and count the blows for each of the 6-in. increments. If the blow count in the first 6 in. is substantially different than the other two, it is discarded. Otherwise, the blow counts for the two increments totaling the lowest number are combined to determine N. Before taking a sample, the spoon should be lowered to rest on the bottom of the bore hole, then tapped a few times to seat it on undisturbed soil before the driving starts. This procedure should also reveal when

(a)

Fig. 5.1   (*a*) Standard penetration soil sampler.

Fig. 5.1   (*b*) Driving mechanism for standard penetration test.

the spoon has been stopped by an accumulation of gravel which has settled at the bottom of the hole.

To drive the sampler, the drive weight is raised with a length of rope reaved over a single sheave and wrapped several turns on a winch head. After the weight has been raised 30 in., the tension on the winch is fully released so that the weight has virtually a completely free fall.

Because the standard penetration test is largely a manual operation, it is a rough (not precise) measure of soil density or stiffness. A more detailed discussion of its uses and limitations may be found in Ref. 3.

The standard penetration test may be used to classify the density of or stiffness of soil formations as follows:

Granular Soils (N)	Cohesive Soils (N)
0 – 10 loose	0 – 5 soft
11 – 20 medium	6 – 10 medium
21 – 30 firm	11 – 20 firm
31 – 50 dense	21 – 30 stiff
51 or more – very dense	31 or more – very compact

The standard penetration test is less expensive than "undisturbed sampling" and laboratory testing. Therefore, it still is used on many projects and furnishes valuable information.

5.1.2   Shelby Tube

The Shelby tube is a thin-walled steel tube which can be fastened to the drill stem of a boring rig, and pushed into the soil below the bottom of the boring to obtain soil samples. Usually, these soil samples are relatively undisturbed, since the thin-wall tubing causes little displacement of the soil. Also, they can be pushed or driven into the soil fairly easily. After samples are brought to the surface, the tubes are disconnected from the drill stem; the tubes are capped at each end, or also may be capped with hot paraffin poured into each end. The tubes then are taken to the laboratory for testing.

The tubes come in several sizes. Popular sizes are 2.0 and 2.5 in., OD wall thicknesses are from 18 to 11 gauge.

5.1.3   Piston Sampler

The piston sampler uses a Shelby tube, plus a piston inside the tube. When the sampler is lowered to the bottom of a test boring, the tube is pulled up so that the piston is flush with the bottom of the tube. After being seated on the bottom, the piston is held in place on top of the soil, while the tube is pushed down through the soil.

It has been found that this sampling method reduces the tendency for the soils to be disturbed during sampling. Also, in withdrawing

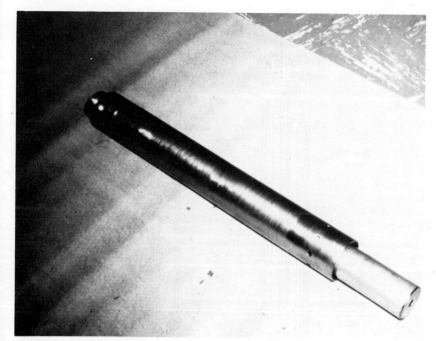

Fig. 5.2 Piston sampler.

the sample, the chance of a sample sliding out of the tube is reduced greatly, since a vacuum would be produced between the top of the sample and the bottom of the piston (see Figs. 5.2 and 5.3).

5.1.4 Split Barrel

Large diameter split barrel samples are commonly used for obtaining "relatively undisturbed" samples of soil and soft rock. Their convenience in use has made them popular; common sizes are $2\frac{1}{2}$, $2\frac{3}{4}$, and 3 in. ID. Plastic or metal lining tubes or rings are placed inside the split barrel. After a soil sample is obtained and brought to the surface, the barrel of the sampler can be separated so that the sample can be removed for packaging and shipment to the laboratory. When liner rings are used, they can be placed directly into the testing equipment in the laboratory. A commonly used split barrel sampler is shown in Fig. 5.4.

This particular sampler has catcher leaves in the bit. If the soil

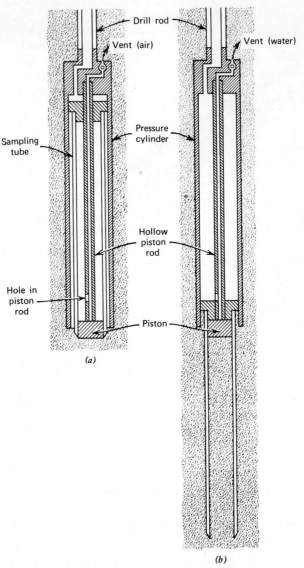

Fig. 5.3 Piston sampler of hydraulically operated type. (*a*) Lowered to bottom of drill hole, drill rod clamped in fixed position at ground surface. (*b*) Sampling tube after being forced into soil by water supplied through drill rod. From Ref. 4.

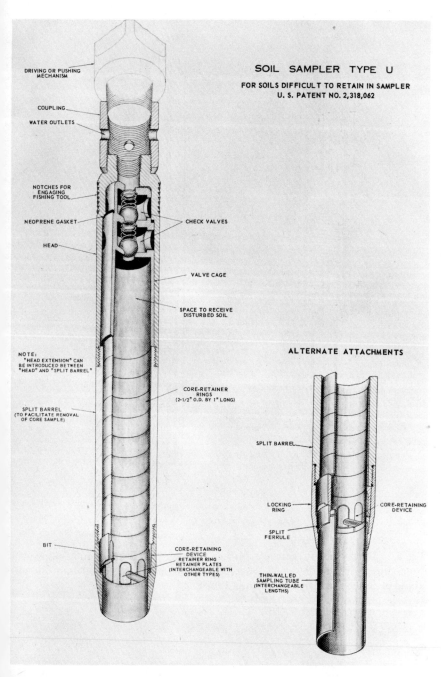

DRIVING OR PUSHING
MECHANISM

COUPLING

WATER OUTLETS

NOTCHES FOR
ENGAGING
FISHING TOOL

NEOPRENE GASKET

HEAD

NOTE:
"HEAD EXTENSION" CAN
BE INTRODUCED BETWEEN
"HEAD" AND "SPLIT BARREL"

SPLIT BARREL
(TO FACILITATE REMOVAL
OF CORE SAMPLE)

BIT

SOIL SAMPLER TYPE U

FOR SOILS DIFFICULT TO RETAIN IN SAMPLER
U. S. PATENT NO. 2,318,062

CHECK VALVES

VALVE CAGE

SPACE TO RECEIVE
DISTURBED SOIL

CORE-RETAINER
RINGS
(2-1/2" O.D. BY 1" LONG)

CORE-RETAINING
DEVICE
RETAINER RING
RETAINER PLATES
(INTERCHANGEABLE WITH
OTHER TYPES)

ALTERNATE ATTACHMENTS

SPLIT BARREL

LOCKING
RING

SPLIT
FERRULE

CORE-RETAINING
DEVICE

THIN-WALLED
SAMPLING TUBE
(INTERCHANGEABLE
LENGTHS)

Fig. 5.4 Commonly used split barrel sampler.

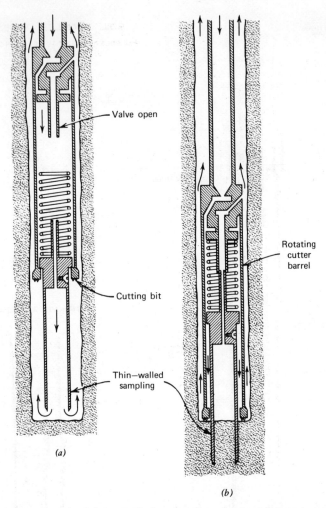

Valve open

Rotating
cutter
barrel

Cutting bit

Thin—walled
sampling

(a)

(b)

Fig. 5.5 Diagrammatic sketch of Pitcher sampler. *(a)* Sampling tube suspended from cutter barrel while being lowered into hole. *(b)* Tube forced into soft soil ahead of cutter barrel by spring. From Ref. 4.

Fig. 5.6   Pitcher sampler.

sample tends to slide out, the leaves open and catch the sample. Also, the ball valve at the top of the sampler prevents water pressure from pushing the sample out.

5.1.5   Rotary Barrels

In many firm soils or soft rock, it is difficult to obtain suitable samples by pushing or driving a soil sampler into the soil.

Rotary barrels use a sampling tube such as a Shelby tube, which is pushed into the soil. At the same time, a rotary bit digs away the soil just behind the cutting edge of the sample tube.

Two commonly used soil samplers are the Denison sampler and the Pitcher sampler. A diagram of the Pitcher sampler is shown on Fig. 5.5.

5.1.6   Aids to Sampling

In some cases, soils are extremely difficult to sample without serious disturbance. Also, caving of borings in sandy soils can allow sloughed material to deposit on the bottom of the boring.

A commonly used method of stabilizing soils in a boring is to use a mixture called driller's mud, which is a mixture of bentonite clay and water. Other chemicals are sometimes added to improve the weight or consistency of the mud. This work is usually done with a churn drill and with a rotary rig. It can be done also with a wash boring rig (see Fig. 4.3). The mud forms a cake on the wall of the boring and stabilizes the wall. The mud also forms a cake on the exposed surface of sand samples, which stabilizes them during removal from the borings.

In some extreme cases soils have been frozen. Brine tubes are inserted in the ground around the area to be sampled. The frozen soil is cored, then packaged in dry ice during transportation to the laboratory. An alternate is a cryogenic sampler, which uses liquified nitrogen to freeze the soil in the bit of the sampler.

5.1.7   Offshore Sampling

A number of unique types of soil samplers have been devised for sampling offshore on lake, river, or ocean bottom soils. Generally, these samplers penetrate to a depth of 2 or 3 ft below the mudline. However, some samplers are long pipes which are either driven or vibrated into the ground. Such a sampling device is shown on Fig. 5.7.

5.1.8   Auger Equipment

Many test borings are drilled using auger equipment. The soils which come to the surface can be gathered, placed in bags, and taken to the laboratory for testing.

The bag samples can be used in tests to determine the compaction characteristics and suitability of the soils for compacted fills.

Soil samplers can be lowered down the hole, and then driven into the soil by hand-operated driving equipment, as shown in Fig. 5.8. Also, in holes 24 in. in diameter or larger, it is possible for a man to go down the hole to take soil samples. Short samplers have been devised which can be hammered or jacked sideways into the wall of the boring to take samples (see Ref. 5).

Fig. 5.7 Vibracore.

Fig. 5.8　Hand-driven sampling device.

5.2   Rock Sampling

5.2.1   Obtaining Samples

Samples of rock generally are obtained by a tube which is set on the surface of the rock. The tube is rotated, and water is flushed through it. At the bottom of the tube, a cutting edge is built up, which may consist of hardened steel teeth, or of rows of small industrial diamonds. These are called "single tube" barrels and should be used only in hard, massive rock.

"Double tube" or core barrels are better. They have an inner liner floating free into which the rock core moves during the coring operation. The liner protects the core sample from the turning action of the core itself and from the flow of circulating water. On removal from the hole, the core barrel is disassembled and the rock core removed. Normally, the cores are packed in wooden boxes.

Core barrels vary from 5 to 20 or 30 ft in length. Commonly used core barrels are 5 or 10 feet in length. When the cores are removed, the total core length is carefully measured and logged. Frequently, the length of core retrieved is on the order of 50 to 80% of the distance cored into the rock. This indicates that some of the rock was soft or fractured and was lost during the coring operations, or that soil in the rock seams was washed away. The length of core recovered versus the distance drilled is called the "core recovery," expressed in percentage. The condition of the drilling equipment and drill bit, and the skill of the operator, also can affect the core recovery.

It is also helpful to log the pieces of rock core, and in particular to measure the lengths of all of the unbroken pieces of rock core. Such information can be used in a statistical method for comparing rock soundness, called the RQD method (see Ref. 6).

5.2.2   Sedimentary Formations

Some rocks, particularly sedimentary formations, are only moderately hard and can be successfully sampled by soil samplers built of high-strength steel. Core recovery length may be 6 in. to a foot. However, this method is much faster than use of core barrels. Sometimes it is helpful in obtaining samples of weathered zones in the rock, which cannot be obtained by the usual rock coring methods.

5.2.3   Problems

Residual rock formations are produced by weathering, leaching, and chemical action which cause disintegration. However, nodules, slabs, and pieces up to rip rap size resist the weathering, remaining hard and unaffected. These solid inclusions are usually scattered throughout the mass, like raisins in a cake. The cores recovered from diamond drilling in residual rock will reveal low percentages of recovery in the disintegrated zones. By contrast, good cores will be secured of the unaffected hard inclusions. Bearing capacities should be assigned by evaluating the strength of the weathered, softer rock, rather than the cores of hard rock recovered. Otherwise, upon exposure by excavation it may be found that the assigned bearing capacity is too high and the job endangered.

6

Geophysical Exploration

*By Henry Maxwell and Noel M. Ravneberg**

6.1 General

Unknown subsurface conditions often cause costly time delays, and
sometimes financial disaster. A contractor courts disaster if he is
guessing about subsurface conditions or is relying on subsurface data
from a few widely spaced borings. Geophysical exploration is an
additional tool that can minimize the guesswork about the soil and
bedrock conditions on a project.

The objective of a geophysical exploration as applied to construction work is to detect and locate subsurface soil and rock bodies, to
measure certain of their physical properties and dimensions, and to
locate other features such as ground water. The physical properties
of soils and rocks measured commonly by geophysical surveying are
density, elasticity, magnetic susceptibility, electrical conductivity, or
resistivity.

Geophysical methods can be separated into four general classes.
Only two are applied to construction projects, which are (*a*) static
methods in which the distortions of a static physical field are detected
and measured accurately to delineate the features producing them,
such as the natural fields produced by geomagnetism, gravity, and
thermal gradient or by an artificially applied electrical field; and (*b*)
dynamic methods in which signals or energy are sent into the earth,
and the returning signals are detected and measured. The dimensions
of time and distance always are needed for use of the data.

* Henry Maxwell is an Engineering Geologist and Noel M. Ravneberg is Vice
President of Woodward, Moorhouse & Associates, Inc., Clifton, N.J.

6.2   Advantages

The advantages of geophysical techniques over conventional exploration methods are that they are fast, economical and, especially of advantage in these days of environmental consciousness, nondestructive at the test area; also because geophysical equipment is readily portable, the building of access roads for heavy equipment is not required. The disadvantage of geophysics is that the results are derived from indirect measurements and therefore geophysical methods cannot completely replace conventional subsurface exploration methods. Geophysics can, however, enhance an exploration program by providing early data to help in the selection of locations to drill borings, and also to provide a profile between boring locations.

6.3   Commonly Used Methods

Two geophysical methods that are well-known and the most widely used are electrical resistivity and seismic refraction. Both techniques have long, and most successful, histories. There have been a few cases where geophysical results have been wrong, causing some engineers and contractors to distrust geophysics. Mistakes were made, especially in the early days of geophysics. However, the methods, equipment, and field techniques have been greatly improved. Geophysics has become more dependable, especially the electrical resistivity and seismic refraction methods.

6.4   Electrical Resistivity

The electrical-resistivity technique is based on the ability of a soil or rock to conduct electricity. This depends on the salts in the water which occupy the pore spaces in soil or rock. Therefore, the resistance of soils and rocks to the flow of electricity is largely dependent on soil density and moisture. This resistivity gives to the materials characteristic resistances to a current flow. These characteristic resistances, or resistivities, may be used to locate and often to identify subsurface materials and conditions.

The foundation for electrical-resistivity methods used in applied geophysics was developed by Wenner in 1915. He introduced a method designed to give a value of apparent resistivity of an earth material below two electrodes. The technique in Wenner system of electrical-resistivity consists of four electrodes equally spaced and in a straight line. An electric current is passed through the ground from a source of direct-current applied to the two outer electrodes. Measurement is made of the potential drop between the two inner electrodes (see Fig. 6.1).

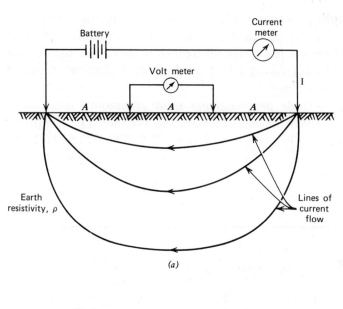

(a)

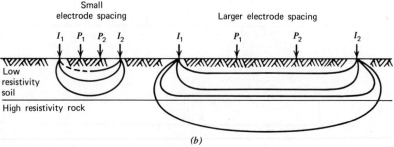

(b)

Fig. 6.1   (a) Electrical resistivity setup showing lines of current flow. (b) The effect of electrode spacing on current distribution and depth of exploration.

Current flow is measured with a milliammeter, and voltage potential drop with a potentiometer, from which the apparent resistivity of the material is computed by use of the formula

$$\text{(apparent resistivity) } R = 2\pi A \frac{E}{I}$$

where A = electrode spacing (centimeters, meters, feet)
E = potential drop (volts)
I = current flowing in circuit (amphere)
R = apparent resistivity (ohm-meters, or ohm-feet)

The depth penetration of the current flow in the Wenner system is considered, for practical purposes, to be equal to one-third the distance between the outer electrodes or equal to the A spacing. Therefore by increasing the A spacing, the "effective" depth of exploration is increased.

Three electrode arrangements most commonly used for engineering resistivity investigations are the Wenner, Lee partition, and Schlumberger. These are shown in Fig. 6.2. The C_1 and C_2 represent

Wenner

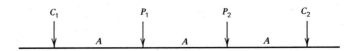

Lee modification of Wenner

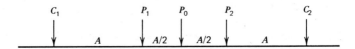

Schlumberger

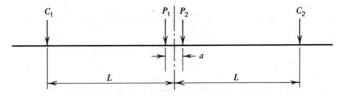

Fig. 6.2   Three popular electrical resistivity electrode arrangements.

the locations of the current electrodes, and P_1 and P_2 the potential electrodes.

The Wenner arrangement, discussed earlier, consists of four electrodes placed at equal intervals, A, along a line. This arrangement is used for most profiling measurements.

The Lee partition or Lee modification of Wenner introduces a fifth electrode at the center of the spread. The purpose is to distinguish between the effects of horizontal and vertical variations of subsurface conditions on the measured resistivity. By switching from the left side to the right side of the center point, the lateral extent of a subsurface condition can be delineated. This is an excellent technique for locating the lateral boundary between different materials.

In the Schlumberger arrangement, the potential electrodes are placed relatively close together. The mathematics of this arrangement is more complicated than the others but is considered by many as an excellent method for resistivity sounding measurements. For more information see Ref. 7.

6.5   Seismic Refraction

The seismic refraction technique of subsurface investigation consists of creating impact or vibration waves within the ground. This can be done by striking the ground surface with a sledge hammer or drop weight, or by exploding a small explosive charge buried in the ground. The elastic waves created by the impact travel at specific velocities through different materials. The denser the material, the faster the wave moves through the material. Velocities range from less than 1000 ft/sec in loose and dry soils to more than 20,000 ft/sec in a crystaline rock, such as granite. Simply stated, refraction surveys consist of measuring the travel time of an elastic wave between its starting point and its arrival at a detector, located a known distance from the starting point. This concept is shown on Fig. 6.1. The velocity is calculated by dividing the distance traveled by the travel time. Table 6.1 presents the range of velocities typical for earth materials.

In order for the refraction method to work, two conditions must exist, as follows: The velocity must increase with depth.

Table 6.1   Typical Velocities of Materials

Material	Velocity of Sound (ft/sec)
Top soil	
Loose and dry	500 – 800
Moist loam or silt	900 – 1300
Clayey, dry	1300 – 2000
Wet loam	1500 – 2500
Frozen	5000 – 6000
Loose rock, talus	1200 – 2500
Clay	
Dense, wet	3000 – 5000
Gravel	
Mixed with soil	1000 – 2500
Compacted	4000 – 6000
Water bearing soils	5000 – 6000
Basalt	8500 – 13000
Breccia	
Weathered	3000 – 7000
Solid	6000 – 11000
Chalk	3000 – 8000
Gneiss	
Weathered	2000 – 7000
Solid	6000 – 14000
Granite	
Weathered	2000 – 8000
Solid	8000 – 20000
Greenstone	13000 – 18000
Limestone	
Weathered	3000 – 8000
Solid	8000 – 20000
Quartzite	10000 – 20000
Schist	
Weathered	3000 – 6000
Solid	6000 – 11000
Shale	
Weathered	2500 – 5000
Solid	5000 – 13000

The various layers through which the refracted wave travels horizontally must have sufficient thickness to transmit the refracted wave.

The seismic refraction method is relatively simple in principle. If subsurface strata consist of homogeneous materials in well-defined horizontally stratified layers, interpretation is easy and straightforward. However, interpretation is seldom simple, because subsurface soils and rocks are usually not homogeneous and occur generally in layers varying in thickness and having complex interface relationships. Interpretation of the seismic data should be done by an experienced person possessing a knowledge of geology and geophysics. Also, the seismic data should be correlated with other existing subsurface information, such as borings.

Seismic refraction surveys are made with multichannel or single-channel seismograph instruments. Multichannel instruments consist of a recording unit that receives and records the arrival time of a seismic wave from a number of detectors (geophones), usually 12 or 24. Figure 6.3 shows a typical field layout for a multichannel instrument. A seismic wave is created by a blow from a sledge hammer or by exploding a small explosive charge at the point being investigated, usually at the ends of the detector spread.

Single-channel seismographs consist of one recording channel for one detector. Figure 6.4 shows a typical field layout. In single-channel work, the detector is located at the point being investigated, and the energy source, usually a hammer blow, is moved at measured intervals, along a straight line away from the detector (see Fig. 6.5).

Multichannel instruments are more sophisticated and have more capabilities than single-channel instruments. However, single-channel instruments perform quite well and can be used effectively in most instances of normal seismic refraction surveying.

6.6 General Applications

When, where, and what geophysical method should be used is a question often asked by an engineer or contractor. The answer depends on the problem. The problems include the following. How deep is bedrock? Is the bedrock surface flat, sloping, or irregular? Is the rock rippable? Where is the water table? What is the nature of the soils? Do sands and/or gravels exist in the project area, and if so how much?

The method to use depends on the information required. For depth to rock, identification of materials, and rock rippability, the seismic refraction method gives the best results. Locating the water

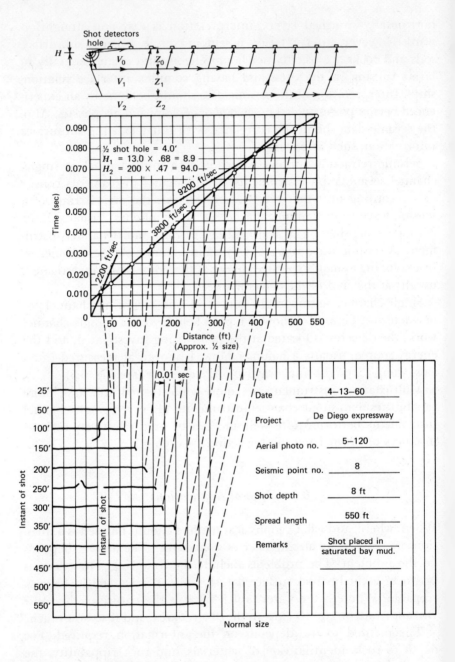

Fig. 6.3 Composite illustration of record, time-distance graph and profile.

48

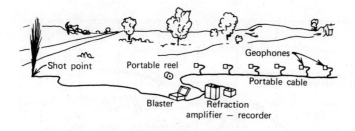

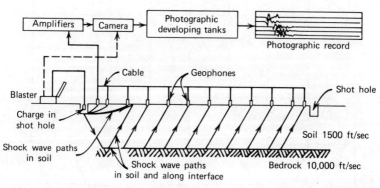

Fig. 6.4 Typical multichannel field layout. Schematic diagram shows how system works. Detectors between shot holes pick up and relay shock wave energy through amplifier to photorecorder.

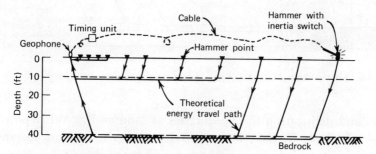

Fig. 6.5 Typical single channel field layout.

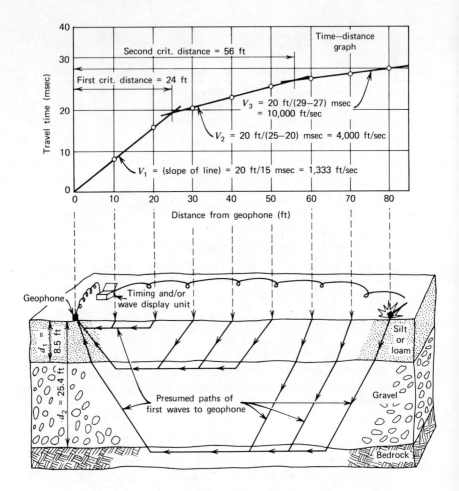

Fig. 6.6 Single channel field technique and resultant time-distance graph.

table and delineating the boundaries of sand and gravel deposits is done effectively by electrical resistivity methods. In some instances, a combination of the two methods would be necessary.

As an example, a highway contractor used both the seismic and electrical-resistivity methods for a prebid investigation, since the test borings drilled for the job were widely spaced. The seismic investigation found an area in which the velocities indicated sand and gravel. The area was very heavily overgrown with thorn bushes and sapling trees, and was inaccessible to vehicles. The presence of a sand and gravel deposit was confirmed and its boundaries delineated by the electrical resistivity method. Competitors had not found this deposit; thus their price for the sand and gravel item in the specifications was high. The discovery of the sand and gravel in the right-of-way gave the contractor an advantage over the competition and he won the job.

In another case, an industrial land developer had options on two large tracts of land. Both tracts had similar topographic features in glacialed terrain. The developer decided to build on only one tract. Some borings had been made on each of the tracts and showed similar subsurface conditions. To help in selecting which of the two parcels should be developed, a geophysical study was made using both the seismic refraction and electrical resistivity methods.

On tract *A* the seismic investigation found that the bedrock surface was reflected approximately by the ground surface. Grading at the area would encounter considerable bedrock. Seismic profiling across tract *B* found a buried valley. Bedrock would not be encountered in areas of major regrading. In the area of the buried valley, several electric-resistivity traverses were made to search for an aquifer of sand and/or gravel. A zone of low resistivity 15 to 20 ft thick was found at a depth from 75 to 95 ft.

Tract *B* was purchased, and a test well was drilled at the location of low resistivity. A 20-ft-thick layer of sand and gravel was found, which produced 750 gpm of potable water.

6.7   Rippability of Rocks

The velocity at which impact waves travel through rock varies with the hardness of the rock. On many jobs, seismic velocities have been compared with the observed hardness of the rock to be excavated and the difficulty encountered in excavating the rock. It has been found that the rippability of rocks can be estimated on the basis of seismic velocities. This is a very helpful application of the seismic method. Figure 6.7 is a rippability chart developed by Caterpillar Tractor Company. A separate chart has been developed for each combination of tractor and ripper.

This method has been used successfully on many excavating proj-

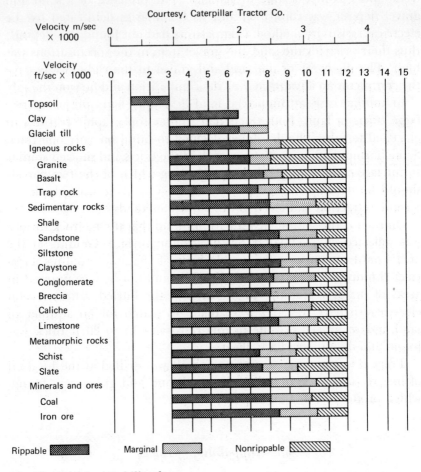

Fig. 6.7 Seismic rippability chart.

ects. However, it must be applied with care. First, be sure the velocity measurements for the rock are truly representative. Has the velocity been lowered by open fractures or voids in the rock, or does the velocity represent an average through soft and hard zones? Sometimes a rock will give a high velocity but will still be rippable. Before committing all equipment and personnel to ripping, be sure the velocity truly represents the condition of the rock. If possible make a field test with the proposed ripping equipment.

As an example, a 12-mile section of highway was up for bid. Contractor *A* and *B* decided to bid the job. The highway was located in hilly terrain that was heavily wooded. Borings had been made along the centerline on 1000-ft. centers and at all structure locations. Contractor *A* had a seismic refraction survey made in all the cut sections and based his bid on the seismic data. Contractor *B* used a power auger and a backhoe, and investigated those areas that were accessible to his equipment. Contractor *B* was low bidder by over one million dollars. He had won the bid on a low excavation price for rock, expecting to use a ripper-scraper combination. Unfortunately only about 30% of the rock was rippable. Contractor *B* had made two serious mistakes. He relied only on the boring data, and the borings were too far apart and too shallow.

6.7.1   Accuracy

The question of accuracy of geophysical surveying applies most frequently to the depth to bedrock. The depth is usually compared with boring data. It has been found that the shallow-refraction seismic method yields results which are generally within a ±10% of the true depth. This accuracy can be as much as 20% or more in error, but more often is less than 5%. The percentage of error diminishes when there are borings with which to correlate overburden velocities and rock depth.

Electrical resistivity is usually the second or third choice if the primary purpose is to find depth to bedrock, because the average margin of error is generally in the range of ±20%. With ideal subsurface conditions (relatively homogeneous strata, mineral and moisture content) and nearby boring information, the accuracy can be improved considerably. However, ideal subsurface conditions for electrical resistivity methods seldom exist.

6.8   Costs

The cost of a geophysical investigation by a consultant or geophysical contractor is usually on a daily or linear foot basis, depending on the size and complexity of the investigation. Projects that only require a day or a few days of work range in price from $300 to $600 per day plus expenses. Large projects where tens of thousands of linear feet of investigation are required may cost anywhere from 25 to 70 cents a linear foot for land work and between 50 cents to $1.25 per linear foot for water work.

Construction firms have found that the benefits derived from geophysical investigations are well worth the costs. By having a better knowledge of subsurface conditions much of the guess work in bidding and operational planning for excavation projects is eliminated resulting in more realistic bids and reduced costs.

7

Soil and Rock Characteristics

7.1 Bedrock

To most people, bedrock is considered to be hard material which cannot be excavated without blasting. Generally, the hardest rocks are igneous rocks. These may be granite, basalt, diorite, "traprock," or other similar materials. These rocks resulted from the cooling of molten material underlying the mantle of soil and softer rocks which form the earth's surface. They are generally excellent for construction purposes.

7.2 Sedimentary Formations

Many areas are covered by sedimentary rocks of various thicknesses. Usually, these rocks are soft, although some are moderately hard or hard. These rock formations are layered, since they were formed of soil particles of sand, silt, or clay laid down in sheets on the bottom of the ocean or lakes. The alternating layers of soil become firm with time, and are classified as sandstone, siltstone, shale, or mudstone.

If the original material consists of sea shells and calcareous marine materials, it may be consolidated and altered to form limestone or coral reefs. Limestone may be relatively strong, but is soluble and sometimes develops cavities or sinkholes. Most calcareous formations are loose, easily crushed, and are treacherous.

7.3   Metamorphic Rocks

These rocks may originally have been igneous or sedimentary, but they have been altered to form new rocks with different characteristics. Common rocks of this type are gneiss, schist, and slate. Most of these rocks are hard. They have well-developed cleavage planes and tend to flake off in small pieces. For a more detailed discussion of rocks, see Ref. 8.

7.4   Soil

Soil originated from various rocks. Soil consists of chunks, pieces, fragments, and tiny bits of rock.

Rocks gradually weather, decompose, and soften in place. This decomposed and altered rock changes into soil, which is called residual soil.

If the decomposed rock materials are washed away, usually by rain water and streams, it is washed down to a lower area where it is deposited in valley bottoms. This soil is classified as alluvial soil.

In some cases the decomposed soil is blown by the wind. The sandy soils form sand dunes. In the midwest United States and other areas of the world, silty soils have been blown great distances in "dust storms." This material frequently builds up in layers hundreds of feet thick. Such soil is called loess. Loess has peculiar characteristics, requiring experience in working with this kind of soil (see Section 7.18).

If alluvial soils are carried by streams and rivers out to the ocean and deposited on the floor, they are called marine deposits. Such deposits on the bottom of lakes are called Lacustrine. Marine deposits of sand and silt or clay may become very thick formations. Contrary to some beliefs, sand does not come from the ocean; it is brought to the ocean by rivers and streams. Sometimes uplifting of ocean floors can cause these formations to become mountains and other forms of dry land. These marine sedimentary deposits are the upper soil and rock materials in many areas of the United States. These generally are firm soils—or soft rock.

Some soils are compressed and hardened under the load of glaciers which have previously covered much of the northern half of the United States. They may be called hardpan.

In some western states, volcanoes erupted in the past. Large lava flows covered the surface of the earth for hundreds of square miles. Also, volcanic ash has been blown out to form cinder cones. Many smaller mountains are composed of volcanic ash. This material is used for construction of asphalt roadways in Arizona and New Mexico.

Soil, as we see it in the typical construction job, is a mixture of many mineral grains, coming generally from several kinds of rocks. In addition to the mineral grains, the soil contains water, air, or perhaps some gas and organic material—such as roots and humus—; it also may contain chemicals.

7.5   *Sand*

Sand and coarser grained soils are classified in terms of the diameter of the particle sizes. This is indicated by the particle size gradation table (Fig. 8.1).

Sand also can be classified in terms of its grain shape, such as angular, subangular, or round.

Sand generally is considered to be a favorable construction material, and usually sandy soils are considered to be favorable from the standpoint of foundation support. Sand is unjustly criticized in the Bible. It becomes a problem in some circumstances, usually due to water. Sand deposits too near the sea or streams, may be washed away from under building foundations. Water rising through a sand deposit, due to artesian water flow or other reasons, may create an unstable condition, sometimes called quicksand. On "dry" sites, sand is a good foundation material. It is less likely to develop unexpected bad performance and is good construction material.

Sand does not hold water; water flows easily through it. Any sand which *does* hold water is a mixture of sand and other finer grained soils which plug up the sand. If a sand layer is plugged at the bottom by a silt or clay soil, water can be trapped in the sand. This sometimes is called perched water.

Excavations in sand generally do not stand very well. Dry excavations cave off at slopes of about 1–1/2 horizontal to 1 vertical. Damp sand may temporarily stand steeper, even vertical, for short periods of time. However, sand cut steeper than about 1:1 is very likely to fail within a few days or weeks, and will slide down to a flatter angle, more like 1–1/2 to 1. This is called the angle of repose.

7.6   Silt

Silt commonly is found in flat flood plains or around lakes. It generally has been deposited either by flowing water or by dust storms. It is composed of finely groundup pieces of rock and is inorganic. Sometimes black organic material is incorrectly called silt.

A dry chunk of silt generally can be broken easily by hand. It is dry and powdery.

Silt holds water reasonably well and is generally soft when wet. A chunk of wet silty soil, held in the hand and shaken back and forth, will flatten out like a pancake and appear to be "quick." It turns shiny as water comes to the surface.

Silt frequently is found in mixtures with sand or fine sand. Many times a "dirty sand" is a mixture of silt and sand.

Silt generally is not a very good foundation material, unless it has been compressed and hardened like a siltstone formation, or has been dried out. Silt is found in many valleys and stream beds. It is usually loose and wet and generally is easily compressible under low foundation loads, thus causing building settlements.

As a construction material, silt is difficult to use in compacted fill. It is difficult to mix with water. Also, silt tends to be fluffy if it is dry, or tends to weave under compaction equipment if it is slightly too wet.

Some silts are composed of particle sizes which are flat plates or needles. These silts perform in a manner similar to clay. However, other silts are composed of angular particles, resembling extremely fine sand. Such silt has many of the characteristics of sand. If slow drainage is permitted, its strength characteristics may be similar to fine sand.

7.7   *Clay*

Clay is composed of extremely fine ground particles of rock. These particles may be round, flat plates, needles, and other shapes. A chunk of dry clay is hard and difficult to break apart by hand. Wet clay can be rolled and moulded, like modeling clay.

The characteristics of clay can be explained in terms of the small size of the particles. In Fig. 7.1, a piece of rock 1 by 1 by 1 in. is cut down to form clay soil. Each slice is one-millionth of an inch thick. If this cube is cut into a million slices, the surface area of the resulting plates is 2 million in.^{2} If this cube also is sliced in the other two directions, we end up with a total surface of 6 million in.^{2} A thimble full of clay has the same surface area as about five truck loads of gravel.

Clay soil usually contains some water; natural clay soils generally have moisture contents of 10 to 50% by weight.

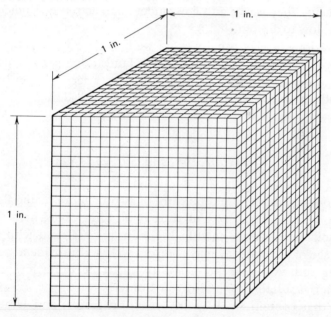

Fig. 7.1   A piece of rock is sliced a million times, in three directions, resulting in a clay soil. The exposed surface area is 6 million in.,^{2} or approximately 1 acre.

Water tends to hold things together and has surface tension. It acts like weak glue. If the layer of water becomes very thin, surface tension increases and the glue effect becomes stronger. Chunks of nearly dry clay become very hard.

Although the water surface tension force is small, it becomes large for clay because of the tremendous surface areas, described previously. The small particles are literally "held together by the water." When water is withdrawn, by drying, the clay shrinks, cracks, and becomes very hard. This drying process sometimes is called *dessication*.

Clay soils vary from very soft (and wet) to firm (and relatively dry). Usually firm clay is a good foundation material. However, the tendency to absorb water causes firm clay to swell. Then, it can lift foundations, and can impose greater soil pressures behind retaining walls (see Section 7.11).

Soft (and wet) clays slowly drain and compress when foundations are placed on them. They are difficult to use as construction materials because they weave and flow under compaction equipment, and are very slow to dry out.

Excavations in clay usually stand well. Firm clays stand in steep, high banks. Too high or steep results in landsliding (see Chapter 25). Adding water to the clay and reducing the surface tension between the small clay particles is a primary cause of landsliding.

7.8   *Mixtures of Sand, Silt, and Clay*

Soils more commonly are a mixture of two or more materials. Sand and silt, or silt and clay, or a mixture of all three. The characteristics of the soil therefore are modified. For instance, a sand with several percentage of silt and clay may compact well and provide a very firm resulting soil. Also, the permeability might be quite low, making this material suitable for a reservoir lining.

Soils that contain small grains, medium grains, and large grain sizes are called well graded. Soils with mainly one grain size are called poorly graded. These characteristics are shown in Fig. 8.1.

7.9   Mud

Mud generally is silt or clay or a mixture of the two, which contains a large amount of water. Also, muds may contain some organic material. Even sand with some clay or silt can be called "mud" when it is too wet. When muds dry out, they shrink and crack severely.

7.10   Peat

In forests, swamps, thick grass, and other heavy vegetation, dead organic material accumulates on the ground or underwater. Thick beds of decaying organic material may build up. This material may be brown or black and may contain various amounts of soil.

Peat soils are very compressible and provide very poor support for fills or for structures. Also, rotting organic material produces gas such as methane or "swamp gas." If this gas accumulates in manholes or under floor slabs, it can become a hazard. Frequently, such gas kills men working in confined areas.

7.11   Adobe

Certain sticky or "fatty" clays are described as adobe or gumbo. These soils will absorb water and swell. When they dry, they shrink and crack. These soils occur in many areas of the south central and southwestern states, generally in dry climates. Adobe soils have caused great damage to houses and other structures, and to pavement and sidewalks. The swelling action causes foundations or pavements to move up and down at various seasons of the year. See Section 7.15, Chapter 8, Section 8.10, and Chapter 14, Section 14.14.

7.12   Caliche

Caliche is a soil containing some chemicals. Caliche occurs in areas of high evaporation rates, typically in desert areas. Evaporation of subsurface water results in chemicals being deposited in the upper layers of soil.

Some caliche soils are extremely hard, like soft limestone. Other caliche materials are more variable and are only moderately hard.

In some areas where caliche is hard, it is difficult to excavate.

7.13   Other Chemicals

Soils may contain various quantities of other chemicals. Some soils are high in sulphides or chlorides, making them "hot soils." Hot soils may cause corrosion of buried utility lines or cause deterioration of concrete and reinforcing steel. See Chapter 8, Section 8.10 and Chapter 14, Section 14.11.

Calcite is a chemical (calcium sulphate) frequently found in soils. It is slightly soluble in water. There could be concern in a situation such as a dam or embankment subject to continued percolation of large volumes of water. Prolonged leeching may cause failure.

7.14   Water Sensitive Soil

In many desert regions, particularly where flash flooding may have happened in the past, mud flows have occurred resulting in soil of very low density. This soil generally is hard, because it has dried out in the arid climate. Such soils may have densities on the order of 60 lb/ft^3.

Many residential developments have been thrust into desert areas. In many cases, luxuriant lawns and other landscaping have been supported by imported water.

The low density soils quickly absorb water. Reduction of surface tension and lubrication permits the soil particles to slide more closely together, with a substantial decrease in the volume of the soil. This sometimes is called collapsing soil. The result is rapid settlement or subsidence of the ground and damage to the structures.

Subsidence of several feet due to collapsing soil has been measured in several locations, such as in the western portions of the San Joaquin Valley in California.

7.15   Expansive Soils

As described in Section 7.11, some soils expand or contract with changes in moisture content. This is due to a type of clay called montmorillonite. Soils containing montmorillonite minerals will swell, or shrink, when water is added or removed. A common source of montmorillonite is a material called bentonite.

7.16   Frost Sensitive Soils

Nearly all of the northern half of the United States is subjected to sustained cold weather in the winter, sufficient to cause the soils to freeze. The depth of freezing varies from 7 or 8 ft in Maine to 3 or 4 ft in New York and New Jersey to 2 to 3 ft in Kansas City and a foot to 18 in. in Seattle.

During freezing, the water in the soil expands slightly. More important, if a source of water is available, the soils may draw additional moisture, forming an ice lens or lenses, resulting in expansion of the soils. This uplifting can cause serious damage to structures. In the spring when the soil thaws, the excess ice in the soil turns to water, and the soil turns to mud. Soils which drain easily, such as clean sand or gravel, are not affected. Silt expands most during freezing and turns to mud when it thaws. Clay soils have low permeability and limit the drawing of water. Therefore, expansion is much less than for silt.

7.17   Shock Sensitive Soils

Clean soil containing no binder or other cementing material may be sensitive to shock or to vibration. This applies particularly to clean loose sand above the water table or below the water table.

Severe shocks, such as may be caused by earthquakes, piledriving, or dynamite explosions, may cause the particles of sand to rearrange and become more compact, resulting in subsidence of the ground.

Loose sands, underwater, which are in the process of densifying, may temporarily lose strength. In this short period, the sand temporarily will not provide support for foundations. This condition may be called liquefaction.

7.18   Blow Sand and Wind Deposited Silt

These soils have been moved to their present position by wind. They are likely to be moved away from their present position by future winds.

Frequently, new embankments of sand are eroded seriously by wind or rain. A wind-resistant surfacing must be placed over the sand to prevent further wind erosion.

Loess is a wind-deposited silt of very uniform grain size and low natural density. It typically contains vertical tubes or "root holes," and may be somewhat cemented. Vertical cliffs stand well. However, slopes tend to erode and gully, since rainfall softens the soil structure and permits it to flow like sugar when water hits it. If vertical cliffs develop bird nests or gopher holes on top that channelize the water, channel erosion can become severe. This soil is difficult to compact, except with exceptionally close control on the moisture content of the soil. Foundations on loess may settle if the loess becomes saturated.

7.19   Laterite Soils

In tropical areas, the heavy rainfall causes weathering of igneous rocks, or leaching of clay soils. This continuous washing may dissolve and remove some of the minerals resulting in a red colored soil of low density. These soils may appear to be firm, and steep cuts can be made into them. However, these soils usually contain a large amount of water. When used as a construction material, these soils become soft and unstable and can be very unsatisfactory.

7.20   Limestone Sinks

Thick deposits of limestone or limey soils occur in the central eastern and southeastern parts of the United States, particularly in Pennsylvania, West Virginia, Kentucky, Tennessee, and Florida. Limestone sinks or sink holes are characteristic of the bedrock formation. Where they occur, they have an effect on the overlying soils.

Limestone is water-soluble to some extent. It may be dissolved slowly by a continuous flow of fresh rain water, either from the ground surface down through the limestone or by subsurface water coming up to the surface. The water may be slightly acid due to surface organic material or due to acids in the soil. This speeds up the removal of lime. The removal of limestone gradually causes large cavities or "solution channels." The soil overlying the limestone eventually caves in. Sinks generally are round, frequently are full of water, and may contain stands of dense forest growth.

7.21 Hardpan

Hardpan is generally a soil which has become compact and very hard through consolidation under extremely heavy loads. Such a load might have been due to previous glacier. Hardpan may be developed by other processes, such as natural cementing of a soil layer. Hardpan generally is a good foundation material.

7.22 Dumps

Dumps and sanitary fills are becoming more common in and near many of the major cities. Present practice is to place alternating layers of trash and soil.

Generally, even well constructed dumps—above water table—consolidate under load. The settlement may continue for many years. In addition, gases may be generated by decomposition of organic material, creating a hazard.

Dumps frequently are converted into parks or golf courses, where subsidence is no problem, and the escaping gases pose no problem. However, some old dumps are used for construction of housing or industrial or commercial structures. Generally, there are some problems. Pavements and surface grading have been misaligned due to general subsidence. Local differential settlements affect structures, utilities, and floor slabs.

7.23 *Summary*

Primary points in this chapter are as follows:

FACTS: Soils vary greatly in behavior. Not all soils are good for engineering purposes. Silt seems to be a problem more frequently than sand or clay.

WATCH OUT FOR: Silty soils in areas of deep freezing. Sandy or silty soils having a low density. Silty soils in general. Sandy soils where there is exposure to erosion. Clay soils which expand or contract with changes in moisture content.

8

Tests of Soil Samples

8.1 Soil Classification

8.1.1 General Identification

Soil samples usually are described in terms of such basic features as:

Color.
Apparent grain size (gravel, sand, or fine grained).
Firm or soft.
Compact or loose.
Wet or dry.
Uniform or variable.
Stratified.
Roots or organic material.
Chemicals such as lime or caliche.

8.1.2 Grain Size

The grain size of the soil is important in identification. Therefore, soil samples are passed through sieves of various sizes to calculate the percentage of the sample, which is gravel, sand, silt, and clay. The diameter of the soil particles for each classification is shown on Fig. 8.1.

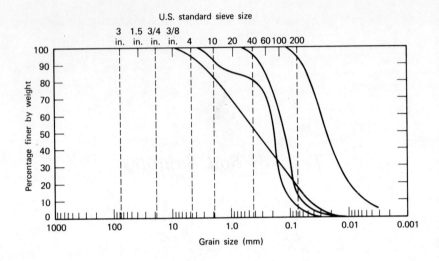

Fig. 8.1 Gradation curve.

Sieves go down only to about number 200 (permits soil particles smaller than 0.74 mm or 0.003 in. to pass through the sieve) or number 270, which is at the borderline between fine sand and silt. To distinguish between silt and clay, it is necessary to go to another technique. This is done by a "hydrometer test." The results of the sieve test and the hydrometer test are matched to give the full grain size curve.

Typical grain size curves are shown on Fig. 8.1.

Several important features can be read from the grain size curves.

8.1.2.1 *Vertical Curves.* These indicate that the soils have been sorted into one particular grain size and can be described as poorly graded.

8.1.2.2 *Flat Sloping Curves.* These indicate a variety of different sizes of soil particles, called well graded.

8.1.2.3 *Horizontal Line.* This indicates that some particle sizes are completely missing. An example would be sandy clay. This sometimes is referred to as skip graded. See curve 4 on Fig. 8.1, which shows a minimum amount of medium sand.

Frequently, materials specified for use on a job are identified by a gradation curve or by a tabulation; examples of specified gradations are given below:

Soil Usually Acceptable for Compacted Fill

Sieve Size	Percentage Passing
3 in.	100
200 mesh	20 – 30

Select Soil for Compacted Fill

Sieve Size	Percentage Passing
2 in.	100
No. 4	50 – 85
40 mesh	20 – 50
200 mesh	5 – 15

Road Base Course

Sieve Size	Percentage Passing
2 in.	100
1½ in.	90 – 100
¾ in.	50 – 90
4 mesh	25 – 50
200 mesh	3 – 10

For comparison, a typical gradation for sand to be used in concrete is as follows:

Concrete Sand

Sieve Size	Percentage Passing
⅜ in.	100
4 mesh	90 – 100
8 mesh	65 – 90
16 mesh	45 – 75
30 mesh	30 – 50
50 mesh	10 – 22
100 mesh	2 – 8
200 mesh	0 – 4

Frequently it is difficult to keep the imported soil materials within the gradation allowances of the specifications. Therefore, the design engineer usually specifies that laboratory tests will be made at frequent intervals on the materials to make sure they satisfy the specifications. If the contractor plans to obtain his material from a supplier, it is the contractor's responsibility to check the source and make sure the material he plans to buy actually will satisfy the requirements.

8.2   Moisture Content

The moisture content of a soil is a percentage, comparing the weight of water to the weight of dry soil. It is determined by the following procedure:

1. Weigh a sample of the soil.
2. Dry the sample in the oven. Reweigh the sample to determine the loss of moisture. The weight of water lost, compared to the weight of dry soil, is called the moisture content. It usually is expressed as a percent. Therefore,

$$\text{moisture content} = \frac{\text{weight of water}}{\text{weight of dry soil}} \times 100$$

The moisture content of various soils generally ranges from about 10 to 15% for sand, 15 to 30% for silt, and 30 to 50% for clay. Some soils, such as a bay muds, may have water contents of 100 to 200%.

Assuming that a sample of mud has a moisture content of 100%, this would indicate that a cubic foot of soil is composed of approximately 45 lb of water and 45 lb of soil grains. By contrast, in desert areas sandy soils may have moisture contents of 5% or less.

8.3   Dry Density

The dry density is the weight of soil particles in a sample. Dry density usually is expressed in terms of a cubic foot of soil.

Most soils have dry densities on the order of 80 to 120 lb/ft³. However, in the example given above for bay mud, the dry density is only 45 lb/ft³.

As a general ryle, soils having a density of 100 lb/ft³ or higher generally are considered to be fairly good. Sandy soils and well-graded soils generally have higher densities. Silty and clay soils generally have lower densities.

The soil density depends on two factors: how closely the soil particles are packed together, and the specific gravity of the rock from which the soil particles were derived. Most rocks have a specific gravity on the order of 2.6 to 2.7. Rock weighs on the order of 160 to 170 lb/ft³ in place.

If a soil has a dry density of 100 lb/ft³, about two-thirds of the soil is soil particles, and the remainder is air or water. Soils with a dry density in excess of 125 lb/³ are abnormally dense and should be recognized as being abnormal. They may contain iron or other heavier minerals. By contrast, a soil containing organic material generally will have a lower dry density, frequently in the range of 50 to 70 lb/ft³.

8.4   Plastic Index

Silty and clayey soils frequently are tested to determine their consistency.

Within a certain range of moisture contents, a given clay or silt can be described as being plastic. Below this moisture content, the soil becomes semisolid. At higher moisture contents, the soil changes from plastic to a semiliquid condition. The moisture content of the soil sample can be measured at the limit between plastic and semisolid, and at the limit between plastic and semiliquid. These moisture content numbers are called Atterberg limits.

The range of moisture contents through which a soil remains plastic is an important characteristic. This range is called the plasticity index or PI. It is the arithmetic difference between liquid limit and plastic limit. A soil with a plasticity index of two has a very narrow range of plasticity. A soil with a PI of 30 has highly plastic characteristics.

Frequently, soils for construction purposes are specified which have a PI below some given amount. Because soils forming the subgrade for roads and highways will become wet sometime in the future, highway departments require frequently that the base course for roadways have a PI less than 4.

Generally, clayey soils which feel slippery, and can easily be molded and rolled out into long strings, have a high PI and would be unsatisfactory materials for a roadway base (see Chapter 30, Section 30.6).

Occasionally, it is necessary to determine the PI to identify precisely certain soils, see Ref. 9, p. 30.

8.5   Strength

Several procedures have been devised for measuring the strength of soils in the laboratory. The types of tests normally run are as follows.

Direct shear tests
Double shear tests
Torsional shear tests
Vane shear tests
Unconfined compression tests
Triaxial compression tests

The essential features of a direct shear test are shown on Fig. 8.2. A shear test device is shown in Fig. 8.3. As the shearing force gradually causes the sample to fail, the amount of force applied and deflec-

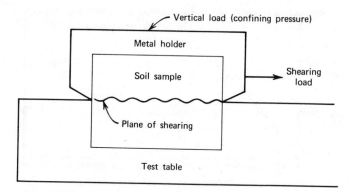

Fig. 8.2 Direct shear test. In this test, the vertical load is usually made equal to natural loading on the soil when it was in the ground.

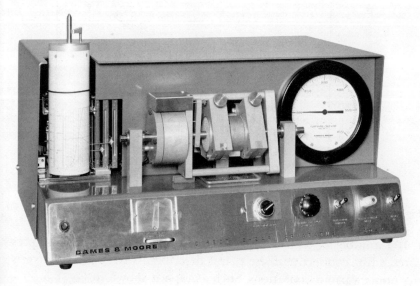

Fig. 8.3 Direct shear test machine.

tion resulting from that force are plotted on a graph. Such a graph is shown on Fig. 8.4. A point called the yield point, the peak strength point, or the ultimate strength may be picked from this curve and used in later calculations.

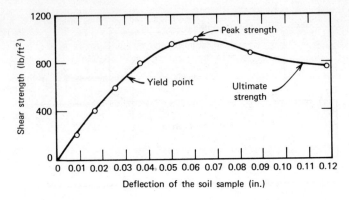

Fig. 8.4 Soil shear strength. Soil strength usually is measured in pounds per square foot (lb/ft²).

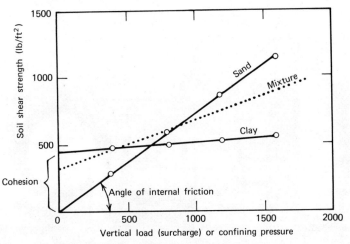

Fig. 8.5 Graph of shear strength versus loading intensity.

If a number of tests are performed using different surcharge pressures, a line connecting these points describes its strength characteristics under various conditions. Such a graph is shown in Fig. 8.5.

A soil which increases in shearing strength with increases in surcharge pressure generally is considered to be granular soil and develops internal friction. Internal friction may be likened to placing two pieces of sandpaper face to face; with no pressure on top of the sheets of sandpaper, they can slide back and forth over each other. However, if moderate pressure is placed on the sandpaper, forcing them together, it takes considerable force to slide one sandpaper over the other.

The soil may have another characteristic called cohesion. This is a characteristic of clay and silty soils. These soils have some strength, even with no confining pressure. Cohesion strength is indicated in Fig. 8.5.

Many soils are a combination of granular soils and cohesive soils, and therefore have both cohesion and internal friction. This is shown in Fig. 8.5. Such drawings usually are contained in soils reports.

During the direct shear test, the soil sample may expand or contract under the confining pressure. This expansion or contraction is measured during the test. If the sample contracts, it indicates a very loose condition, and a soil which could become unstable. If the sample expands, it indicates a dense soil structure, which generally would be stable under load or vibration or saturation.

Frequently, loads must be placed on soils that are saturated with water. These soils may have low strengths. However, if the loading is applied slowly, the soil has a chance to drain out excess water. Then it gains strength. The amount of gain in strength varies with the kind of soil and the density of the soil. Laboratory tests can be made to measure the gain in strength. Usually, triaxial compression tests are used to measure the shear strength (Fig. 8.6). Drainage can be permitted during the test. An example of "gain in strength" is shown on Fig. 8.7. The required time can have an effect on construction schedules.

Some soils are described as being "sensitive." If the soil is remolded, without change of volume or moisture content, and tested immediately thereafter, the strength may be appreciably less than in the undisturbed condition. The loss in strength is a measure of its sensitivity. In most cases, soil samples allowed to rest for some time will regain their original strength. This characteristic, however, can be very important on some construction operations in which soils can be temporarily weakened due to construction operations.

Samples tested in the laboratory generally are undisturbed core samples. However, in many cases it is desirable to check the characteristics of a soil when compacted as a fill. Therefore, samples can be compacted to various densities and similar strength tests can be performed (see Chapter 23).

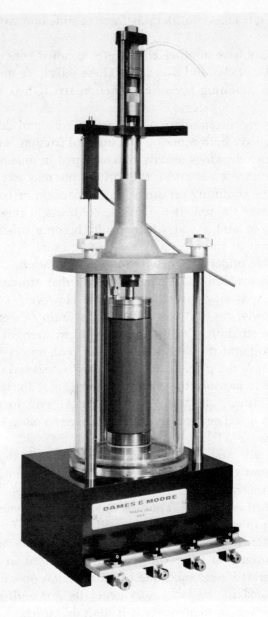

Fig. 8.6 Triaxial compression test device.

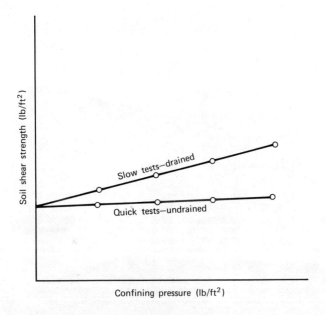

Fig. 8.7 Tests on silt or clay soil.

8.6 *Consolidation*

Consolidation tests are performed to estimate compression or consolidation of soil layers under load. In this way, the settlements of foundations can be estimated. Also, settlements due to placing of earth embankments or heavy loads on the soil can be estimated. The methods of estimating settlements are described in many textbooks and are not repeated herein (see Ref. 10, Chapter 12). A typical consolidation test machine is shown on Fig. 8.8.

As a general rule, consolidation tests are performed on samples 1 in. in height. Consolidation under laboratory loads varies from fractions of a percent up to several percentage. For an example, let us assume that in a particular case a load on the soil sample of 4000 lb/ft² results in a consolidation of 1% of the sample height. Assume that under a proposed-foundation there is a layer of this soil approximately 8 ft thick. If the average increase in stress in this soil layer is 4000 lb/ft², the soil layer will consolidate 1% of its thickness,

Fig. 8.8   Typical consolidation test machine.

or approximately 1 in. The resulting foundation settlement therefore would be approximately 1 in. This example is very rough, but demonstrates the procedure for calculating settlements (see Chapter 15).

The consolidation test can also be checked to determine the speed at which settlement occurs. For sandy or free-draining soils, consolidation occurs quickly. For clayey soils which are very slow draining,

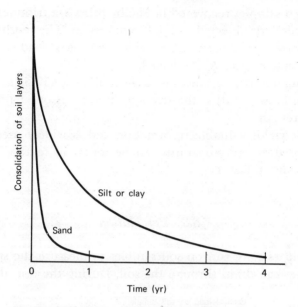

Fig. 8.9 Graph of consolidation vs. time.

consolidation takes a long time (see Fig. 8.9). Calculations can be made of the speed of settlement to be expected for foundations placed on various soils. For foundations on sandy soils, settlements may occur as the building loads are applied, and be completed within a few months after the building is completed. By contrast, foundations on clay soils may settle over a period of several years. The term "consolidation" is different from "compaction" used elsewhere in the book. Consolidation usually is considered to be a process in which water is squeezed out of the soil, allowing the soil grains to move a little closer together. Consolidation is vertical downward movement of the soil surface. By contrast, compaction usually is considered to be mechanical rearrangement and densification of soil particles, performed rapidly by rollers or tampers or other machinery.

8.7 Unconfined Compression Test

The purpose of the test is to determine the ultimate compressive strength and ultimate shear strength of cohesive soils. Typically, undisturbed samples recovered in Shelby tubes are trimmed to twice the diameter and subjected to axial compression. The results are plotted as a stress-strain curve from which the peak load or ultimate compression strength (Q_u) is selected.

Assuming that the sample fails in shear along a 45° plane from the axis, it can be shown that the strength in shear is one half the compressive strength.

The test yields valuable information and is widely used. Details of the procedure and apparatus can be found in textbooks on soil mechanics and in Ref. 4.

8.8   Percolation

Percolation tests are run on soil samples to measure the speed with which water can drain through the soil. During the test, the sample

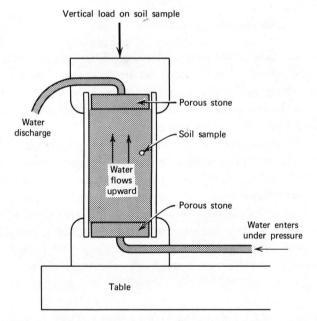

Fig. 8.10 Percolation test device. Rate of flow of water through the system is measured.

usually is confined by pressure equal to the overburden soil pressure at the depth from which the sample was obtained (see Fig. 8.10). Typical percolation rates for various soils are listed below. Percolation rates are used to select dewatering methods for excavations below water level, as well as for other purposes.

Typical Percolation Rates

Soil Type	Cm/sec	ft/day
Gravel	10	30,000
Coarse sand	1	3,000
Medium sand	0.1	300
Fine sand	0.01	30
Very fine sand	0.001	3
Silt	0.0001	0.3
Silty clay	0.000001	0.003
Plastic clay	0.00000001	0.00003

For more information, see Ref. 11, Chapter 2. Percolation rates can be reduced greatly by compaction of soil. For instance, reservoir linings frequently are made of compacted soil. In one case, a silty sand after compaction worked well as the lining of a reservoir.

8.9   *Compaction*

Compaction tests are run on soils proposed for use in compacted fills. A number of different procedures have been set up for compacting the soils. A summary of some of these test methods is presented in Fig. 8.11.

The laboratory tests are intended to duplicate the rolling action of compactors in the field. The original Proctor test, using a 5.5-lb hammer dropping 12 in. to compact soil into a mold in three layers, represented the energy level of rollers in use at that time.

With higher demands for roadway and airport pavements, heavier rollers have been developed. Laboratory test procedures have changed to use heavier hammers and more energy in compacting the soil. A commonly used test uses a hammer weighing 10 lb, dropping 18 in., and compacting the soil in five layers.

In Figure 8.11, the compactive energy in foot-pounds per cubic

METHODS OF PERFORMING COMPACTION TESTS

NO.	TEST NAME AND NUMBER	CYLINDER			HAMMER		BLOWS PER LAYER	LAYERS IN NUMBER	SOIL PASSING SIEVE	COMPACTIVE ENERGY ft.-lb./cu. ft.	REFERENCE
		D in.	H in.	V ft.³	WT. lbs.	DROP in.					
1a	STANDARD PROCTOR			1/30	5-1/2	12	25	3		12,400	
b	STANDARD AASHO			"	"	"	"	"		"	
c	ASTM D698-42 T	4.0	4.6	"	"	"	"	"	#4		ASTM PROC. FOR TEST. SOILS (1944) p.59
d	ASTM D698-57 T A	"	"	"	"	"	"	"	"		ASTM PROC. FOR TEST. SOILS (1958) p.102
e	AASHO T99-38	"	"	"	"	"	"	"	"		ASTM PROC. FOR TEST. SOILS (1944) p.59
f	AASHO T99-49	"	"	"	"	"	"	"	"		AASHO (1958) VOL. II p.284
g	AASHO T99-57 A	"	"	"	"	"	"	"	"		AASHO (1958) VOL. III p.305
2a	ASTM D698-57 C	4.0	4.6	1/30	5-1/2	12	25	3	3/4	12,400	ASTM PROC. FOR TEST. SOILS (1958) p.102
b	AASHO T99-57 C	"	"	"	"	"	"	"	"		AASHO (1958) VOL. III p.305
3a	ASTM D698-57 T B	6.0	4.6	1/13.33	5-1/2	12	56	3	#4	12,400	ASTM PROC. FOR TEST. SOILS (1958) p.102
b	AASHO T99-57 B	"	"	"	"	"	"	"	"		AASHO (1958) VOL. III p.305
4a	ASTM D698-57 D	6.0	4.6	1/13.33	5-1/2	12	56	3	3/4	12,400	ASTM PROC. FOR TEST. SOILS (1958) p.102
b	AASHO T99-57 D	"	"	"	"	"	"	"	"		AASHO (1958) VOL. III p.305
5	THREE LAYER MODIFIED									33,700	
6a	MODIFIED AASHO			1/30	10	18	25	5		56,300	
b	ASTM D1557-58T METHOD A	4.0	4.6	1/30	10	18	25	5	#4		ASTM STAND. FOR TEST. SOILS (1958) p.110
c	AASHO T180-57 A	"	"	"	"	"	"	"	"		AASHO (1958) VOL. III p.310
7a	ASTM D1557-58T METHOD C	4.0	4.6	1/30	10	18	25	5	3/4	56,300	ASTM STAND. FOR TEST. SOILS (1958) p.110
b	AASHO T180-57 C	"	"	"	"	"	"	"	"		AASHO (1958) VOL. III p.310
8a	ASTM D1557-58T METHOD B	6.0	4.6	1/13.33	10	18	56	5	#4	56,300	ASTM STAND. FOR TEST. SOILS (1958) p.110
b	AASHO T180-57 B	"	"	"	"	"	"	"	"		AASHO (1958) VOL. III p.310
9a	ASTM D1557-58T METHOD D	6.0	4.6	1/13.33	10	18	56	5	3/4	56,300	ASTM STAND. FOR TEST. SOILS (1958) p.110
b	AASHO T180-57 D	"	"	"	"	"	"	"	"		AASHO (1958) VOL. III p.310
10	C B R	6.0	4.5	1/13.61	10	18	55	5	3/4	56,000	ASTM PROC. FOR TEST. SOILS (1958) p.459
11	CORPS OF ENGINEERS			1/20	10	18	50	5		56,300	"DESIGN OF SMALL DAMS" USBR p.505
12	CALIFORNIA (H) STATE 216	2-7/8	36	FACTORS 2.816	10	18	20	5-10	3/4	33,600 MIN. TO 80,500 MAX.	ASTM PROC. FOR TEST. SOILS (1958) p.136
13	HARVARD MINIATURE	1-5/16	2.816	1/454	40	PUSH	10	5	#4		ASTM PROC. FOR TEST. SOILS (1958) p.133

Fig. 8.11 Compaction test methods.

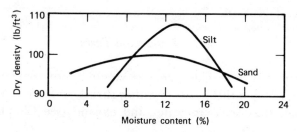

Fig. 8.12   Typical compaction curves.

foot of soil is shown for various types of tests. This indicates that the modified compaction test, with 56,300 ft-lb of energy, delivers approximately four and one-half times as much energy to the soil sample as the original standard Proctor test. Since the contractor bids to obtain a certain compaction (such as 90% of modified), he should clearly understand the amount of work required for each test method.

A typical set of compaction curves is shown on Fig. 8.12. Note that one curve is fairly flat; the other is steep. The steep curve indicates trouble if the soils are too dry or too wet. Compaction of this soil is not possible if the moisture content is too low or too high (see Fig. 23.2).

8.10   Chemical Tests

Chemical tests may be performed on soils to ascertain whether the soil is acid, alkaline, or neutral and to determine if it contains sulphides or chlorides or other chemicals which might cause deterioration of concrete or steel foundations or pipelines placed in the soil. Chemical tests also may be needed on samples of water and samples of filter materials for the design of drains or wells. It is common to test the pH of soil samples first. If the soil is about neutral (pH = 7), usually no other tests are run. If the pH is high or low, indicating alkaline or acid conditions, additional tests usually are run to measure the sodium, the chlorides, or the sulfates in the soil. This may indicate the need for special protection for concrete or steel structures placed in the ground (see Chapter 14, Section 14.16).

8.11   Expansion Tests

Some clayey soils and shales, change volume with changes in moisture content. When these soils dry, they shrink and crack. When they become wet, they soak up water and expand (see Chapter 7, Section 7.15).

Common names for such soils are as follows:
Adobe
Gumbo
Bentonite

Samples of soil can be tested to determine the likelihood that a soil will expand or contract. The sample is placed in a machine similar to the consolidation test. The sample is permitted to soak up water and expand. The expansion is measured. Usually, a surcharge pressure (of 60, or 100, or 144 lb/ft² or perhaps 500 lb/ft²) is applied during testing. In some cases, in which a predetermined bearing pressure is to be used on foundations placed on the soil, a higher surcharge pressure will be used during the expansion test. Expansion of the sample is measured. Then, the sample is placed in an oven and dried out. The shrinkage is measured. If the change in volume from saturated to oven-dry exceeds 4% of the height of the sample, it is generally considered to be expansive. Change in volume of over 10% is to be considered to be very expansive (see Fig. 8.13).

8.12   Rock Tests

Samples of rock also are tested in the laboratory. This includes tests of rock samples from the area to be excavated or built on, and also includes tests of rock to be imported as a construction material. Some tests are similar to soil tests. Different tests include:

Abrasion tests measure wear and breaking of pieces of rock in a rotating drum.
Freeze-thaw tests measure rock splitting or deterioration.
Chemical tests measure lack of resistance to chemicals.

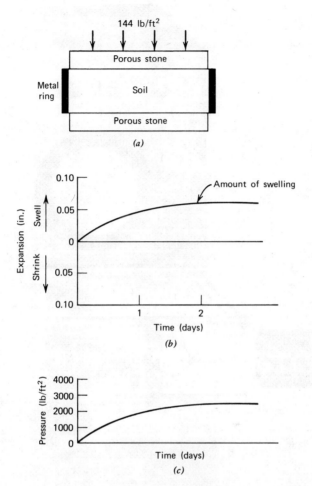

Fig. 8.13 Expansion test. (*a*) Soil sample is placed under a confining pressure of 144 lb/ft². (2) Water is added to the soil sample. (3) Sample swells, and the swelling is measured in inches (*b*). The test can also be run to measure the pressure required to prevent expansion. The test data might look as shown in (*c*).

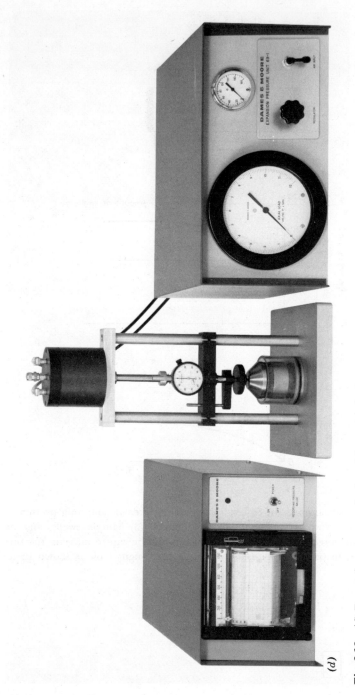

Fig. 8.13 (d) Expansion-pressure device with an attached recorder.

Laboratory tests of soil and of rock are discussed in more detail in publications of the American Society for Testing Materials (ASTM), see Ref. 12.

8.13 Summary

Primary points in this chapter are as follows:

FACTS: Laboratory tests can tell a lot about the soils the contractor will be working with.

WATCH OUT FOR: The kind of tests which were run on the soil samples. For instance, there are several kinds of compaction tests. When the specifications ask for 90% compaction, what is 100%? It varies considerably depending on what kind of test is run to measure 100%.

9

The Soils Report

Soils reports frequently are available at the time of bidding of jobs. Reports can be very helpful in gaining an understanding of the site conditions, construction planning, water problems, soils that may be difficult to work with, and the bad effects or delays that may result from bad weather.

9.1 Types of Reports

Reports may be made at various stages in planning or design of a project. Sometimes, reports during early feasibility studies are limited in scope, and present only generalized opinions based on limited data. Usually such reports are marked "preliminary" or "feasibility" report.

During the course of design, a more detailed report is made. This report usually involves drilling test borings, or digging test pits, and spending some money for undisturbed soil samples for laboratory testing, soil bearing tests, or even driving test piles or performing pile load tests to provide information needed for the design of foundations.

Reports also may be needed on special problems in excavation, foundation construction, or the suitability of compacted fills, backfills, or other materials. Sometimes reports are needed for planning a system of site dewatering or a system of shoring and bracing.

Occasionally, completion reports concerning the soils and foundation construction are prepared for use of the owner.

Should a foundation failure, settlement, or other unfortunate occurrence develop after construction has been completed, reports generally are obtained with opinions regarding the cause of damage and necessary repair work.

9.2 *Usual Contents of Reports*

A report of a foundation investigation usually would include the following items:

Scope or outline of the work.
Proposed construction site investigation method.
Site conditions found.
Results of laboratory tests or of field tests.
Results of geological or other examination.
Site history or problems characteristic of the area.
Recommended type of foundations.
Recommended design values for foundations. This would include bearing values for spread foundations or the supporting capacities of piles. This should include the depth for bearing of foundations, and the soil type at that depth.
Foundation settlements. Frequently estimates are made of the likely settlements of spread foundations of various sizes and depths, and estimates of settlement are also made for individual or groups of piles.

9.3 *Log of Borings*

There is no standard form of log of borings. Each foundation company, and other organizations preparing boring logs, has its own method of preparing boring logs. However, a typical log of borings is shown on Figure 9.1.

Information which should be contained on a boring log includes:

1. Boring number.
2. Location of boring or coordinates.

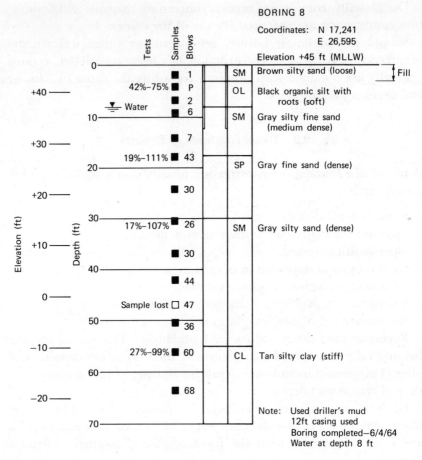

Fig. 9.1   Typical log of borings.

3. Ground surface elevation.

4. Depth of boring.

5. Date drilled.

6. Name of drilling inspector, drilling contractor, and driller on the job.

7. Depth of casing, if used.

8. Type of drilling equipment, such as auger drill, churn drill, rotary drill, or wash boring. Also, whether the hole was drilled dry, with water, with driller's mud, or was cleaned out by compressed air.

9. Whether caving occurred in the boring, and if so at what depths, and the severity of the caving.

10. If a boring was abandoned, the cause for abandoning and the locations of offset borings.

11. The water level, levels at which water seepage occurs, any perched water.

12. The level at which drilling water (or mud) was lost into the formation.

13. The thickness of the various soil layers encountered.

14. Any topsoil, or organic or peaty material, or man-made fill which overlies the site.

15. The colors of each of the soil layers.

16. A classification of each of these soil layers.

17. The relative firmness or compactness of each soil layer.

18. Materials contained in each layer, such as roots, vegetation, and chemicals such as gypsum.

19. Depths at which samples of the soil were obtained. Also, are the samples cuttings, disturbed cores, or undisturbed cores?

20. The type of sampler used.

21. The method of driving, rotating, or pushing the sampler into the ground.

22. The blow count to drive the sampler, or resistance encountered in pushing the sampler into the soil.

23. Any soil samples that were attempted but lost.

24. Results of laboratory tests frequently are also listed on the log of borings. In Fig. 9.1 the laboratory test data listed for the sample at Elevation +42 are moisture content (42%) and dry density of the soil (75 lb/ft^3).

9.4   Soil Classification

A number of systems have been devised for classification of soils. Earlier systems were for agricultural uses. Later, a classification system developed by the United States Bureau of Roads became popular. It described many of these soils as loam. Later, the Highway Research Board created a system classifying soils in eight categories listed as A-1 through A-7.

The Federal Aviation Agency prepared a somewhat different classification of soils, setting eleven categories listed as E-1 through E-13, where E-13 is extremely bad soil or muck.

In an effort to improve the system of soil classification, a system was designed and titled "the unified soil classification system." This classification system is presented on Figure 9.2. This is an abbreviated version of this classification system.

Basically, the requirements for describing and classifying soils include the following items:

Color.

The grain size of the major portion of the soil.

The grain sizes of other portions of the soil.

The firmness of the soil: whether soft, moderately firm, firm or stiff; whether the soil is compact or loose. The moisture content: whether wet, moderately dry, or dry.

Apparent engineering properties.

For more information, see Ref. 13.

9.5   Water Level

The water level underlying a site is very important in planning excavations, or in constructing basements.

Normally, logs of borings will show the water level. This is the water level encountered at the time the borings were drilled.

The water level may be different at the time of construction. Recent rains may cause the ground water level to rise. The water level may be lowered after a long period of low rainfall. The water level measurements shown on the borings logs may have been done carefully, or they may reflect a single observation during drilling. Sometimes it is necessary to leave a boring open for a period of time, and perhaps insert a perforated casing and then bail down the fluid in a boring to obtain a true measure of the water level. Sometimes it is necessary to flush out a boring several times to remove the drilling mud.

Frequently, water level information can be obtained from other

MAJOR DIVISIONS			GRAPH SYMBOL	LETTER SYMBOL	TYPICAL DESCRIPTIONS
COARSE GRAINED SOILS MORE THAN 50% OF MATERIAL IS LARGER THAN NO. 200 SIEVE SIZE	GRAVEL AND GRAVELLY SOILS MORE THAN 50% OF COARSE FRAC-TION RETAINED ON NO. 4 SIEVE	CLEAN GRAVELS (LITTLE OR NO FINES)		GW	WELL-GRADED GRAVELS, GRAVEL-SAND MIXTURES, LITTLE OR NO FINES
				GP	POORLY-GRADED GRAVELS, GRAVEL-SAND MIXTURES, LITTLE OR NO FINES
		GRAVELS WITH FINES (APPRECIABLE AMOUNT OF FINES)		GM	SILTY GRAVELS, GRAVEL-SAND-SILT MIXTURES
				GC	CLAYEY GRAVELS, GRAVEL-SAND-CLAY MIXTURES
	SAND AND SANDY SOILS MORE THAN 50% OF COARSE FRAC-TION PASSING NO. 4 SIEVE	CLEAN SAND (LITTLE OR NO FINES)		SW	WELL-GRADED SANDS, GRAVELLY SANDS, LITTLE OR NO FINES
				SP	POORLY-GRADED SANDS, GRAVELLY SANDS, LITTLE OR NO FINES
		SANDS WITH FINES (APPRECIABLE AMOUNT OF FINES)		SM	SILTY SANDS, SAND-SILT MIXTURES
				SC	CLAYEY SANDS, SAND-CLAY MIXTURES
FINE GRAINED SOILS MORE THAN 50% OF MATERIAL IS SMALLER THAN NO. 200 SIEVE SIZE	SILTS AND CLAYS	LIQUID LIMIT LESS THAN 50		ML	INORGANIC SILTS AND VERY FINE SANDS, ROCK FLOUR, SILTY OR CLAYEY FINE SANDS OR CLAYEY SILTS WITH SLIGHT PLASTICITY
				CL	INORGANIC CLAYS OF LOW TO MEDIUM PLASTICITY, GRAVELLY CLAYS, SANDY CLAYS, SILTY CLAYS, LEAN CLAYS
				OL	ORGANIC SILTS AND ORGANIC SILTY CLAYS OF LOW PLASTICITY
	SILTS AND CLAYS	LIQUID LIMIT GREATER THAN 50		MH	INORGANIC SILTS, MICACEOUS OR DIATOMACEOUS FINE SAND OR SILTY SOILS
				CH	INORGANIC CLAYS OF HIGH PLASTICITY, FAT CLAYS
				OH	ORGANIC CLAYS OF MEDIUM TO HIGH PLASTICITY, ORGANIC SILTS
HIGHLY ORGANIC SOILS				PT	PEAT, HUMUS, SWAMP SOILS WITH HIGH ORGANIC CONTENTS

NOTE: DUAL SYMBOLS ARE USED TO INDICATE BORDERLINE SOIL CLASSIFICATIONS.

PLATE

Fig. 9.2 Unified soil classification system. For more information, see Ref. 13, Chap. 1.

93

sources. This may include water levels in nearby water wells, seepage of water into basements in nearby buildings.

9.6   Recommendations

Most reports contain recommendations for the design of foundations. Some comments may also be made regarding construction procedures.

It is important for the contractor to understand the intent of many recommendations. For instance, it may be recommended that foundations be placed at a depth of 5 ft on a gray sandy clay layer. Which is more important, founding at a depth of 5 ft or founding on the sandy clay? If the sandy clay is 7 ft deep over portions of the site, should the foundations be placed at a depth of 7 ft, or may they also be placed at a depth of 5 ft? The report might recommend that slopes cut into the soil be at an angle of one and one-half horizontal to one vertical. This slope, however, might refer to permanent slopes. Temporary slopes might be one-to-one, or perhaps three-quarters horizontal to one vertical. Permanent slopes should have a higher factor of safety, and generally are flatter for erosion and maintenance purposes than may be necessary for a temporary construction slope.

9.7   Construction Planning

It is to the advantage of the contractor to have the soils engineer provide some input during construction planning. Questions regarding slope angles and foundation depths can be clarified. The approach to various phases of construction can be reviewed. Many times the on-site soil after it is excavated can be reused as compacted fill around the perimeter of the basement. The soil may need to be protected from rain. Also, it may be wet when excavated or need to be dried out. In some cases, however, the excavated material may be very difficult to work. In this case, compaction tests performed by the foundation engineer would indicate a potential problem (see Chapter 8, Section 8.8). In such a case, it may be to the advantage of the contractor to plan on disposing of the excavated material, and importing backfill which is easy to compact.

9.8   Limitations and Professional Liability

The soils report generally is an expression of opinions and recommendations by a professional person. The report is not a warranty or an insurance policy.

Recently, more and more lawsuits have been filed against engineers. Soils engineers have been particularly vulnerable. The soils engineer generally is called on to reach a reasonable answer with far less real information regarding the site than he would like to have.

Generally, the grounds for a reasonable suit is carelessness. It is recognized that opinions and recommendations are of a variable nature—not subject to precise calculations. Therefore, some recommendations are based on judgment. Judgment may be different between various professionals, and who is to say that the judgment of one engineer is in error?

The matter of professional liability is being written in much more detail in a separate volume to be published as part of this series.

9.9   Summary

Primary points in this chapter are as follows:

FACTS: The soils report should contain facts and give opinions on such things as how to design foundations or how to make an excavation.

WATCH OUT FOR: Reports that do not give specific answers should be questioned. Do not accept vague answers. Force the designer and the soils engineer to give specific answers covering problem soils, safe slope angles, and backfill requirements.

10

Field Tests

10.1 Bearing Tests

The strength of soil at a proposed foundation level is sometimes tested by making static load tests on model footings. A pit is excavated to the depth proposed for testing. The pit generally is made considerably wider than the area of the test footing, usually four to five times the width of the test footing. Test footings generally are at least 1 by 1 ft in size, and so the pit would be at least 4 by 4 ft in size.

A loading platform or reaction frame can be constructed over the plate, or for convenience sometimes a loaded truck trailer is positioned over the test footing. A jack is used to apply load on the test footing. Dial gauges or a surveyor's level is used to measure settlements of the footing as load is applied.

Usually, load is applied in several steps. A plot of load versus settlement is made for each increment of load applied. The test is continued until settlement becomes progressively larger under each increment of load, or until the capacity of the testing apparatus is reached. Readings of rebound are taken as the load is removed. A typical test setup is shown in Fig. 10.1. A typical load-settlement curve is also shown in Fig. 10.1. A detailed specification for such tests is contained in ASTM, test designation D1194.

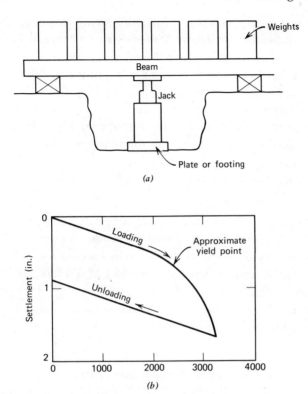

Fig. 10.1   (*a*) Soil bearing test. Read settlement of the footing with a surveyor's level, or with dial gauges mounted on an independent reference beam. (*b*) Typical graph of load vs. settlement and rebound derived from test.

Usually two or more load tests are performed. Two sizes of test foundations may be used, such as 12 by 12 in. and 17 by 17 in. (2 ft²).

The results of the tests can be examined to determine a point at which yield of the soil starts. The indicated bearing pressure usually is divided by two or three or some other number (to provide a factor of safety) to determine a "design bearing value."

Limitations to this method of test are as follows:

1. The soil tested extends to a depth of one to two times the size of the test footing. A true full-size footing would stress the soils to greater depth. A soft layer at a depth of 4 ft could affect a large footing. Therefore, borings or some deeper information is also necessary to go along with load test data.

2. The test results indicate primarily bearing capacity, and are not a reliable indication of likely settlement of proposed foundations. As an example, if a test footing 2 by 2 ft in size settled 1 in. at the proposed design bearing pressure, a real footing 8 by 8 ft in size would be expected to settle about 4 in. A footing 4 by 4 ft in size would be expected to settle approximately 2 in.

3. Settlements of clay soils occur slowly, over a long period of time. Long-term settlements of building foundations may be much larger than would be estimated from a load test.

4. A change in water level could affect the bearing capacity of the soil.

Soil bearing tests are made on the subgrade soils for airport runways and highways. Static load tests are made on circular plates. The test plate usually is 30 in. in diameter. A specific test procedure has been developed and is described in ASTM D1196. In this test, a plate 18 in. in diameter is used as the "test footing." Interpolation of test results and use of the data is much different from footing load tests previously described.

10.2   Vane Shear Tests

Vane shear tests can be made in test borings. Usually they are performed in clay soils, particularly soft clays free of sand layers or gravel.

The test boring is stopped at the depth proposed for testing and is cleaned out. The vane apparatus is lowered to the bottom of the borings, and pressed into the soil below the bottom of the boring. A sketch of a vane test apparatus is shown on Fig. 10.2.

The vane is then rotated at a constant rate, and the force required to cause rotation is measured until the strength of the soil is exceeded.

By using the dimensions of the vane and the force required to cause rotation, the stress required to shear the soil is determined.

10.3   Penetrometer Tests

A variety of tests have been devised to measure the resistance of the soil to penetration. This might include a penetration of:

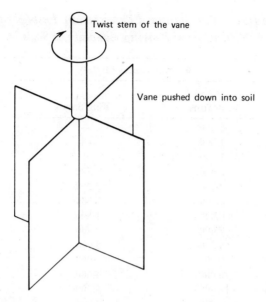

Fig. 10.2   Vane test device. For example, if the vane is 1 in. in diameter and 1 in. high, then soil cohesion in $lb/in.^2 = \frac{1}{2}$ torque in in.-lb to turn the vane. Therefore, if torque is 2 lb at the end of a 10-in. wrench, the torque is 20 in-lb and the cohesion is 10 $lb/in.^2$. This represents a fairly strong soil.

The boring casing.
A sample pipe.
The 2-in. diameter "standard penetrometer."
A small-diameter cone.
Soil samplers of various sizes.

Penetration of these devices in the soil may be caused by pushing on the drill pipe or rods with hydraulic jacks, or by hammering on the drill rods using a falling weight as a driving hammer.

These results give a qualitative indication of the soil characteristics and strengths. Usually, these strength indications are used to correlate with laboratory test data. However, in some cases the results of penetrometer tests are used directly to estimate soil bearing capacity, or the probable penetration of piles into the soil.

There is no generally accepted conversion from blow counts (N values) to bearing values for a soil, and there is considerable difference in opinion as to whether it is even practical to attempt to use

*Table 10.1   The Standard Penetration Test (N) as an
Indication of Bearing Capacity of Soils*

	Bearing Values (lb/ft²)		
	Clay and Silty	Sandy Soils	
N	Clay Soils	Fine Sands	Coarse Sands
2 Blows[a]	500	—	—
4	1,200	—	—
5	1,500	500	1,500
6	2,500	700	1,800
8	4,500	1,200	2,000
10	5,500	1,500	2,500
12	6,000	1,800	3,000
15	7,000	2,000	3,500
20	8,000	3,000	4,500
25	9,000	4,000	6,000
30	10,000	4,500	6,500
40	12,000	5,500	8,000
50	14,000	6,000	9,000
60	15,500	6,500	10,500
70	17,000	7,000	12,000

[a] Only to be used for unimportant structures with light loadings.

blow counts for this purpose. However, Table 10.1 is one suggested conversion table. It may be of some guidance, but *should not be used alone* as the basis for selecting a design bearing value.

Blow counts certainly can be helpful to a contractor in estimating difficulty in making excavations and in driving piles and sheet piles.

These values do not consider submerged conditions, deep foundations, or mat foundations. These values are considered to be "safe" bearing values, rather than being almost at the failure point.

10.4   Menard Pressure Meter

This device is a special type of balloon operated somewhat similar to a hydraulic jack. It is lowered down the boring to the desired depth of testing. The diameter of the pressure meter is only slightly smaller than the borings. "Guard cells" on either side of the "balloon" are first inflated so that they press against the walls of the boring. Then, the balloon itself is expanded by hydraulic pressure. Hydraulic pressure is applied inside of the balloon until it forces itself out sufficiently to cause failure of the soil surrounding the boring.

Special techniques are required for interpretation of the test results.

10.5 Air-Operated Percussion Drills

Occasionally, percussion drills are used as a crude method of probing firm soil or rock. The rate of penetration is some indication of the firmness of the material. Fractures, voids, and other soft conditions can be discovered.

10.6 Pocket Penetrometer

A small device which is used frequently to make approximate measurements of the strength of clay or silty soil is called the pocket penetrometer. It can be used on the job site to measure strength of soil in trenches, the strength of soil samples obtained from borings, or the strength of soil on the bottom of footing excavations, (see Ref. 14).

10.7 Pile Load Tests

Proposed types of piles frequently are driven at a site for testing. The testing may be to verify "design pile capacity," or to determine pile lengths for precasting of concrete piles. Pile load tests are run in a manner fairly similar to bearing tests on soil. A typical test set up and load-settlement diagram is shown on Figure 10.3. Specifications for such tests are given in Ref. 15. Also, most building codes specify procedures for running the tests and also for evaluating the results (see Ref. 16 and also Ref. 17, p. 240).

In evaluating test results, bear in mind that (a) a group of several piles will perform differently from a single pile. Settlements will usu-

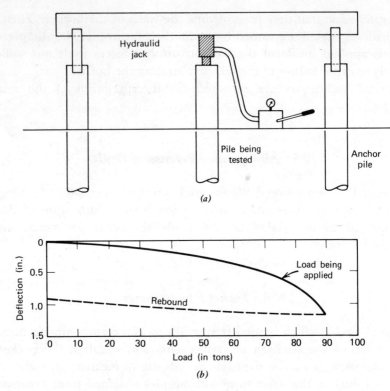

Fig. 10.3   (*a*) Pile load test setup. (*b*) Load settlement diagram.

ally be more. It is possible that a "bearing stratum" is underlain by a soft layer. This may not show up in testing one pile, but could result in settlement of a group of piles. (b) Long-term settlements may be more than settlements measured during the test. (c) Production piles must penetrate into the same bearing stratum (for end bearing piles), even though the bearing stratum may be deeper (or shallower) in other parts of the site. For more discussion, see Chapter 16, Section 16.4.

10.8   Dry Density

Frequently, the density of soil is measured in the field. This can be done by taking samples of the soil by pushing or driving in a soil sampler. This procedure is used commonly for testing of compacted fills. Therefore, the test procedure is described under Chapter 8, Section 8.3.

In testing fills, however, it is more common to dig a hole into the compacted soil as a means of obtaining a sample of the soil. The volume of the hole must be measured. An alternate is nuclear testing. These methods are described in Chapter 23, Section 23.13.

Moisture content of the soil is also tested frequently in the field. The method is described in Chapter 8, Section 8.3.

10.9   Percolation Tests

Percolation tests frequently are run in the field to obtain some approximate values of the percolation rate of the upper soils. These tests are particularly helpful for establishing suitable locations for leaching fields for sewage effluent disposal, and also the required area of leaching fields.

The tests can be run in open dug pits or in shallow uncased borings. The tests can be performed by filling the boring or pit and measuring the rate at which the water level goes down. Before the test is run, the soils should be presaturated by running water into the pit or boring for a period of at least several hours. Then any silty materials should be cleaned out, before the test is run. The test should be run two or three times.

A commonly used test in a pit or in a shallow boring is shown on Figure 10.4a. This is a simple test to run, and results in guideline-type answers.

More sophisticated percolation rates can be run in shallow borings (see Fig. 10.4b). Mathematical solutions are available for calculating percolation rates. Rates usually are expressed in terms of the velocity at which water flows through the soil, using a water head (or driving force) equal to the thickness of soil through which the water is traveling. Typical percolation rates are listed in Chapter 8, Section 8.8. One method of calculation is given on pg. 541 of Ref. 13 and on Ref. 18, p. 29.

Permeability also can be determined by pumping tests. Usually such tests are performed in wells or in well points. At a given rate of pumping, the drawdown of the water surface is measured in other nearby observation wells. The water level draws down in a broad fun-

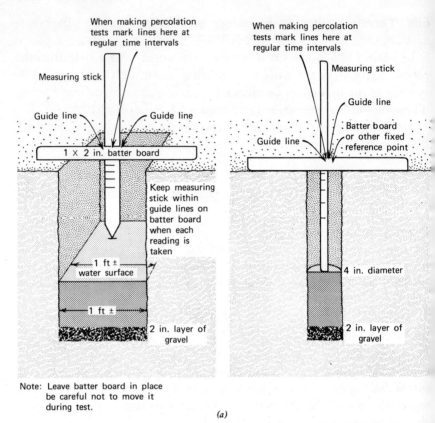

Fig. 10.4 (a) Automatic field Percolation test with readout system and strip chart recorder. An auger drill rig used to drill the percolation holes is in the background (photo courtesy of Soiltest, Inc.).

nel shape. A knowledge of the rate of pumping and of the shape of the funnel is sufficient to calculate the permeability of the formation being pumped. (See Table 10.2 page 106.)

10.10 Electrical Resistance

Soils resist the flow of electricity through them. Usually, dry firm soils have a high resistance. Wet and soft soils have a low resistance. Also

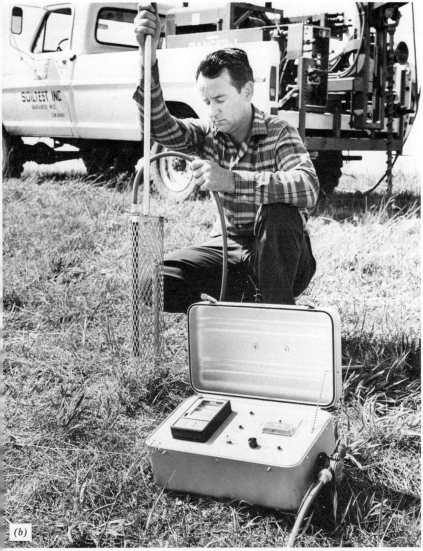

Fig. 10.4 (*b*) Field percolation test (from U. S. Public Health Service; method developed at Robert A. Taft Sanitary Engineering Center).

Table 10.2   Absorption-Area Requirements
for Individual Residences (a)[a]

Percolation Rate (Time Required for Water to Fall 1 inch, min.)	Required Absorption Area, ft^2 per Bedroom (b), Standard Trench (c), Seepage Beds (c), and Seepage Pits (d)	Percolation Rate (Time Required for Water to Fall 1 in. min.)	Required Absorption Area in ft^2 per Bedroom (b), Standard Trench (c), Seepage Beds (c), and Seepage Pits (d)
1 or less	70	10	165
2	85	15	190
3	100	30 (c)	250
4	115	45 (c)	300
5	125	60 (c), (f)	330

Source. U.S. Public Health Service; method developed at Robert A. Taft Sanitary Engineering Center.

[a] Provides for garbage grinder and automatic clothes washing machines.

soils containing chemicals have a low resistance. Resistance is important for several reasons, including:

Ground of electrical transmission lines.

Need for protection of foundations and buried structures from "hot" soils.

Electrical resistance is frequently measured by a device which pumps electrical energy into the ground through a steel stake, and measures the flow to another steel stake. A device for making such measurements is shown on Figure 10.5.

This kind of survey, taking several measurements, can be used to estimate the depth to bedrock (see Ref. 8, p. 445).

10.11   Water Level Measurements

It may be necessary to measure ground water levels for months or years. Commonly used methods are an open dug pit or drilled hole, installation of cased wells, or installation of piezometers.

In pits or wells a tape or electric probe device can be lowered to measure the depth to free-standing water.

Fig. 10.5   Device for measuring electric resistivity of soils. Survey crew uses the soiltest Michimho resistivity Meter in a subsurface investigation. Unlike the seismic instruments, the Michimho uses electrical current to determine the electrical resistivity of earth materials. This is then correlated to depth, thickness, and makeup of materials underlying the earth's surface [Soiltest, Inc., 2205 Lee Street, Evanston, Ill. 60202 Phone: (312) 869-5500]

The piezometer is a pressure device which measures water pressure in any selected layer of soil. Therefore, a piezometer can measure any artesian water pressures in a deeper layer of soil. Also, if a clay layer is overloaded by an embankment of new fill, the excess water pressures can be measured. These measurements can warn of likely failures or landslides. A piezometer is shown in Fig. 10.6.

Fig. 10.6   (*a*) Piezometer (air actuated type).

10.12   *Measurement of Earth Deformations*

Lateral ground movements are more difficult to measure than vertical movements, which can be measured relatively well with surveyors' levels and other leveling devices. Installed special cased holes are commonly used to measure horizontal movements. Instruments are run down and back up the holes to measure any bending or leaning of the casing. If the casing crosses a landslide slip plane where movement is occurring slowly, the casing will bend in an S shape, and this will be detected by the instrument when it is lowered down the casing. The most commonly used instrument is the slope indicator (see Ref. 18, p. 1042). Another typical instrument of this type called the "earth deformation recorder" is shown in Fig. 10.7.

On Fig. 10.7, the instrument is shown entering a casing. Wheels on the side of the instrument track into grooves which are machined into the casing to orient the instrument.

(b)

Fig. 10.6   (b) Piezometer (atmospheric type).

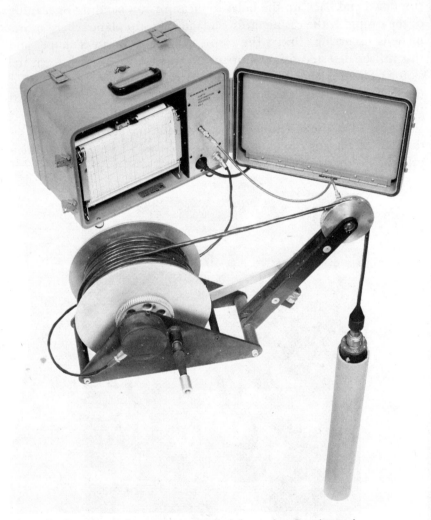

Fig. 10.7 Instrument for measuring earth deformation entering casing.

10.13   Summary

Primary points in this chapter are as follows:

FACTS: Many field tests have been devised. The major problem is how to use the test results.

WATCH OUT FOR: Changing conditions in the area being tested, such as future rise in water level, or unnoticed soft layers under a firm top layer. Make sure there are other data to back up the field test results.

11

Excavations

Most general contractors do well on vertical construction above grade. However, many have difficulties underground. Many lose money on their project due to difficulties underground.

Frequently, the project manager is selected for his ability to erect steel, pour concrete, or perform other vertical construction. Too many times he does not understand underground problems and gets into serious difficulty before recognizing that he needs assistance.

Earth construction is as difficult and demanding as above-ground construction.

11.1 Slope Stability

11.1.1 Slope Angle

Many excavations are started with a vertical cut. Some soils will stand to considerable depths when cut vertically, although most will not. When vertical slopes slough off to a stable angle, large blocks of material may slide down into the excavation.

In sandy soils, generally the sand will tend to slough and cave in during the process of excavation. Usually, this results in a fairly stable angle, without serious hazard.

However, cemented sands and silty or clay soils sometimes are excavated to considerable depths before a large block of soil slides into the excavation.

The angle at which soil can be expected to stand temporarily during excavation can be calculated. Some rough rule-of-thumb slope angles are presented in Table 11.1.

Table 11.1 [a]

Soil Type	Some Typical Temporary Slope Angles
1. Sand or sand and gravel	45 degrees for damp slopes; 35 degrees or 1½ to 1 for dry slopes; flatter for wet slopes.
2. Cemented sand	Vertical to 10 ft; ½ to 1 to 20 ft or more; ¾ to 1 for high slopes.
3. Soft silt or soft clay	Vertical to 3 ft; ½ to 1 to 6 ft; ¾ to 1 to 10 ft; 1½ to 1 for high slopes. Flatter slopes, like 4 to 1, for wet slopes.
4. Moderately firm silt or clay	Vertical to 6 ft; ½ to 1 to 10 ft; ¾ to 1 to 20 ft; 1 to 1 for higher slopes, except flatter slopes for wet soil conditions.
5. Firm silt or clay	Vertical to 10 ft; ½ to 1 to 20 ft; ¾ to 1 to 30 ft; 1 to 1 for higher slopes, except flatter slopes for wet soil conditions.
6. Mud	Silt or clay soils containing high amounts of moisture may require very flat slopes, like 4 to 1 or 6 to 1 or flatter, unless dewatering or drainage is used to reduce the water problem.

[a] There are many exceptions—the "typical values" above are not intended for use for design of slopes. The Federal Act entitled "Occupational Safety and Health Act," as well as state industrial codes, limit the height of unbraced vertical cuts where workmen are located. Typical slope angles for permanent slopes are given in Chapter 22, Section 22.2.

In starting an excavation, it is easier to start the cut at the proposed slope angle. If the desired temporary slope angle is one horizontal to one vertical, and the depth of excavation is to be 15 ft, the top of excavation should be started 15 ft outside of the proposed toe of excavation.

11.1.2 Undermining

After a slope has been cut, it sometimes is necessary to undermine the slope to get in certain foundations or utilities.

Where undermining is necessary, and it is not possible to lay back the slope at a stable angle, undermining should be done in narrow sections or windows. The top of the slope should be unloaded as much as possible, and construction equipment should not be on the top of the slope.

Sometimes, slopes are undermined in the process of excavation. The soil caves and runs to the excavation machine. This is not too hazardous in clean sand, which will slide back to its angle of repose. This can be hazardous in cemented soils, damp sands with apparent cohesion, or silts or clays which will stand vertical temporarily, and then a large block will break off and come down like a landslide.

11.1.3   Erosion

Excavation slopes have been denuded of natural cover and protection, and are usually very susceptible to erosion in heavy rains.

It is particularly important to limit the amount of water running down over the excavation slope. This can be done by building a curb or dike at the top of the slope, which forces water to run away from the excavation rather than over the excavation slope.

The face of the excavation also can be protected prior to an imminent rainfall by covering with plastic sheets, or by spraying with various waterproofing materials. Sodium silicate is one material used for this purpose (a modification of the Joosten process). This material can be injected into a slope, or can be sprayed on the surface of a slope (see Chapter 30, Section 30.4).

11.1.4   Cracking

Cracking of steep excavated slopes may become a problem, as a result of severe drying of the soil. The soil will tend to ravel and run down the slope. Even worse, deep cracks may allow blocks of material to fall out of the slope. Often slopes appear to be at a stable slope, but a block of material can drop off the wall of the excavation. Much damage and injury result from just this one problem.

Later, when backfilling is completed, the soil can become moist again. The soil could swell, and possibly crack concrete walls or concrete slabs placed over the slope.

Cracking can most easily be reduced by limiting the evaporation of water. Occasionally this is done by frequent sprinkling or "fog spraying" the slope.

This also can be accomplished by a protective cover over the slope. Protective covers may consist of plastic sheets, sprayed-on chemicals, sprayed-on bitumastic materials, or other waterproofing materials (see Ref. 19).

11.1.5   Loads on Top of Slope

It is natural for the contractor to put machinery on top of the slope, to stack excess excavated soil on top of the soil, or to store construction materials at the top of the excavated slope. In addition, heavy machinery may produce vibration, increasing the hazard to the slope.

The stability of a slope with added surcharge load at the edge can be analyzed, as described in Chapter 25, Section 25.2. Also, building codes, or the Federal and State Safety codes, may spell out limitations to loading the edge of an excavation. Also, it is possible to calculate a "safe distance back" of the edge for placing loads.

As a crude guide, the distance back from the top of a slope can be estimated by assuming that the slope could be considered safe if it were higher but placed at the slope angle used in making the excavation. If this slope angle is $3/4$ to 1, for instance, and the weight on the tracks of a piece of equipment is 500 lb/ft^2, this would be equivalent to making the excavation 5 ft deeper. This is shown on Fig. 11.1a. Since the equipment may be used for making lifts, the maximum pressure on the tread closest to the excavation may be increased. This increase should be added to the track load in making the calculation. If, for instance, the track load should be increased to 1000 lb/ft^2 during making of a lift, the equivalent height of new soil is 1000 lb/ft^2. The 10 ft of soil can be replaced with a block of soil, as shown in Fig. 11.1b. The edge of the block is approximately 4 ft back from the edge of the slope. The crane track also should be kept at least 4 ft back from the edge of the excavation.

11.1.6   Detection of Movement

Landslides and slope failure do not occur unexpectedly and without warning. They show some signs of impending failure before the

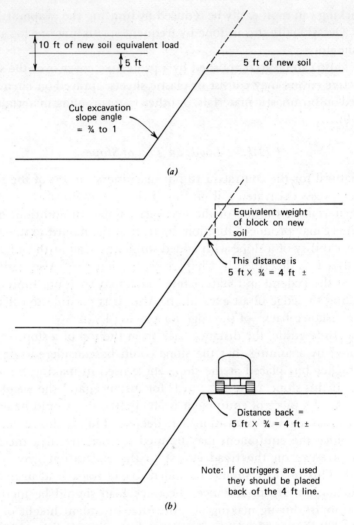

Fig. 11.1 Guide to safe distance back from top of slope for storage of materials or placing equipment.

actual failure occurs. The primary problem is that in many cases these indications are not observed or heeded.

During operation of equipment in a precarious position at the top of a slope, someone should be given the specific assignment of frequent inspection of the top and the slope. He should look for signs of cracking back of the top of the slope back to a distance that is equal to the height of the slope. Also, he should watch for bulging at the center or toe of the slope, and for soil particles running off the slope below the piece of machinery.

Small slope movements can be detected by surveying on fixed reference points. A more convenient but more expensive method is to install special casings in drilled holes. These casings and instruments to measure movement of the casings can be obtained from several sources. However, it would be better to work with a soils engineer familiar with the operation of this equipment (see Chapter 10, Section 10.12).

11.1.7 *Vertical Cuts*

In some cases, vertical cuts can be made in soils that are cemented or are stiff cohesive silts or clays. In addition, vertical cuts sometimes are made in sandy soils exhibiting temporary "apparent cohesion" due to water in the sand.

In general, vertical cuts should be considered as temporary and should be backfilled or otherwise stabilized in a short period of time.

In general, the maximum vertical height to which a silt or clay soil can stand is equal to the following expression:

$$\text{height} = \frac{2 \times \text{cohesion}}{\text{soil weight}}$$

Cohesion is measured in laboratory tests, as described in Chapter 7, Section 7.4 and should be described in the soils report.

For a clay having a cohesion of 500 lb/ft^2 and a weight of 100 lb/ft^3, the temporary height at which a vertical bank could be cut is 10 ft. This calculation includes no factor of safety. With a safety factor of 1.5 the allowable height of cut would be 6½ ft.

In general, vertical cuts should be avoided. Equipment operators should not start out an excavation digging vertically, and then after the excavation is completed, find that it would be extremely difficult to go back and flatten the slope. Excavations should be started by digging out to the required cut lines for the desired slope.

11.1.8   Slope Stabilization

If a slope is cut too steep and starts to fail, the obvious method of stabilizing is to flatten the slope. If there is not room to flatten, some other action is necessary. Hopefully, this action will be taken before excavation starts, or before it has gone too far.

Stabilization methods include:

Dewatering: In many cases, dewatering, substantially back from the slopes, using well points or wells, will increase the stability of the slope.

Guniting: If the slope is not badly oversteepened, sometimes a gunite surface will hold in soil moisture and add some strength.

Chemicals: Where steep slopes must be cut in areas of tight space limitations, it is possible to stabilize certain soils by injecting chemicals. See Chapter 30, Section 30.4.

Bracing: Slopes are more often stabilized by shoring and bracing, as described in Chapter 12.

11.2   Bottom Protection

11.2.1   Drying and Cracking

Soils at the bottom of an excavation may become excessively dry and crack and shrink if they are exposed for a long period of time to dry, hot weather. This may create a problem after the building floor slabs are poured if the soils swell when they regain their natural moisture content. Therefore, the soil may need to be sprinkled or temporarily covered with sand or plastic sheets to limit evaporation.

11.2.2   Saturation

More frequently, the soils at the bottom of an excavation may be saturated. Even though the ground water level may be below the bottom of the excavation, or the site may be dewatered by rim trenches, wellpoints, or wells, it is common to find that the bottom of an excavation becomes unstable for operation of front-end loaders, dump trucks, and other heavy-wheeled equipment.

Also, soils which are saturated and soft may be undesirable soils on which to pour spread foundations for support of the building columns. Such soils may have swelled or "rebounded" on removal of the overburdened soils. The soils therefore would recompress on application of the foundation load. In such cases where the subgrade is in wet clay or silty soils, it frequently is less expensive to over-excavate 12 to 18 in., and backfill with select free-draining soils to provide a "working course."

Occasionally, equipment breakdown may cause the dewatering operation to stop for hours or even days. In this case, the ground water rises upward and may fill the excavation. During the time the water is flowing upward into the excavation, the soils on the bottom of the excavation may be severely loosened and disturbed.

When the dewatering system is again in operation, and the excavation has been dewatered and dried out, it may be necessary to remove the loosened soil. The excavations may be backfilled with select soil. If the soils at the bottom of the excavation are sandy soils, similar to what might be imported as "select soil," it is possible that the loose soils can be recompacted adequately. The entire bottom of the excavation should be recompacted.

Heavy rainfall or freezing also can soften the bottom of the excavation. Rainfall protection should include curbs or small dikes around the perimeter of the excavation to prevent the job site from becoming a sump for the whole neighborhood. Also, in at least one case, a contractor erected a circus tent over the site during the rainy season. Freezing is more difficult to protect against. Sandy soils are not affected much, but silty or clay soils can expand when they freeze and turn into mud when they thaw. It is very bad to build foundations on frozen ground, for they settle a lot the next spring when it thaws. If it is not possible to prevent freezing by covering with soil, or heating, then it may be necessary to excavate all frozen soil below footings and replace with gravel or lean concrete. These costs should be figured into the bid.

11.2.3   Heaving

During driving of pile foundations, the excavations for pile caps have in many cases been found to heave upward. Figure 11.2 shows the excavation for the foundation for a tall stack. Approximately 70 piles were driven at a spacing of 3½ ft center-to-center. The piles were approximately 60 ft long, step tapered, with an average diameter of 12 in.

During driving, the ground was observed to heave upward. The ground also lifted up previously driven piles. By the completion of driving, uplifting of piles was measured and varied from 0 to 16 in. Average heaving was around 4 to 5 in.

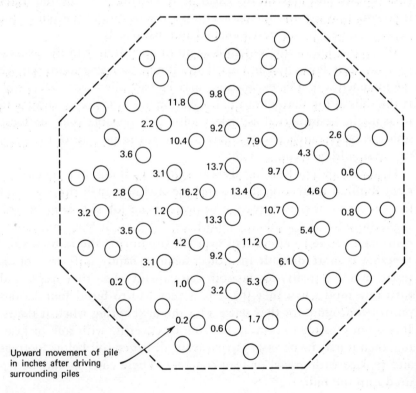

Upward movement of pile in inches after driving surrounding piles

Fig. 11.2   Smoke stack foundation showing vertical heave of piles.

In many cases, the pile cap is overexcavated to accommodate ground heave. Also, predrilling may be used at each pile location to remove excess soil and thus prevent heaving. Heaving is described in more detail in Chapter 16, Sections 16.8, 16.9, and 16.10.

11.2.4 Accidental Overexcavation

Occasionally, an excavation is made too deep, either by surveying error or by mistake on the part of equipment operators. Also, excavations may be cut deeper in order that the corners can be cut out with large machinery.

It is a natural tendency for equipment operators to backfill overexcavated spots by dragging bulldozer blades or loader buckets across the bottom of the excavation, thus disguising areas which have been overexcavated. This is discussed further in Chapter 14, Section 14.11.

11.3 Selection of Equipment

The selection of equipment for excavation is important to the economics of the work. Soil characteristics affecting the choice of equipment include:

Hardness of the soil.
Stickiness or cohesiveness of the soil.
Amount of water present in the soil.
Ability of the soil to support heavy equipment without rutting and becoming mired.

Some indication of the hardness of soils to be encountered in an excavation can be obtained from the soil investigation report. Indicators would be as follows:

The description of the soil.
The sampler blow count.
The plastic nature of the soil.
The design bearing value for the soil.
The recommended slope angle for excavations.

The method of excavation may be important in some cases. The soil generally lies in layers. It may be desirable to excavate top soil off as one procedure and secondly excavate and save the good material which can be used as a select fill or backfill. By contrast, if a general filling operation is to be done with the material excavated, it may be desirable to cut across layers, thereby mixing the poor and the good soils together.

More detailed discussions of selection of equipment are given in Ref. 20.

11.4 Dewatering

11.4.1 Symptoms of Trouble

As an excavation reaches the ground-water level, it may not be immediately evident that ground water is being reached. However, bulldozers or wheeled construction or hauling equipment in the bottom of the excavation may develop trouble with rutting or weaving and pumping of the soil. In some cases, it appears that the construction equipment may be in danger of sinking out of sight if it continues to excavate. On removal of equipment from the excavation, occasionally water will break through the surface bringing up soil. The water appears to "boil" as it comes out of the ground, forming small cones which look like volcanoes. Such a "sand boil" is shown on Fig. 11.3.

11.4.2 Methods

The most common method of dewatering an excavation is to construct a sump or several sumps in the bottom of the excavation. Frequently, sumps will be placed outside of the proposed building lines. It may be necessary to dig ditches (rim trenches) around the perimeter of the excavation leading to the sumps. As water flows into the sumps, they are dewatered by pumps. Pumps used should be designed for this purpose. Flyght submersible electric pumps are frequently used. Detailed discussion of methods of dewatering is contained in Refs. 21 and 22. Other methods may include well points, wells, gravel blankets, and French drains.

Fig. 11.3 Sand boil.

11.4.3 Underground Tanks

Large tanks are placed underground for storage of oil, petroleum products, and other fluid storage. Frequently, such tanks are placed in an area of high water, requiring dewatering. In such cases, dewatering must be continued so that backfilling of the excavation can be done in the dry.

There have been a number of cases in which tanks have popped out of the ground during backfilling. In many of these cases, water jets were used as a means of compacting the backfill soil. In other cases, water was drawn down by pumping during placing of the tank, and then was allowed to run into the excavation during the period of backfilling. If the water level comes back to its original level, it exerts a considerable upward or buoyance effect on the tank. If the backfill has not yet been completed, sufficient fill over the tanks or tie downs will be required to prevent the tanks from rising out of the ground when they are emptied.

11.4.4 Underground Pipelines

Excavations for pipelines are discussed in Chapter 13, Section 13.4.

11.5 Rock Excavation

Excavations into rock are not covered in this book, except for a few comments.

Many excavations will intercept weak planes in rock. These planes may be the bedding planes in sedimentary rocks or fractures in hard rock, or fault zones in any kind of rock. If the weak plane lies at an angle, it can cause one of the sides of the excavation to be in trouble, as shown in Fig. 11.4.

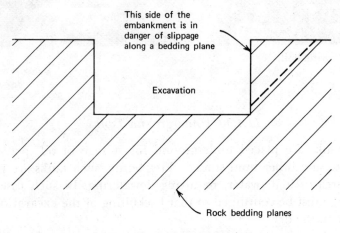

This side of the embankment is in danger of slippage along a bedding plane

Excavation

Rock bedding planes

Fig. 11.4   Example of potential slippage of rock along bedding planes.

11.6 Summary

Primary points in this chapter are as follows:

FACTS: Major excavations require planning for safety and economy. They may look easy but can turn into serious and expensive problems.

WATCH OUT FOR: Cracking of slopes. Blocks of material "pop out" and come thundering down into the work area. Heavy loads at the top of an excavation are bad and should be placed back as far as possible. Over-excavation of footing excavations.

12

Shoring and Bracing

The design of shoring and bracing usually is done by the contractor or by a subcontractor specializing in such work. The design generally is the responsibility of the contractor; however, the design is done by his own engineers or by a specialty subcontractor. In this case, the specialty contractor hires or retains registered professional engineers to prepare the design. The laws concerning responsibility for design may vary among the states.

Occasionally, the owner may have the shoring system designed and then he takes the responsibility for proper performance.

Some building departments have made efforts to set standards for shoring systems and for approval or disapproval of designs proposed by the contractor, because they do not take any responsibility.

OSHA, in some states the Department of Industrial Safety, or the local building department may require approval of proposed shoring systems by their safety engineers. Any of these agencies can close down a job.

The design of shoring systems is based on the expected pressure of a wedge of soil on the back of the shoring. A typical assumed wedge is shown in Figure 12.1.

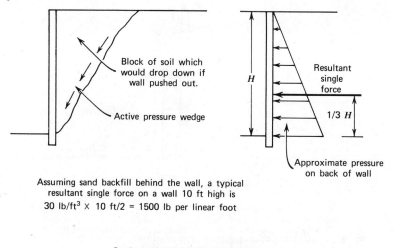

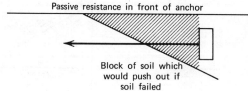

Fig. 12.1 Active soil pressure on wall. Passive resistance restraining tie back anchor.

12.1 Sheet Piles

Sheet piles may be constructed of steel, reinforced concrete, or wood. Steel sheet piles have interlocks which tie the sheet piles together. Concrete or wooden sheet piles usually have tongue-and-groove connections at their edges, which partially tie the sheet piles together.

Sheet piles are driven around the perimeter of a proposed excavation; usually the sheet piles are installed before excavation has started, or when excavation has proceeded to a moderate depth or until water is encountered. Sheet piles usually are driven with hammers similar to pile-driving hammers, except smaller and usually double acting. Smaller sheet piling may be driven with adaptations to jack hammers.

Usually a template or guide is set on the ground to assist in alignment of the sheets. The permanent wale may be set as the front face

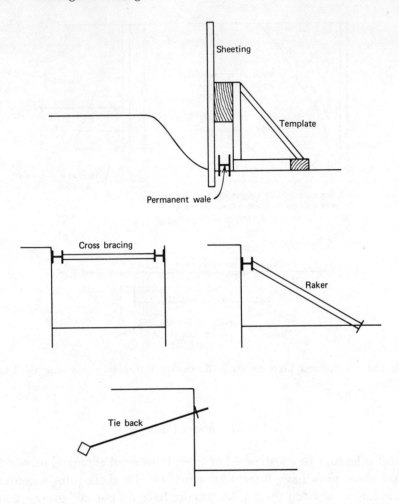

Fig. 12.2   Template and permanent wale used to align sheet piles during driving.

guide for the sheets, as shown in Fig. 12.2. Usually the corner piles are set in position first. The other sheets are pitched from each end so that closure is made at the center. Sheets should be driven in lifts, not over 5 ft each, to prevent sheets from being driven out of their interlocks. In harder ground, the lifts should be shorter.

After the sheet piles are driven, and an excavation is made down to a depth of approximately one-quarter of the depth of the proposed excavation, the sheet piles are restrained. The restraint may be developed by cross bracing, rakers, or by tieback anchors. Examples are indicated in Fig. 12.2.

Sheet piling normally is designed by a design engineer. The proportions depend considerably on methods of construction, the type of soil involved, and water conditions. The proportions indicated in Fig. 12.3 are average for reasonably good sandy soil above the water table.

It is common to place "walers" in front of the sheet piles as part of the bracing system. Anchor rods, or internal bracing, push against the walers. When the anchor rods are installed, they normally are pretensioned by turnbuckles on the anchor rods or by other methods. The pretensioning should be approximately equal to the expected force to be carried by the tie rods. Therefore, as excavation proceeds, it would be expected that the deflection of the sheet piles would be limited to bending of the piles, and not to stretching of the anchor rods. This tends to limit lateral deflection, and to protect streets or buildings adjacent to the excavation. Some deflection of sheeting is inevitable; therefore, this system is never as positive as underpinning an adjacent structure. If bracing is done by internal inclined posts,

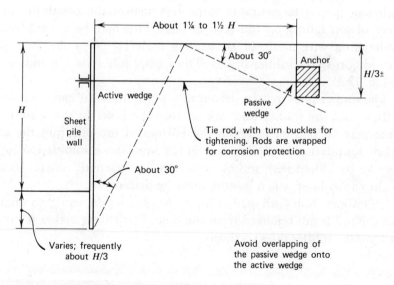

Fig. 12.3   Sheet pile wall with tiebacks and anchors.

sometimes called "rakers," or "kickers," it is common to use jacks to preload the rakers so that they push against the walers with a force equal to the expected design force. In this manner, deflections are limited as the excavation proceeds.

12.2 Soldier Piles

Soldier piles frequently are more economical than sheet piles and are commonly used in excavations for buildings.

Soldier piles are strong beams placed vertically along the perimeter of the proposed excavation. Spacing between soldier piles may vary from 4 or 5 ft to 10 or 15 ft.

In most cases, lagging is placed between the soldier piles. Lagging may consist of boards, but sometimes consists of precast concrete panels, or of cast-in-place concrete. If cast-in-place concrete is used, it may be the permanent final wall of the building.

In some cases, the soil is strong enough to bridge between the soldier piles. In these cases, lagging may not be used. If not, the soil between soldier piles may be protected from drying out. The protection may consist of chemical spray, plastic covering, or gunite. In addition, it may be desirable to protect against the possibility of a piece of soil falling off the vertical face. This may be accomplished by hanging wire mesh, or by fencing material down the face and attaching it to the soldier beams. The soldier pile system is indicated in Fig. 12.4.

The soldier piles may be driven into place. In many cases, a hole is drilled, and the soldier piles are set into the hole. In this case, concrete may be poured to fasten the bottom of the pile into the soil below foundation level. The soil in the hole above foundation level may be backfilled with soil or with lean, low-strength concrete, easy to chip away later, when lagging must be placed.

Sometimes, holes are drilled for each soldier pile, using an auger, but the soil is not removed from the hole. Predrilling makes it easier to drive the soldier piles vertically.

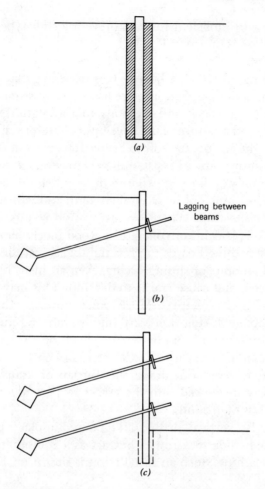

Fig. 12.4 (*a*) Step 1—Drill hole. Set soldier pile in hole. Backfill with concrete. Pile spacing generally about 6 to 8 ft on center. (*b*) Step 2—Excavate for first row of tie backs. Prestress the tie backs. Put wood lagging between the soldier beams. (*c*) Step 3—Excavate and install second row of tie backs.

12.3   Sheathing

Sheathing may consist of sheet piles, wood lagging between soldier piles, or boards held against the sides of trenches. Sheathing prevents soil from falling off the vertical bank, and also must push against the vertical face with sufficient force to prevent a slide-type failure. Such a failure surface is shown in Fig. 12.1.

Lagging usually is set behind the flanges of the soldier beams. In placing lagging, or wooden boards, it is necessary that the sheathing be tight against the soil. Soil in place has a certain strength. However, many soils, such as clayey and silty soils, lose strength if some slippage is permitted, and a failure plane develops. Therefore, sheathing must be pushed tight against the soil to keep slippage from starting. Then the soil strength helps to resist sliding. However, if the soil should slide, even if only an inch or two into the gap behind loose sheathing, this soil has lost much of its natural strength and will impose greater forces on the sheeting. Where overexcavation results in the sheathing being loose, backfill or concrete or wood blocks should be placed behind the sheathing boards to press tightly against the soil face.

If a small amount of sliding occurs, even an inch, blocks of material may stretch and cause cracks to develop. This may damage adjacent pavements or structures. Much worse, however, the cracked soil becomes a sponge during rains, soaking up water rapidly and becoming much heavier and imposing greater loads on the sheathing.

Lagging should be separated, with cracks $1/2$ to 1 in. wide between boards, so that water can drain out. Burlap or "salt hay" (treated excelsior) may be tucked into the cracks to pass water but prevent loss of soil (loss of ground).

Occasionally, vertical drilled and poured-in-place piles are constructed side-by-side in a row. They act as a combination of soldier piles and sheathing. Such an installation is shown on Fig. 12.5.

12.4   Bracing

The rakers or kickers usually are placed at an angle on the order of 30 to 40 degrees from the horizontal (see Fig. 12.6). If the excavation is not too wide, cross-excavation bracing can be used.

The forces used to design the bracing should be calculated by a design engineer. A discussion of such calculations is presented in Ref 17.

The rakers must be supported at the bottom by a footing, or foot block as shown in Fig. 12.6. The design of such footings is discussed in Chapter 14, Section 14.13.

Fig. 12.5   Continuous wall of poured-in-place concrete piles.

12.5 Anchors

Anchors, or deadmen, usually are placed several feet below the ground surface. They may be individual blocks or can be a continuous beam. Generally, they can be designed by assuming that the passive resistance of the soil is approximately equal to the weight of the wedge of soil which would be pushed out if the soil failed. This "passive wedge" is indicated in Fig. 12.1. However, to take care of uncertainties regarding variations in soil conditions, it is general practice to use a factor of safety, in the range of $1\frac{1}{2}$ to 2 in designing the anchors. Therefore, the anchor geometry should be such that it would try to pull out a somewhat larger wedge of soil.

For deep excavations, it is sometimes convenient to put in anchors which are installed with drilling equipment. Such drilled-in anchors can extend down to bedrock and be fastened into the bedrock. As

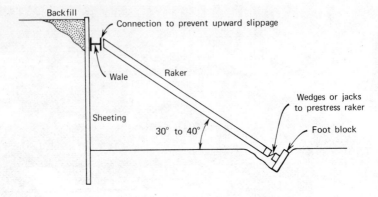

Fig. 12.6 Footblock may be wood, concrete steel, piles, batter piles, or sheet piles. It is best, if possible to brace against a permanent interior foundation.

an alternate, the drilled-in anchors can extend far back into the soil and take their resistance by friction between the soil and a concrete cylinder. This is indicated in Fig. 12.7. A third alternate is to bell out a circular anchor, using a special belling tool. This scheme also is indicated in Fig. 12.7. This method is described in Ref. 17, p. 375. The required length or size of anchors extending into rock or into soil will depend on the strength of the rock or soil. All anchors should extend behind a line which can be defined as the "line behind which failure is unlikely." If we examine the sketch in Fig. 12.7, the line along which failure is most likely might be Line *A*. A stability calculation would indicate that the factor of safety is 0.7.

Further back, at line *B,* failure is less likely. At this location, the factor of safety might be 1.0.

Even further back, at line *C,* the chance of failure is very unlikely. At this point, the factor of safety might be 1.5.

Depending on the degree of safety, or factor of safety desired, a line such as line *C* would be picked as the area which is safe against sliding, or the "line behind which failure is unlikely."

The anchor should derive its strength in the soil or rock behind line *C*.

The pull-out strength of a cylinder of concrete can be estimated as the perimeter area of the concrete cylinder, times the shear strength of the soil along the cylinder. As an example, assume:

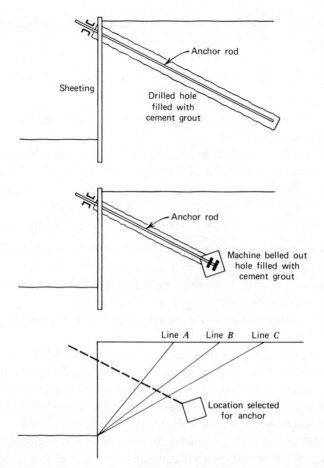

Fig. 12.7 Drilled tie back systems selection of depth of embedment.

Soil strength $= 1000 \text{ lb/ft}^2$ average at depth of anchor.
Anchor diameter $= 1$ ft; surface area $= 3$ ft per foot of length.
Desired capacity $= 50,000$ lb.
Desired factor of safety $= 1.5$.
Required length $= 25$ ft.

For a belled anchor, the depth below grade greatly influences the bearing capacity. Assume that at the depth involved, the bearing capacity equals $20,000 \text{ lb/ft}^2$. Then, the required size of the anchor is

$$\text{area} = 3.75 \text{ ft}^2; \qquad \text{diameter} = 27 \text{ in.}$$

Pull-out tests are performed on most jobs to verify the capacity of the anchors.

Construction of anchors requires some skill, experience, and considerable cooperation from the soil. The soil characteristics required include:

1. The soil must be strong enough to stand in an open hole without caving.

2. The hole should be dry, although it is possible with some modification in construction methods to develop satisfactorily an anchor when the hole is below the water level.

3. Absence of boulders or rock ledges which make drilling difficult, or deflects the drill bit and causes a crooked hole.

In most cases, anchors are considered to be temporary and useful in holding the excavation open during construction operations. In some cases, however, it may be desirable for the anchors to be permanent. In this case, the primary requirement is for the steel tie rod to be adequately covered by concrete, or other protection to resist rusting and deterioration.

Anchor rods usually carry loads on the order of 30,000 to as much as 100,000 lb. The most common loads are on the order of 50,000 lb. The rods usually are on the order of 1 in. in diameter and are made of high strength steel. The horizontal spacing between tie rods usually is on the order of 8 to 15 ft. Where deep excavations are required, the ties can be placed in rows, one below the other. The vertical spacing between ties is generally on the order of 6 to 8 ft. See Refs. 23 and 24.

The following formula may be used in determining the depth of embedment required to resist lateral loads where no constraint is provided at the ground surface, such as rigid or ground surface pavement. See following Section 12.6.

12.6   Free Standing Posts

Occasionally soldier piles are used to hold the shoring as free standing posts (see Fig. 12.8). The post develops resistance against leaning over by the soil's passive resistance. There are several ways to calculate

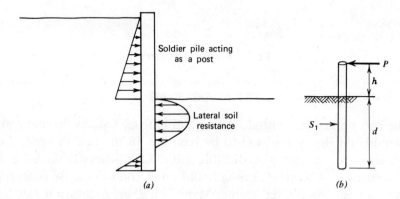

Fig. 12.8 Flagpole formula for calculating resistance to bending (From Uniform Building Code).

the strength against leaning over. Some such ways are formulas described as flagpole formulas (see formula below and Fig. 12.8).

$$d = \frac{A}{2}\left(1 + \sqrt{1 + \frac{4.36h}{A}}\right)$$

WHERE A = 2.34$P/S_1 b$

P = Applied lateral force in pounds.

S_1 = Allowable lateral soil-bearing pressure based on a depth of one-third the depth of embedment.

b = Diameter of round post or footing or diagonal dimension of square post or footing (ft).

h = Distance in feet from ground surface to point of application of P.

d = Depth of embedment in earth in feet but not over 12 ft. for purpose of computing lateral pressure.

12.7   Earth Pressures

12.7.1   Soil Types

The earth pressures behind shoring and bracing systems depend considerably on the type of soil to be retained. In the case of sand, the pressures are reasonably predictable and remain generally unchanged with changes in weather, rainfall, and other conditions. By contrast, clay soils can be unpredictable. Many times, an excavation can be made to the planned depth vertically, with the clay soil standing without shoring. Shoring is needed primarily to avoid risk as a clay tends to dry out, and blocks of clay fall into the excavation. However, if an excavation in clay is left open for a period of several months, as may be necessary on a construction job, it may go through a variety of weather conditions such as rainfall, snow, or freezing.

After shoring has been installed, the primary concern is rainfall and saturation of the soil. Saturation can cause the soil to lose strength and to become heavier. This greatly increases the pressure on the shoring.

Assuming that a shoring system to hold a clay bank was designed using an equivalent fluid pressure of 30 lb/ft² per foot of depth of soil. This same clay after saturation might lose most of its strength, and weigh well over 100 lb/ft³. The combined soil and water pressure might be on the order of 70 or 80 lb/ft² per foot of depth. This is more than twice the design pressure.

An even greater hazard can develop for shoring of soils which are expansive, such as adobe and gumbo clays. These soils expand when they become wet, and exert greater lateral pressures and tend to heave and to expand laterally. The lateral pressure on the shoring system may be increased by several hundred pounds per square foot.

12.7.2   Construction Methods

Soils require some deformation to develop their strength. This deformation may be in the range of 0.1 to 1.0% of the height of the excavation. A flexible design, which presses consistently against the soil embankment, but can permit some deformation to occur, may develop the optimum condition, sometimes called the "active" pressure. For this condition, the shoring system can be the minimum strength.

On the other hand, if the shoring system is very rigid, and no deformation of the soil is permitted, the soil remains in a condition which sometimes is called "at rest." In this case, the soil pressure acting on the shoring system may be 50% to as much as 100% greater. Rigid shoring frequently is required in congested city areas; otherwise, deformation will crack utility lines or buildings near the excavation.

Sandy soil behind a shoring system may dry out. If cracks or holes are open through the sheeting, the sand may tend to flow out through these openings. Continued bleeding of soil may undermine large blocks of soil which then may develop greater instability and exert greater force on the sheeting system.

Proper drainage of retained soil is essential for permanent and also temporary retaining systems. Where sheeting extends below water level, or where saturation may occur due to rainfall, it may be necessary to build in sand or gravel pervious filters and weepholes.

Constructing the sheeting or lagging so that it is not in uniform contact with the embankment is a potential cause for change in soil pressure. This was described previously.

12.7.3   Surcharge Loads

Surcharge loads, which may be applied from storing excavated soil, building materials, or equipment adjacent to the edge of the excavation, can impose considerably increased loads on the shoring system. A graph indicating increases in lateral pressure due to a wheel load placed adjacent to an excavation is shown in Fig. 12.9.

12.8   Slurry Trench

The slurry trench method has been used for many years in Europe. It was introduced in the United States in connection with major dam construction work, and more recently has been successfully used on

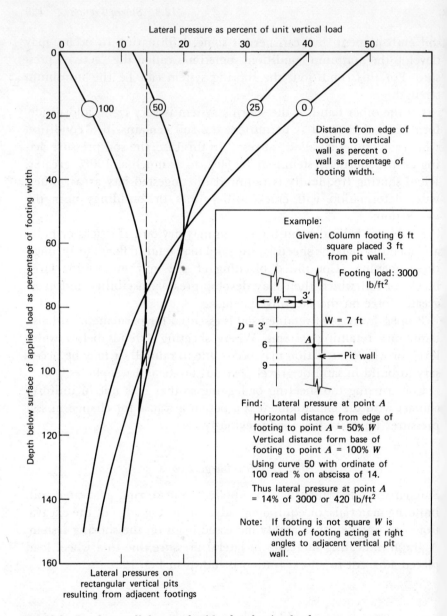

Fig. 12.9 Load on wall due to wheel load or footing load.

several large commercial buildings in New York, San Francisco, and other cities.

Essentially, a trench is excavated in sections. Each section is kept continuously full of slurry. The slurry is basically a mixture of water and clay or mud. Frequently the "mud" is bentonite. The slurry may be made heavier by certain additives, such as Baroid. The hydrostatic pressure of the slurry is sufficient to support the banks and prevent failure. In addition, the mud cake on the walls of the excavation prevents the slurry water from entering the soil and causing it to soften.

After the trench has been dug to the desired depth, a concrete tremie pipe is lowered to the bottom of the trench. Concrete is poured on the bottom and gradually rises and fills the trench, forcing out the slurry. This method is described in more detail in Ref. 26. One drawback to this method is that boulders, old wood piles, or other obstructions create problems in making the excavations.

12.9 Permanent Walls

In some cases, it is economical to make the temporary sheeting and lagging out of poured-in-place concrete. This concrete later becomes the permanent basement wall.

12.10 Trench Excavations

Deep trenches are required on more and more city streets for bigger and deeper utility lines. Many trenches are 50 ft deep. Trench excavations normally are cross-braced as they are dug.

Based on extensive measurements for deep excavations in clay soils, a lateral pressure diagram was developed which is considerably different from the common "equivalent fluid" system. This diagram is indicated in Fig. 12.10. A more detailed description of this method is given in Refs. 17 and 26.

Since trenches may be of great length, sometimes many miles in length, the amount of shoring and bracing is a major expense. Occasionally, contractors build a test excavation, and experiment with one

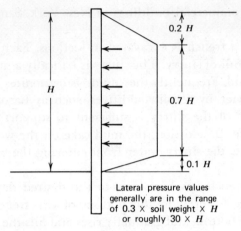

Lateral pressure values
generally are in the range
of 0.3 × soil weight × *H*
or roughly 30 × *H*

Fig. 12.10 *Note:* Horizontal pressure diagram for trench excavations in clay soils. The shape of the pressure diagram varies for various soils. Also, water levels higher than the bottom of the excavation impose additional loads.

or more methods of shoring and bracing to devise a workable and economical system.

Typical problems involved in projects include:

1. Loss of ground adjacent to the bracing system.

2. Serious bending of walers, or bending of cross-bracing or trench jacks.

3. Instability of bottom of excavation due to inadequate dewatering.

4. Softness of bottom of excavation due to inadequate underdrainage, resulting in settlement of pipeline when trench is backfilled.

5. Adjacent building foundations, requiring underpinning, additional bracing, or stabilization of soil under the foundations.

6. Long sustained dewatering may lower water under nearby structures supported on wood piles. These piles may rot in the "dry period" and lose so much strength that building settlements occur.

7. Undercutting of bedding planes or joints or fractures in rock, permitting a block of material to slide downward on a weak plane.

An article in *Civil Engineering Magazine* states:

Cave-ins are rated the number one cause of construction-worker deaths. At a recent meeting of the Construction Section of the National Safety Congress, it was revealed that, in the past two years, trench cave-ins were responsible for the death of more than 125 workers. A survey, conducted by the L. B. Foster Company and reported at the meeting, showed that most cave-ins are caused by unshored trenches, improper shoring, and excavated material stored too close to the edge of the trenches. It was found that half of the trenches, at accident sites, had no shoring at all.

And a recent news brief from *Civil Engineering-ASCE,* May 1973 states:

More than 110 fatalities occurred in trenching accidents at construction sites last year. This and several other startling statistics were revealed in a conference on the subject, held in late March by the Occupational Safety and Health Administration in Washington, D.C.

A half-day conference, attended by about 200 construction contractors, labor union officials, some architects and engineers, and OSHA officials, was hailed as the launching of a nation-wide drive to reduce the number of fatalities and injuries caused by cave-ins on construction excavations.

As is often the case in construction injury statistics, figures on loss of life and injury in such accidents are sketchy—for many reasons including the disparity of most state reporting systems. Nevertheless, Chain Robbins, deputy assistant secretary of Labor for OSHA, said that "more than 110" fatalities occurred in such accidents last year, along with many more injuries and near-fatal occurrences. Like Labor Secretary Peter J. Brennan, Robbins said that special emphasis on cave-in accidents and their prevention is "one of the first orders of business for the Labor department."

Discussions by a number of speakers, plus some slides and a joint Associated General Contractors-Laborers' Union film, quickly made it clear that the problem is one on which there is nearly complete agreement on all sides, and on which considerable effort has already been expended. Leonard E. Dodson, president of Olson Construction Co., Lincoln, Neb., speaking for AGC, outlined the establishment of a number of short-course "schools" throughout the U.S. providing one-day "courses" for construction foremen and others in proper trenching, shoring and protection methods; the preparation of the film and other training aids; and considerable general educational efforts. W. Vernon Reed, speaking for the AFL-CIO Building Trades department, enthusiastically supported contractor and OSHA efforts in this matter—and added that the unions would support what he called "capital punishment" (loss of jobs) for members who fail to abide by employers' safety regulations. "There is no enthusiasm among the unions," he said, "to protect men who fail to follow safety orders." Reed—an officer of the Laborers' International Union, added that union "job action" (picketing and other pressures) "are not unreasonable when (safety) matters are not going according to plan."

The labor representative offered the opinion that most accidents on construction jobs seem to be affecting younger workers over the past several years.

What emerged as a sort of theme for the meeting was the need for education, particularly of smaller contractors; plus the need for careful engineering planning of any excavation work (including soil studies to determine the type of treatment—shoring, sloping, bracing, etc.) that may be required to make excavation safer.

12.11   Summary

Primary points in this chapter are as follows:

FACTS: Cave-ins occur frequently. Newspapers and trade magazines are full of accounts of cave-ins and bracing failures. Shoring systems must be built better than has been the past practice. The shoring system should be a cooperative design by the builder and the designer.

WATCH OUT FOR: Loose shoring which would permit large movements of a large block of soil. The starting of movements should be watched for—signs include subsidence adjacent to shoring, cracks in the ground, frequent noise, and creaking of the system.

13

Backfills

Probably the most important filling operation on most conventional building jobs, and one which is given the least attention, is backfilling. This includes backfilling around basement walls and backfills over utility lines and other buried service lines. These backfills frequently become important, because so many of them are done carelessly, resulting in broken water lines and also in settlements of floor slabs, sidewalks, streets, and highways. This leads to many lawsuits against contractors.

Backfills must be placed in restricted spaces, limiting the choice of equipment. Backfills should be compacted with mechanical equipment such as small sheepsfoot rollers, small vibrating rollers, or small rubber-tire wheel rollers.

Where space is more restricted, tamping equipment such as Ingersoll-Rand "simplex" or "triplex" tampers or Barco tampers or Wacker tampers frequently are used.

In special circumstances, such as in clean sandy soils, backfills can be compacted by jetting. In most cases, however, jetting, ponding, or flooding produce a low-density fill. Such fills usually settle later.

13.1   Selection of Material

Backfills placed around structures are relatively small in volume. Therefore, the cost of material becomes small compared to the time of men and equipment required to compact it into place. Many times, it is more economical to import good quality material, which will compact easily, rather than to deal with on-site excavated soils which are difficult to compact.

13.2   Backfills Behind Walls

Backfills behind walls generally are in deep and narrow slots. The biggest problem is to get men and equipment down into the work area. Hand-operated tampers such as Ingersoll-Rand "powder puffs," Barco rammers, Wacker tampers, and similar machines generally are used. In most cases, engineers specify that the backfill be placed by mechanical methods. It takes energy and work to shove the soil down into a compact condition. Most soils will not compact by dropping into the hole, or by flooding or jetting. Only very occasionally are the soil conditions "right" so that jetting will work (see Section 13.4).

In some cases, the lower part of a narrow excavation is filled by dumping in pea-gravel. As soon as the backfill is up high enough to permit normal working operations, the pea-gravel is tamped on top, and then soil backfill is placed in layers to complete the remainder of the backfill.

It is important that soil backfill be placed in layers, similar to general site grading fills, as described in Chapter 23. Generally, the layers should be on the order of 6 to 8 in. thick, and each layer should be tamped before the next layer is placed. After the working area becomes about 5 or 6 ft wide, many kinds of small rolling compacters and vibrating compacters are available which are more efficient. Typical pieces of equipment include vibrating machines on the order of 3 ft wide. Manufacturers of such equipment are listed in Ref. 27.

In addition, it is possible to use a piece of machinery on top of the bank with a boom extending down in the hole, with a vibrating tamper attached to the end of the boom. Such a machine can reach to depths on the order of 20 ft. It is more efficient than tamping with hand-operated small machines, and also increases safety, since a man does not have to be at the bottom of the excavation.

After basement walls have been poured and stripped, the narrow slot between the back of the wall and the sloping face of the excavation can be a hazardous place to work. In most states, an area restricted by basement walls adjacent to an embankment is considered to be a trench, and the safety laws apply to men working in such locations in the same manner as for men working in pipeline trenches.

Lateral pressures develop on the basement wall as the fill is placed and compacted. Usually, there is a slight yielding of the wall. This yielding is usually small, probably less than 1/10 of 1% of the height of the wall. For a wall 20 ft deep, the yielding of the wall might be ¼ in. Compacting of soil behind the wall may exert a fairly strong pressure on the wall. Therefore, temporary bracing frequently is placed to restrain the walls during placing of fill. An alternate is to place the interior floor slabs in position as cross bracing before the backfill is placed.

Soils engineers sometimes make the mistake of calculating lateral pressures on a retaining wall by considering the natural soil existing before start of construction. In construction, however, the natural soil usually is all ripped out. The wall is built and then some of the removed soil, or other soil, is backfilled behind the wall. The lateral pressures on the wall are generated primarily by the backfill. Therefore, the wall cannot be properly designed until the designer knows what the backfill will be. Generally, this is handled by requiring that the natural soil be reused as backfill, or that a better soil be used, and that the soil be compacted to a specified density. If the natural soil is silt or clay, or is wet and sloppy, the specifications may require that other soil be used. Backfill generally is described in specifications by sieve sizes or by typical local names. Typical specifications for imported backfill soils are as follows:

The soil shall be predominantly sand or sand and gravel, with not more than 20% passing the number 200 sieve.

The fill shall be free of clods, wood, or masonry debris, or other deleterious material. The fill shall be compacted in layers not exceeding 8 in. in thickness, and shall be compacted to a density of 90% of the maximum, determined by the Modified AASHO Method of Compaction Testing.

Many walls are waterproofed, and drains are placed at the toe of the wall as indicated in Fig. 13.1.

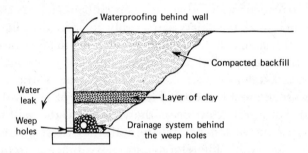

Fig. 13.1   Failure of good drainage system due to improper back filling.

The backfill is placed in layers and compacted. However, the compacted fill may contain a layer of compacted silt or clay soil, as shown in Fig. 13.1. This layer would stop downward natural flow of water. The water would perch on the clay layer. It could not get down to the drain. Therefore, water would build up on top of the clay layer and may find a weakness in the waterproofing on the wall. In this case, the water will flow through the wall.

For basements extending below ground water, drainage will be necessary during construction. Usually, well points, deep wells, perimeter trenches and sumps, or other systems are installed to draw down the water level. A tendency for water to collect at the sides of the excavation will be a problem in attempting to put in a good compacted backfill. Therefore, one approach is to use pea-gravel or clean sand for the first few feet of the backfill. If necessary, small sumps can be installed temporarily to permit pumping out excess water.

13.3   Backfill for Large Culverts

Large corrugated metal culverts are used frequently under roadways. The corrugated metal is quite flexible and is not sufficiently strong to act as a bridge. Therefore, it depends to a great degree on the strength of the soil backfill surrounding the culvert for stability. Detailed construction procedures for placing such fills are outlined in manuals, such as Ref. 28.

13.4   Backfills in Utility Trenches

Utility trenches are constructed inside building sites, from the building sites to streets, through streets, and cross-country. There are many theories about pipeline construction and backfilling.

The bedding and the support for pipes are extremely important. In most cases, the pipes themselves are designed structurally to carry the overburden soil loads only, with some help from the supporting soils. In these cases, bedding or shaping of the bottom of the trench to fit the contours of the pipe, or other schemes for providing support in the lower one-third or one-half of the pipe, are important to prevent the pipe from squashing down and cracking. Several typical cross sections for providing bedding for pipelines are shown on Fig. 13.2. Detailed discussions of culvert or pipeline bedding are contained in Refs. 28 and 29, Chapters 24 and 25.

In some cases, it is considered more economical to put additional money into the pipe itself. It is made structurally strong enough to carry the full overburden soil pressure even though bearing only on a flat hard surface. In this way, special bedding procedures and special care and procedures in placing backfill around and over the pipe can be eliminated.

Pipeline excavations can be cut vertically or with sloping sides. Vertical excavations require removal of less material and can be cut with trenching machines. However, most vertical sided trenches must be braced or shored. In wide open country, it may be cheaper to slope the sides of trenches to eliminate bracing and shoring. The shape of the excavation can have a considerable effect on the load

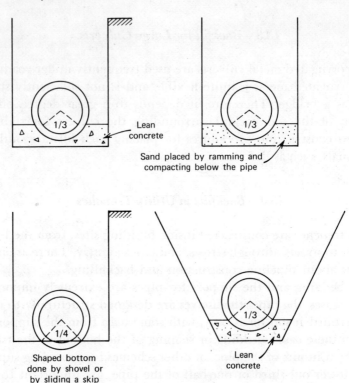

Fig. 13.2 Pipeline bedding. For more information, see Refs. 28 and 29.

that the backfill imposes on the pipe, and sometimes specifications will require a particular shape.

Trench bracing is specified, with typical designs, by federal and state safety codes. However, there is considerable leeway within the codes, since the codes have fairly unspecific definitions for soil conditions. There is a lot of ground between "hard" and "soft." Therefore, the contractor has considerable leeway in selecting a shoring system and must make several decisions.

For deep trenches, some soils engineering information can be helpful in preparing trench designs. Alternately, experiments can be made. Test trenches can be dug, and shored using a particular design, to see if it will work. If trouble develops, then a revised design can be tried. Lateral pressures on shoring in the dry may be on the order of 20 to 30 lb/ft of depth. However, below water level, these pressures can become three times greater, such as 70 to 80 lb/ft per foot of depth.

Backfill in pipelines has traditionally been placed by dumping in the soil, and then flooding or jetting the soil with water to cause settlement. Over the years, however, it has been found that generally such backfills settle and subside. Where they underlie roadways, the roads require repairs continually, and the roads are rough and unsatisfactory to motorists.

When can flooding or jetting be used? Generally, it has been found that clean sand soils will compact moderately well by flooding and jetting. If the soil at the bottom of the trench is free-draining sand, and the water level is below the bottom of the trench, the jetting water will flow downward through the fill soils and out of the bottom of the trench. Generally downward drainage results in reasonably good compaction of sand backfill. Tests on sand backfill under these conditions usually indicate compaction of 85 to 90%, based on modified AASHO. However, for silt or clay backfill soils, or sand containing some silt or clay, jetting is not very effective. The backfill usually remains soft and sloppy for some time and test densities are usually below 85% compaction.

In St. Louis, a committee of the American Society of Civil Engineers performed a 5-year study of backfilling practices. Their report reached the following conclusions:

1. The mechanical (hand) tamper is relatively ineffective in obtaining consistently satisfactory dry densities in cohesive soil backfills for use under sidewalks, pavements, and lightly loaded structures.

2. The mobile trench compacter (under certain conditions and with certain limitations) can produce consistently satisfactory dry densities in cohesive soil backfills for use under pavements and lightly loaded structures.

3. The jetting method of compacting cohesive soils and trenches does not produce satisfactory dry densities for use under sidewalks, pavements, and lightly loaded structures within a reasonable period of time.

For backfills in streets, it is common for the bottom several feet of fill to be placed in fairly thick layers, such as 2 ft thick, with only a moderate amount of compaction. However, the top 2 to 3 ft under-neath the pavement generally is required to be compacted to 90%. It is fairly common for the pavement patch to be considered as temporary, and that new patching and repairs will be required in the future after some settlement has occurred.

For backfills in cross-country pipelines, the backfill generally is thrown in loose, and the top is wheel-rolled. However, compaction is required for road crossings. For crossings of railroad tracks or free-ways, tunneling with a horizontal auger drill is common.

Where pipelines underlie foundations of structures or other facili-ties which cannot permit settlements, it is necessary for fills to be placed in thin layers, 6 to 8 in. thick, and each layer to be compacted with mechanical equipment. For these conditions, mechanical equip-ment is required even for sandy soils. Such backfills usually are tested by the engineer to assure proper compaction.

13.5   Submerged Pipelines

It is extremely difficult to build pipelines under submerged condi-tions. In addition, there may be difficulty in holding a pipeline down. Frequently, pipelines and buried tanks, when empty, have popped out of the ground because of high water level in the ground. For this reason, the commonly used well point system was developed. It is by far the most satisfactory system for dewatering pipeline alignments temporarily, for stabilizing the excavation, and for permitting back-fill to be placed and compacted.

Sometimes pipelines are constructed by placing a gravel base below the pipe invert, and by placing submersible pumps in the gravel to pull out the water. This works well in many soils, but in some cases the upward movement of water through the soil can cause a soft or even a quick condition on the bottom of the trench, which results in wavy inverts and lawsuits.

Frequently, pipelines, such as gas pipelines of large diameter, are fought through by making wide excavations, securing the pipeline in position by use of screwed-in anchors, and then throwing in the backfill loosely. Releveling and grading are done to compensate for large settlements of the backfill. This method is satisfactory on cross-country pipelines, but not under pavements.

A wide variety of equipment is used for compacting backfill in trenches. At the bottom of the trench and around the haunch of the pipe, soil may be shoved into place by shovel or by ramming with sticks, or compacted by small vibrators or hand-operated tampers. As the fill comes up to the top of the pipe, small vibrators can be used. After the fill is about 1 to 2 ft over the top of the pipeline, it is customary to use rubbertire rollers, small tractors, or vibrating drum rollers. After the fill is up to within 2 or 3 ft of the surface, larger equipment such as sheepsfoot rollers or truck wheel rolling is common.

In vertical trenches, the lower portion of the fill is compacted by small hand tools, and only the top 2 or 3 ft of fill can be compacted by large mechanical equipment.

It is difficult to moisten or otherwise condition the fill soil "in place" in the bottom of a trench. Therefore, if the soil must be dried, moisture added, or other changes made, these changes should be made on the top before the material is dumped into the trench. On top, there is room for using trucks with spray bars for moistening the soils, and using scarifying tools for mixing the soil.

Rocks can be a problem in the backfill, since they puncture the protective wrapping. While the excavated soil is on top, soil free from rocks can be selected and placed around the pipe. Otherwise, the pipe wrapping must be thicker or protected by some method.

13.6   Summary

Primary points in this chapter are as follows:

FACTS: Backfills are a nuisance to the contractor. Generally they are done piecemeal, and it is expensive to have compaction machinery sitting around waiting for the next piece of backfill to be ready. Frequently, it rains in the trench about the time the backfill should be placed. Therefore, backfills frequently are loose. They settle, resulting in disagreements with the owner.

WATCH OUT FOR:
1. Contracts involving high ground water.
2. Steep slopes or trench walls which have soil "falling off" or have cracks on top, back from the edge of the slope.
3. Backfill which is too wet or too dry and would be difficult to work in a trench.
4. Large sharp rocks in the soil, which may be a problem in backfilling.

14

Foundations

14.1 Spread Footings

Spread footings generally consist of a pad of concrete placed at a shallow distance below the ground surface to support a building column. Spread footings are the most common type of building foundations.

Typical average bearing values for use in the design of spread footings are listed in Table 14.1 (see table Pg. 156). This is typical of bearing values listed in many building codes. Generally, these bearing values are considered to be conservative. Usually, higher bearing values can be determined as a result of sampling and testing of the soils. Most building departments will accept higher loads based on laboratory tests and soils engineering recommendations.

Sometimes bearing values are presented in graphical form. A typical bearing value graph is presented in Fig. 14.1.

The soil below the footings should be as firm as the soil on which the footings rest, down to a depth of at least 1.5 times the footing width. Also, the foundation soil should be the same classification as shown on the plans. Soil conditions frequently change appreciably from one footing to the next. In general, a footing should bear on uniform soil. If there is a marked change, contact the soils engineer.

Table 14.1 Typical bearing values for design of spread footings from Uniform Building Code 1970.

Class of Material	Minimum Depth of Footing Below Adjacent Virgin Ground (ft)	Value Permissible if Footing is at Minimum Depth, lb/ft²	Increase in Value for Each Foot of Depth that Footing is Below Minimum Depth, lb/ft²	Maximum Value lb/ft²
1	2	3	4	5
Rock	0	20% of ultimate crushing strength	0	20% of ultimate crushing strength
Compact coarse sand	1	1500^a	300^a	8000
Compact fine sand	1	1000^a	200^a	8000
Loose sand	2	500^a	100^a	3000
Hard clay or sandy clay	1	4000	800	8000
Medium-stiff clay or sandy clay	1	2000	200	6000
Soft sandy clay or clay	2	1000	50	2000
Expansive soils	1' 6"	1000^b	50	
Compact inorganic sand and silt mixtures	1	1000	200	4000
Loose inorganic sand silt mixtures	2	500	100	1000
Loose organic sand and silt mixtures and muck or bay mud	0	0	0	0

[a] These values are for footings 1 ft in width and may be increased in direct proportion to the width of footing to a maximum of of three times the designated value.

[b] For depths greater than 8 ft use values given for clay of comparable consistency.

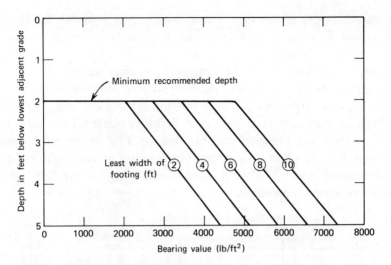

Fig. 14.1   Bearing value graph.

14.2   *Footings on Sloping Ground*

Usually, footings are stepped on sloping ground in staircase fashion. Occasionally, where the ground surface slope is relatively flat, foundations are poured to conform to the slope.

Where one footing will be near another and at a higher elevation, it is common practice to restrict the placement so that a plane drawn from the lower corner of high footing, at an angle of 45 degrees from the horizontal, will not intersect the lower footing. This concept is shown on Fig. 14.2. Obviously, the lower footing should be built and backfilled first. In some cases, however, it will be necessary to dig down below an adjacent footing to install a new footing at a lower elevation. The slope angle above may not always be safe for this condition. If, for instance, the soil is sand with a friction angle of 30 degrees, the stable slope of 30 degrees would mean that the upper footing would fail. Consult the soils engineer on methods of handling this problem.

If it becomes necessary to place a footing closer than the 45-degree line, the bearing value for the upper footing may have to be limited, and it may be expected that the lower footing would experience somewhat larger settlements, since it will carry some of the load of the upper footing. It may be better to place the upper footing at greater depth. Also, the upper footing could be moved back, and the footing-to-column connection designed for eccentricity.

There is another problem—dealing with foundations on sedimentary rock or stratified soil. This condition is shown in Fig. 14.2. Even though the soil or rock is firm, each bedding plane on the right side of the trench is a plane of possible sliding. The wedge *ABC* cannot be used for foundation support. The footing at the right must be kept beyond point *C*. By contrast, the footing at the left can be placed closer to the trench.

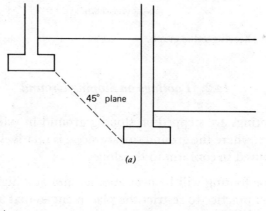

(a)

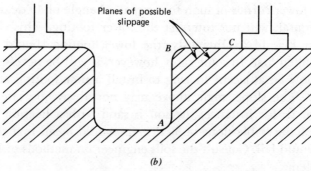

(b)

Fig. 14.2   (a) Limitations affecting adjacent stepped footings. (b) Potential failure along bedding planes of rock into a trench affects location of adjacent spread footings.

14.3   Belled Caissons

Drilling machines have been developed to install belled caissons such as sketched in Fig. 14.3. The type of drilling machine used is shown in Fig. 4.5. Generally, this is a very economical type of foundation, because this caisson generally is not reinforced. It is designed as a short column, not requiring vertical reinforcing steel.

Such caissons are considered to be deep spread footings for design purposes. Bearing values, such as discussed under spread footings, are used for design. Because of the considerable depth of the base of the caissons, higher bearing values generally are used. In calculating the weight of the caisson, the weight of soil removed is deducted from the weight of concrete.

Occasionally, a modified form of belled caisson is installed by drilling a large diameter open shaft, pouring a circular footing on

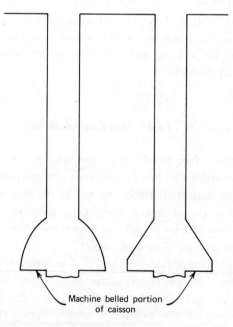

Machine belled portion
of caisson

Fig. 14.3   Belled caisson.

the bottom, and coming up with a pedestal. Frequently, sono-tube paper forms are used for casting the column.

Occasionally, drilled caissons are excavated with straight shafts down to a hard layer or bedrock. The caisson is designed as a spread footing, using the allowable bearing pressure on the base of the footing (see Chapter 21).

14.4   *Continuous Footings*

Continuous footings, such as wall footings, strap footings, girder foundations are elongated spread footings made long enough to carry a wall or a row of several columns.

The excavation for such long footings sometimes can be done with trench diggers which can be a speedy and economical excavation system. Such excavations may be trimmed by hand to the neat size of a proposed continuous footing, and concrete is poured without the use of side forms. Elimination of carpenter work for forming can save time and money. These foundations always are reinforced.

Continuous footings have the advantage of being able to "bridge" or "span" over local soft areas. Therefore, they may offer more uniform support for a long wall or row of columns than individual footings would provide.

14.5   *Mat Foundations*

Mat foundations frequently are used under very heavy structures. They are continuous in both directions and therefore occupy a large area. Mat foundations usually are thick, involve a large volume of concrete and a considerable weight of reinforcing steel, and are expensive. They can be an advantage where there is upward hydrostatic pressure due to high water level.

Since a mat foundation, with the sidewalls of the building, acts somewhat like a barge, it has some advantages. The weight of soil excavated before pouring the mat foundation can be deducted from the total weight of the building, which may substantially reduce settlement. In some cases, mat foundations are placed at such a depth

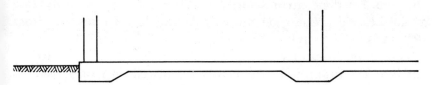

Fig. 14.4   Slab foundation.

that the weight of soil removed will equal the gross weight of the building. In this case, future building settlements usually are very small, since no new load is placed on the soil below the mat foundation.

Mat foundations act like continuous footings, in both directions, and therefore can bridge over soft spots. This results in more uniform support for building columns.

14.6   Slab Foundations

Slab foundations frequently are used under one-story and two-story light structures such as houses, school buildings, and light industrial and commercial buildings.

Usually, the edge of the slab is thickened to form a perimeter footing. In addition, ribs or pads may be placed as thickened parts of the slab to support walls or footings. Such a foundation is shown in Fig. 14.4.

This design is primarily used for economy. It is not suitable in areas of deep freezing, high water levels, or expansive soils.

"Waffle" slabs of this type are a standard design for the Los Angeles City School District.

14.7   Temporary Loads

The bearing values given in Fig. 14.1 apply to static dead loads, static live loads, and frequently applied live loads.

Temporary loads may be applied by wind forces or earthquake lateral forces, impact forces, or other temporary loads of very short duration. For these circumstances, it is common to allow an increase in the bearing pressure on the soil. Allowable increases vary from 10% to as much as 100%. An increase of 33% is common.

Temporary loads may be applied to footings during construction. For instance, tilt-up walls frequently are placed on footing pads at column locations, and then the continuous footing under the tilt-up wall is poured.

In such a case, the footing may be loaded to a much higher bearing pressure than its design pressure when the building is completed.

Generally, there is reserve strength to permit overloading the foundation. This is sometimes called the factor of safety. Factors of safety frequently range from 1.5 to 4.0.

If temporary loads are planned which will considerably exceed the design bearing value, the plan should be reviewed with the structural designer of the building to make sure that the reserve strength of the foundation will not be exceeded. Sometimes foundations are failed by temporary construction loadings.

14.8   Compacted Soils Foundation

Many soils are deposited naturally in a loose state, so that they provide poor support for spread foundations. Therefore, pile foundations or other expensive foundations are used frequently.

In many such cases, it is more economical to excavate the soft or loose soils. Sometimes these soils can be reused for constructing compacted fills; in other cases, imported soils are necessary to construct a suitable soil fill. These soils are used to backfill the excavation. Soil fills can be engineered and constructed to support desired foundation loads. Such fills become part of the foundation structure system, and sometimes are referred to as "structural fills."

In one case of this type, the foundation for a power plant was to bear on a layer 20 ft thick of loose silty fine sand. It was found to be economical to remove the loose soil. After removal, the soil was recompacted into the excavation. It shrank from a thickness of 20 to 15 ft. Additional soil was imported to make up the shrinkage. The foundations for the power plant were placed on this "structural fill" (see Ref. 30).

Occasionally, soils are compacted in place to increase their bearing capacity for support of foundations. Methods of compaction in place are described in Chapter 23.

14.9   Tolerances

14.9.1   Footing Locations

In early stages of construction, some confusion on the site may cause one or more foundations to be poured out of position. A question then develops regarding usability of the footings.

In some cases, the footings were lifted out by crane and reset at the proper locations. In one case, a number of footings were 2 ft out of position. Holes were drilled into the footings. Bolts were grouted into the holes, and the footings were lifted out. The bottoms of the footings were hosed off. New footing excavations were cut, extending 4 in. over depth. Four inches of fresh concrete was poured, and the footings were set on the fresh concrete.

Sliding footings laterally a few inches by use of jacks or heavy construction equipment have been given serious consideration in more than one instance, but the writers do not know of an actual case. This would appear to involve some risk, due to disturbing and loosening the soils under the footings, thus encouraging settlement.

It is possible that the column connection to the footing could take some bending moment, in which case the offset footing still could be used, in its offset position. This must be reviewed with the structural engineer.

Where footing excavations are cut neat into the soil and side forms are not used, foundations occasionally extend out farther on one side than planned. This would appear to result in an eccentric foundation. However, so long as the foundation is as large or larger than planned in the other three directions, no case is known where such possible eccentricity has created a problem.

14.10   Drying or Saturation

The soils in the bottom of a foundation excavation may be altered considerably by drying or by saturation.

Drying should be restricted and can be controlled by frequent sprinkling of the soils, or covering with plastic, canvas, loose dirt, or straw.

Soils which are seriously dried, and which shrink and crack badly, may be expected to regain their moisture content after the footing and the building have been completed. Regaining moisture may cause the soils to swell and heave, possibly lifting some foundations or the floor slab.

Foundation excavations frequently become saturated during heavy rains, since water collects at this low area. Generally, the most satisfactory solution is to overexcavate to remove the soft soil.

If the reinforcing steel already has been placed, other experiments may be worth trying. Probings could be made to determine the thickness of softened soil and the likely increase in settlements. For flexible structures, the anticipated additional settlement may not be too serious a problem.

In a few cases, heaters and blowers have been used to cause rapid drying of saturated soils.

14.11   Overexcavation

Many foundation excavations are made with large excavating machinery. Large machines working in small restricted spaces sometimes are difficult to control, and overexcavation may occur.

In one such case, foundation excavations were made, steel was placed, and the concrete truck was there ready to pour concrete. Inspection of the bottoms of the excavations included probing with a steel rod. In almost all excavations, the rod could be pushed easily 6 to 12 in. into the bottom soils.

The bottom of the excavation was level. It was found that the operator had dug deeper as much as 12 in. Then he put loose soil back in the excavation to level the bottom of the excavation.

Many cases have been noted in which the soils at the bottom of foundation excavations are disturbed as a result of accidental overexcavation. Replacement of the soil was done hurriedly to hide the mistake. Therefore, the replaced soils are not adequately compacted, but are looser than the natural soils.

Generally, it is cheaper to accept overexcavation. The overexcavation can be made up with lean concrete. Lean concrete is simple to pour and may be appreciably less expensive than attempting to recompact soils in a small area. Lean concrete backfill generally is considered to be part of the soil foundation, and is not considered to be an extension of the concrete foundation itself.

Frequently, a foundation bottom is irregular due to problems in excavating the soil. A natural tendency is to "level up" the bottom of the excavation. It looks better and is easier to set the steel. Leveling up is done with soil or gravel. The leveling material should be compacted and tested. However, most soils engineers agree that it is better to leave the bottom rough, in undisturbed soil, and just pour extra concrete to fill in the low areas. The extra concrete can be poured first, if easier to set the reinforcing steel.

14.12   Eccentric Loads

Overturning loads, resulting in eccentric forces on foundations, are common for structures subject to wind or earthquake loads, or for retaining walls.

The common method of analyzing the foundation pressures has been to convert eccentricity into a triangular-shaped soil pressure. This is indicated in Fig. 14.5.

Usually, the designer restricts the maximum edge pressure to the allowable design bearing pressure, or to the design bearing pressure plus an allowable increase for temporary loads.

An alternate solution also is shown. In this case, it is assumed that eccentricity places the center of force at a new location. One end of the footing can be "theoretically trimmed off" so that the resulting remaining portion of the foundation is concentric. In this case, the smaller foundation can be designed using the full design bearing pressures as described previously.

14.13   Inclined Footings

Inclined footings sometimes are used as foot blocks for bracing, as ie-back anchors, and as anchor blocks for pipeline bends. Such foot-

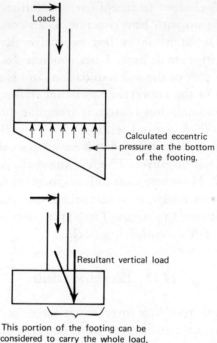

Loads

Calculated eccentric pressure at the bottom of the footing.

Resultant vertical load

This portion of the footing can be considered to carry the whole load, as a concentric load, resulting in larger but uniform bearing pressures on the reduced width of footing.

Fig. 14.5 Distribution of bearing pressure under eccentrically loaded footing.

ings have a lower bearing capacity than for vertically loaded footings at the same average depth. A rough guide for estimating the reduction in bearing capacity is given in Fig. 14.6 and below.

	Usable Bearing Value as a Percentage of Vertical Bearing Value	
Inclination of Load from Vertical (deg)	For Clay (%)	For Sand (%)
0	100	100
30	80	40
45	70	25
60	60	15
90	50	10

Fig. 14.6 See Ref. 17. Typical inclined footing.

14.14 Foundations on Expansive Soils

Several constructors of housing tracts have been hurt financially as a result of constructing numbers of houses on expansive soils. These soils expand when they get wet, and shrink when they dry out. Volume changes may be 5 to 10% or more (see Chapter 7, Section 7.11, Chapter 8, Section 8.10, and Fig. 14.7).

The first problem is to identify the soil. Sometimes a clue can be found by examination of the site. Soils that are expansive usually are hard and cracked when they are dry. Cracks in the ground may be ½ to 1 in. wide and several feet deep. The hard clods of soil are like a brick and cannot be broken easily. When wet, the soil is plastic, like modeling clay.

At least four approaches are used to solve the problem:

1. Keep the moisture content constant.
2. Place foundations below the depth of moisture change.
3. Treat the expansive soil with chemicals such as lime to stabilize it.
4. Excavate and remove the expansive soil in building areas. Replace with stable soil (see Fig. 14.7 *a* and *b*).

14.15 Franki Foundations

A type of foundation popular in Europe and other parts of the world, and used in some parts of the United States, is called the Franki foundation. Foundations may be constructed at shallow depths, which are similar to spread foundations. They are installed by use of a special rig.

In this method, a bulb of low water content concrete is pounded into the ground at the foundation level. This displaces and compacts the surrounding natural soil. The resulting foundation acts

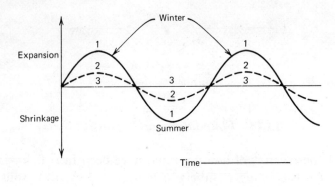

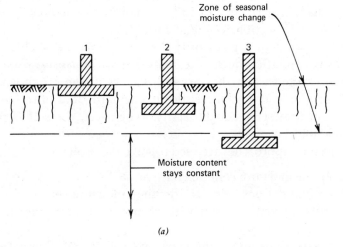

Fig. 14.7   (*a*) Seasonal behavior of expansive soils.

similar to a spread foundation, but bears on soil which has been pre-compacted to a much higher strength. This foundation is described in more detail in Chapter 19, Section 19.6.3.

14.16   *Foundations on Hot Soils*

Chemicals in some soils can corrode steel and deteriorate concrete. They are called hot soils (see Chapter 7, Section 7.13, Chapter 8, Section 8.9, and Chapter 10, Section 10.10). If laboratory tests or field resistivity tests indicate such conditions, special precautions may be

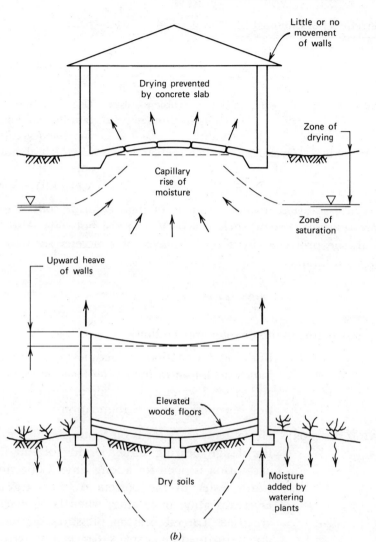

Fig. 14.7 (*b*) Behavior of structures in expansive soils.

necessary to protect the concrete and the reinforcing steel. Based on experience, tables have been prepared showing percentages of chemicals which could cause problems. Based on Ref. 31, an abbreviated table showing the amounts of chemicals which could cause problems is given on Pg. 170.

Percent SO_3 Contained In

Ground Water	Clay Soil	Seriousness	Recommend
0 – 0.03	0 – 0.2	No special problem	No special measures
0.03 – 0.1	0.2 – 0.5	Some problems especially in thin concrete walls	Use sulphate resistant Portland cement concrete (type II)
Over 0.1	Over 0.5	Serious problems	Use high alumina or super-sulphate cement (type V)

A typical solution in high sulphate or high chloride soils is to use more resistant cement, such as type V, to resist hot soils. Also, steel should be protected by a thicker cover of concrete, such as 4-in. cover minimum.

14.17 Summary

Primary points in this chapter are as follows:

FACTS: Building foundations sometimes are poured on loose backfill, or in the wrong location. Some soil and ground water can corrode or cause deterioration of concrete or steel foundations.

WATCH OUT FOR: Heavy temporary loads on footings which exceed the design bearing value. Drying of soil if the excavation is open for a long time. Collection of storm water in the bottom of the excavation. Overexcavation of footings when large machines are used. Lateral bearing pressures on footings due to inclined raker struts. Cracked or expansive soil.

15

Settlement

15.1 General

During construction, as building column loads are placed on foundations, the foundations will settle.

If the foundations are on extremely hard soil or rock, the settlements may be very small. However, if they are on ordinary valley soils, settlement may be a fraction of an inch or several inches. Settlements of $1/2$ to 1 in. are common.

A substantial amount of the settlement may occur during construction. In other cases, settlements occur very slowly, and for many years after construction is complete (see Ref. 32).

15.2 Calculated Settlements

A system of laboratory tests and of calculations has been devised to estimate settlements for a proposed foundation.

Under Chapter 8, Section 8.6, consolidation tests were discussed. These tests measure the compression of soil under load, and the speed at which compression occurs.

When load is placed on a foundation, this load is transferred downward to each of the soil layers underlying the foundation. This pressure distribution is indicated in Fig. 15.1.

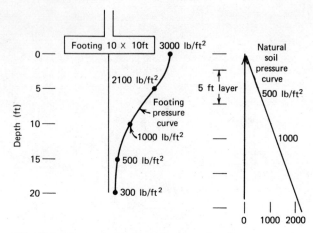

Fig. 15.1   Pressure distribution through soil.

Table 15.1   Typical Settlement values for a column load of
300,000 lb

Soil Type	Bearing Pressure (lb/ft²)	Footing Size (ft)	Settlement (in.)
Hard clay	10,000	5½ × 5½	0.5
Compact sand	10,000	5½ × 5½	0.3
Mod. firm clay	3,000	10 × 10	1.5
Mod. compact sand	3,000	10 × 10	0.8
Soft clay	1,500	14 × 14	3.0
Loose sand	1,500	14 × 14	1.5

Immediately under the footing, the soil pressure is increased to approximately the full bearing pressure load. At depths of 10 or 20 ft below the ground surface, the load is spread out, and the increase in pressure is small.

To estimate settlements, the soil underlying a proposed foundation is divided into layers. The settlement of each layer is estimated; then these numbers are added together for the total settlement.

The natural soil pressure curve in Fig. 15.1 indicates that the soil pressure at a depth of 5 ft is approximately 500 lb/ft² since the soil weighs approximately 100 lb/ft³. The new foundation will have a bearing pressure, due to dead and other static real loads, of 3000 lb/ft². Momentary loads due to wind, seismic, and other infrequent and short-term loadings are deducted generally, since they have relatively little effect on settlement. The soil pressure is distributed through the soil, and therefore increased pressure at a depth of 5 ft is not 3000 lb/ft², but is approximately 2100 lb/ft².

Since the normal pressure at a depth of 5 ft is 500 lb/ft², this pressure will be increased to 2600 lb/ft² as the result of the footing. Based on the laboratory consolidation test, it was found that a sample obtained from a depth of 5 ft consolidated very little when a load of 500 lb/ft² was applied. This is reasonable, since the soil already had been loaded to 500 lb/ft², and already had consolidated. The very small consolidation is taken as the starting point for our measurement. Continuing the consolidation test by applying heavier loads, it is found that the soil consolidates an additional 1%, when the full load of 2600 lb/ft² has been applied to the soil sample.

Assuming this layer is 5 ft thick, the total compression of the layer is 0.6 in. (60 in. × 1% = 0.6 in.).

Similar calculations can be made for all of the other layers under the foundation. The total is the expected settlement of the footing, probably in the range of 1.5 in.

Some typical values of estimated settlements for foundations on various types of soils are indicated in Table 15.1.

15.3 Measured Settlements

Settlements frequently are measured. The measurements can be made most easily and accurately if bench marks are set in columns during early phases of construction.

If no such bench marks were set, settlement surveys are compared back to the "as-built" elevations for foundations or supported floor slabs. These records usually are much less accurate.

15.4 Settlement During Construction

Certain soils, such as sands and free-draining materials, settle quickly under load. These settlements may occur almost entirely during the construction period. Therefore, practically no settlements will occur after the building is completed.

By contrast, silt and clay soils are slow draining. Therefore, settlements will occur during construction but also will continue for many years after construction is completed.

During consolidation testing in the laboratory, the speed at which the test sample compresses can be measured. This is an indicator of the speed of settlement to be expected for a foundation.

A method of calculation has been set up to estimate the time required for most of the settlement to occur. Drainage of a layer of soil depends on its rate of drainage and the thickness of the layer. When a sample of a particular soil layer has been tested, the time required for consolidation of the soil layer can be estimated by comparing the thickness of the test sample with the thickness of the soil layer in the ground.

Test Sample	Soil Layer
Thickness = 1 in.	Thickness = 10 ft.
Speed of settlement = 30 min.	One-half thickness = 60 in.
Note: Drainage from top and bottom applies to the test sample and also to the soil layer. Thus, drainage path is one-half the thickness of the layer.	Time for settlement $$= \frac{30 \text{ min} \times 60 \times 60}{\frac{1}{2} \times \frac{1}{2}}$$
	= 30 days

Generally, a soil layer is considered to be free to drain if there are sand layers above and below it. Frequently, clay soils are interfingered with layers of sand. In such a case, the sand layers act as drainage layers, causing settlements to occur faster than for a body of silt or clay without sand layers.

15.5 Acceptable Settlements

Building settlements can be measured as the total settlement of the building, or as the differential settlement between adjacent footings or between the center and corner of the building.

Generally, total settlements can be tolerated without much difficulty as long as they are uniform. If all foundations in a building settle 3 in., the only problems will be to accommodate utilities coming into the building, and the level of the sidewalk and parking areas around the building.

If foundations settle different amounts, such as one column footing settling 1 in. and a nearby footing settling 2 in., this can create distortion of the building and cracks in walls. This kind of settlement is much more difficult to tolerate. Therefore, differential settlements are of much more importance than total settlements.

Certain kinds of structures, such as large storage tanks, have been known to settle several feet with relatively little difficulty in keeping them in operation. Frequently large oil storage tanks are designed and constructed in anticipation of settlements of a foot. The primary requirement is for the tank shell to settle a reasonably similar amount.

In major commercial structures, it is common to limit the allowable differential settlements between adjacent columns to ¼ in. or less. Settlements between adjacent columns might be acceptable for wood frame structures or light steel frame industrial buildings.

15.6   Methods of Accommodating Settlements

Settlements may be reduced by a change in foundation design. This may include larger or deeper foundations. Also, settlements can be reduced if the site is preloaded or "surcharged" prior to construction of the building (see Section 15.7) or if the soil is precompacted (see Chapter 23). If settlements occur quickly, during construction and initial loading, they can be corrected for and will not be a nuisance when the building is taken over by the owner. It is possible to "speed up" settlement by improving drainage of the compressible soils.

Concerning the use of wider foundations, as a rough guide it can be assumed that settlement reduces as the width increases for square footings. For instance, for a column load of 400 kips, assume that the footing size is 8 by 8 ft and the estimated settlement is 1 in. If the footing is changed to 12 by 12 ft, the settlement will be $8 \div 12 = $ ⅔ in. If the footing is changed to 16 by 16 ft, the settlement will be $8 \div 16 = $ ½ in. This guide applies better to silty and clay soils, than to sandy soils.

Accommodating settlements is accomplished frequently by changing the structure with regard to its method of framing and wall construction to make it more flexible.

The foundations of light buildings can be designed with long anchor bolts and clip angles on the columns which would permit jacks to be inserted and the columns to be jacked up from time to time to relevel the building frame.

Structural separations may be placed in a building at certain intervals. This would permit some distortion of the building and movement to occur along preestablished "breaks."

Side panels which are clipped to steel columns can accommodate appreciable differential movements without distortion. By contrast, block filler walls, brick walls, poured-in-place concrete, or continuous tilt-up concrete walls are brittle, crack easily, and show distress cracks for even small differential settlements. It should be borne in mind, however, that well-reinforced concrete walls may have considerable girder strength and may tend to bridge over foundations which tend to settle too much. Sometimes building walls are designed to act as girders. This appears to work satisfactorily as long as the required span is not too long. A redistribution of stress does occur in the wall, which is indeterminate.

15.7   Preconsolidation Methods

15.7.1   Surcharge Fills

A building site may be forced to settle prior to construction of the building. Surcharge fills are used frequently for this purpose. Generally, the surcharge fill placed on the site is as heavy as or is heavier than the weight of the proposed building. Sufficient time must be available for the settlement to occur prior to construction.

Surcharge fills may be on the order of 4 to 5 ft high for one-story industrial buildings, supermarkets, and school buildings. Surcharge fills may be 15 to 20 ft high for relatively heavy reinforced concrete buildings. Occasionally, surcharge fills 30 to 40 ft are constructed on the sites of proposed heavy storage tanks, power plants, or other extremely heavy structures.

Settlement markers can be placed at the bottom of the surcharge

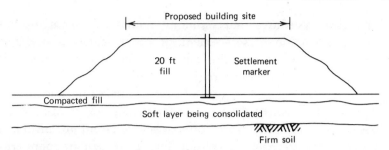

Fig. 15.2 Surcharge fill. Note that the soft layer being consolidated is loaded in the same manner as a laboratory test, see Fig. 8.8. The surcharge process is a "king size" consolidation test. The settlement marker readings give the same answers as can be calculated from laboratory tests.

fills, to measure the settlement and also the termination of settlement. Figure 15.2 shows a typical surcharge fill.

15.7.2   Compacting or Densifying the Soil

Several methods are available for compacting or densifying the soil. These include *(a)* vibroflotation; *(b)* depressing the water level by use of sumps or well points; *(c)* excavating the soil and replacing it as a compacted fill; and *(d)* inserting sand drains, wick drains, or other devices to permit water to drain out of the soil more rapidly. These methods are described in more detail under Chapter 23.

15.8   Correction

Settlement of foundations has been a problem since antiquity. However, many large and heavy structures which have experienced serious foundation settlements have been stabilized, or brought back up to their original positions. The technological and construction capability are available to correct very serious problems of this nature at costs which are reasonable when compared to the replacement value of the structure. This capability applied in time to the Leaning Tower of Pisa could very well stabilize the structure, or possibly relevel it.

Corrective procedures used commonly include *(a)* jacking-up foundations by injection of soil-cement or other materials under the foundation; *(b)* supporting the column while a new foundation is placed under an existing foundation; *(c)* extending the footing to a lower elevation one portion at a time; *(d)* injecting chemicals or grout into porous soils below a foundation; and *(e)* installing piles, drilled caissons, or other new foundations adjacent to an existing footing, and transferring the column load to these new foundations by means of a "needle" beam. Needle beams may be inserted under a footing, or above the footing and be connected directly to the column. A less common method consists of freezing the soil under a foundation and keeping it permanently frozen.

15.9   Settlements of Other Types of Foundations

This chapter has discussed settlements as applied to spread foundations. However, settlements may be a consideration for other types of foundations, such as friction piles, end-bearing piles, groups or clusters of piles, straight shaft piers, drilled and belled caissons, and other deep foundations.

Deep foundations carry their loads down to lower firmer strata or spread out their loads over a greater depth of soil. These foundations also settle when they are loaded. Usually, the settlements are considerably less than for spread foundations. As a crude guide, if spread foundations were used in a particular area, and experienced settlements on the order of 1 to 2 in., it might be expected that pile foundations or other suitable deep foundations might experience settlement of $\frac{1}{4}$ to $\frac{1}{2}$ in. However, if the foundations should reach end-bearing on hard soil or rock, the settlements would be essentially the elastic shortening of the piles as load was applied.

Assume that a building is supported on friction piles. Friction piles gain their support from the full length of soil through which they are driven, and they do not reach hard-end bearing.

If one building column carries a load of 50 tons, it might be supported on a single pile. Another column in the building may support a load of 400 tons and require eight piles. Although each pile is loaded to an equal amount, 50 tons per pile, it should be expected that the eight-pile group will settle more than the single pile. The difference in settlement may not be large; for instance, the single pile might settle $1/4$ in. and the eight-pile group might settle $1/2$ in. The resulting differential settlement of $1/4$ in. would not be a problem structurally and would never be detected unless a precise survey was made.

The settlement of individual piles or of pile groups is more difficult to estimate than for spread foundations. Simplified methods have been developed for rough estimates of settlements. These methods are fairly similar to those used for calculating the settlements of a spread foundation.

Usually, it is assumed that the load on the pile group is spread out, so that the pile group is somewhat equivalent to a spread footing placed at some depth below grade. This concept is illustrated in Fig. 15.3. Having transformed the pile group into an equivalent large spread foundation on soil, the additional soil pressure can be calculated. Using this soil pressure, the consolidation of the various soil layers under the footing can be estimated as described previously, and a total settlement can be estimated. By contrast, if the pile group is driven through soft soil, and then to refusal in a deep, very dense sand and gravel, the "equivalent footing" would be deep, as shown in Fig. 15.4.

Usually, settlements of structures supported on piles are relatively small and are not a problem. However, serious difficulties can develop if a portion of a structure is supported on piles while other portions are supported on spread foundations. Figure 15.5 shows a two-story structure which was supported on pile foundations. Adjacent to it, a lighter one-story structure was supported on spread foundations. It was attached to the original two-story building. Large settlements occurred in the one-story building.

As a general rule, if a portion of a structure is supported on piles, other attachments, even though light, also should be supported on pile foundations. Only after very careful study of likely settlements, should consideration be given using a mixture of foundation types. If the types are mixed, it is better to make a structural separation, with double columns, between the two portions of the structure.

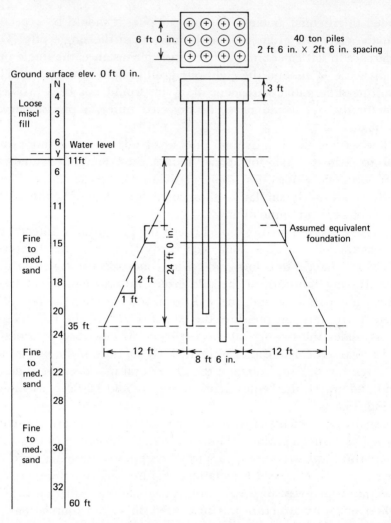

Fig. 15.3 Transformation of a group of friction piles to equivalent spread footing for settlement calculations.

Settlements can be calculated for drilled and belled caissons, deep piers, or a modified form of spread foundations, using the same techniques as for spread footings. This is discussed in Chapter 21.

The Franki foundation also is used as a caisson. The situation is different, however, since in forming the foundation, the soil under

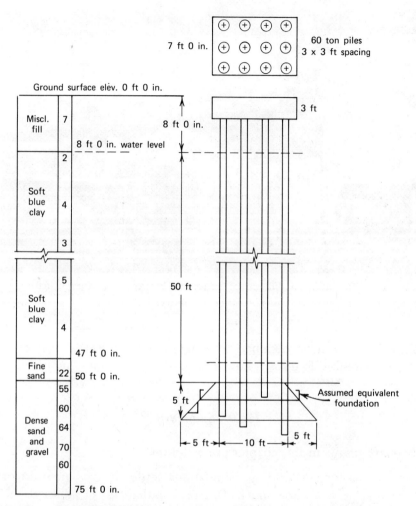

Fig. 15.4   Transformation of group of end bearing piles to equivalent spread footing for settlement calculations.

the foundation is compacted and preconsolidated. Therefore, settlements are appreciably less than would be calculated for other types of caissons supported on soil. This foundation is used generally to bear on sandy soil (see Chapter 19, Section 19.6.3).

Again, it should be pointed out that this discussion of settlement *does not* tell exactly how to perform a settlement calculation. More

Fig. 15.5 Illustration of differential settlement between two story structure on piles connected to a one story structure on spread footings.

information can be obtained from texts, such as Ref. 4, but even these references do not tell how it is done, nor will soils engineers.

15.10 Summary

Primary points in this chapter are as follows:

FACTS: Building foundations settle; it is a question of how much. Different settlements of adjacent columns cause the most trouble. Settlements of footings on sand are fast and occur during construction. Footings on clay settle slowly. Site conditions can be improved to reduce settlement.

WATCH OUT FOR: A building site with firm soils on one side and softer soils on the other side. Heavily loaded footings adjacent to lightly loaded footings.

16

Pile Foundations

It is the usual practice of the general contractor to sublet the pile foundation work to a subcontractor specializing in pile driving. On small projects, piling may be installed by the general contractor. However, in this book the discussion of pile foundations is directed primarily toward the larger projects on which a specialty subcontractor furnishes and drives the piles.

16.1   Contract Documents

The contract documents consist of:

General conditions.
Form of contract.
Specifications.
Drawings.
Soil conditions (may not be included with contract documents).

Equally binding on the contractor are the local building code and any ordinances such as those regulating the use of hoisting procedures and safety provisions.

While engineers are meticulous in preparing specifications for piling to conform to the requirements of the building code, the subcontractor should verify the compatibility of the specifications and the code. Often specifications will restrict the choice of pile types and will contain requirements to fit anticipated soil conditions. These may include acceptable final driving criteria, jetting, or preexcavation of piles which go beyond code provisions.

The selection of the type or types of piles suitable for use on a project is very important. This should be detailed clearly in the specifications. Sometimes specifications can be stretched to include other alternate piles, particularly if money can be saved. Various types of piles are discussed, in Chapter 17, 18, 19, and 20. A brief summary of pile types is presented at the end of Chapter 20.

The insurance provisions require careful review. The limits of insurance coverage called for may be inadequate for the potential risks. This is particularly true of property damage insurance. The procedure outlined in Chapter 27, Section 27.2 will furnish a basis for assessing the risk. Property damage from pile driving occurs principally from the following: (a) rupture or displacement of underground utilities; (b) damage to adjacent structures and equipment from vibration; and (c) soil displacement. Should utilities be damaged, it is incumbent on the contractor to demonstrate that every reasonable effort was made to discover utilities underlying pile locations. Equipment and services are available to measure the effect of vibration on adjacent structures and equipment (see Chapter 29). Soil displacement is discussed under Chapter 16, Section 16.7.

Completed operations insurance coverage should be provided, since claims for damage may not arise until long after the pile work has been completed.

Where the procedures for claims for extra payments require notification of intent to make such claims, strict compliance is important. Changed orders, extra work, or claims based on latent conditions call for the compilation of detailed data, particularly on large complicated projects where unanticipated work in one area sets off a chain reaction in others. At the earliest moment, competent personnel should be assigned to collect and prepare the backup data for claims. The use of a "critical path method" (or similar system) analysis to demonstrate the overall effect of the extra work on both time and costs should not be overlooked.

The determinations to be made from a review of the soil information accompanying the contract documents are as follows:

The contract documents may contain a disclaimer as to the soil information. In many cases the soil data are offered to the contractor to use at his own risk and with a disclaimer as to its accuracy. Often the contractor is invited to make his own soil investigation. The legal aspects affecting any claim for latent or changed conditions are found in Ref. 33.

Whether the soil investigation for a given site is adequate as to the number of borings, their depth, and the data on soil conditions. Where there appear to be deficiencies, that fact should weigh heavily in the decision as to whether to bid the work. The contractor sometimes elects to make check borings at his own expense prior to bidding.

It may not be feasible to drive piles by usual methods to specified depths as based on a review of the soil borings. They may show that special methods, such as jetting, will be needed.

16.2   Bases of Submission of Quotations for Piling

Various forms for requesting quotations for piling work are employed. The three most frequently used are as follows:

Quotations are based on a fixed number of piles of an average length. The price submitted is known as the "principal sum." Unit prices are submitted for adjustment of the principal sum for the addition or omission of an average length pile and a price per lineal foot (l.f.) for piles longer than the average length and separately a credit per l.f. for omitted lengths of shorter piles. In some cases contractors insert their own unit prices; in other cases, the engineers determine what they shall be.

Bids may be requested for a lump sum for mobilization and demobilization of equipment plus a unit price per l.f. based on an aggregate footage for the work.

A lump sum quotation is obtained for a project irrespective of the actual lengths of piles driven. The only adjustments to be made are for added or omitted piles for which unit prices are submitted.

Of these forms of bidding, the use of a principal sum with adjustments may produce the lowest price because the piling contractor assumes the least risk from length variations.

16.3   *Estimating the Bearing Capacity of Piles*

The capacities of piles are estimated by two basic methods. The derivation, application, and limitations of static analysis of capacity and of pile driving formulas are covered in detail in engineering literature (see Refs. 34 and 35). Therefore, the following is only a brief outline of the basic considerations.

In the static analysis method, the load-bearing capacity of a pile is estimated from an evaluation of the soils that provide support for the pile. The soil provides end bearing support and side friction support. Both can be estimated.

The soil profile must be developed from borings, pits, or other explorations. The strength of the various layers in the soil profile can be measured by laboratory tests on samples of the soil or by resistance to penetration. Penetration resistance is usually measured by using a soil sampler, a cone, or other similar device driven or pushed into the soil.

For each layer of soil, the frictional strength is calculated based on the test data. The strength may be adjusted for the side pressure around the pile developed when the pile is driven and shoves the soil sideways. The frictional strength multiplied by the surface area of the pile gives the support in each layer. The support values for the several layers are added up. Also, the bearing capacity of the soil at the proposed pile tip depth is estimated using common bearing value formula, but probably modified for the great depth of the tip. All of the capacity values are added up to obtain the ultimate capacity of the pile. This value usually is reduced to two-thirds or one-half to obtain a "design capacity."

The pile driving formula was developed over a period of many years by comparing driving resistance to results of load tests. The formulas usually consider the weight and fall of the hammer and the number of blows to drive the pile an inch. Further accuracy can be obtained by considering efficiency of driving, the weight of the pile, and other factors. The simpler formulas, such as the *Engineering News* formula, are most commonly used.

As an example of the use of the *Engineering News* formula, take the following data:

Hammer weight $=$ 5000 lb
Hammer drop $\quad=$ 3 ft
Rate of driving $\quad \frac{1}{4}$ in. for each blow

$$\text{Capacity} = \frac{\text{weight} \times \text{drop} \times 2}{\text{rate of driving} + 0.1}$$

$$= \frac{5000 \times 3 \times 2}{\frac{1}{4} + 0.1}$$

$$= \frac{30,000}{0.35} = 86,000 \text{ lb}$$

$$= 43 \text{ tons (factor of safety} = \text{approximately 2)}$$

16.4   Test Piles and Pile Load Tests

In the design of pile foundations, presumptive pile lengths and bearing capacities are determined by engineers prior to construction. These estimates sometimes are verified by driving test piles and conducting load tests on some of the test piles. The test piles also provide the basis for ordering one piece piling, such as timber or H-beam piles.

The need to drive test piles for ordering materials is independent of the presumptive bearing loads. Virtually all building codes exempt lightly loaded piles (up to and, in most cases, including 40-ton working loads) from pile load tests. Verification of bearing capacity by pile driving formula is accepted. The *Engineering News* formula, sometimes with modifications, is generally specified. Load tests are called for by engineers under special circumstances. For example, piles may be driven to a predetermined depth, and driving may be suspended before the indicated final driving resistance has been attained. Load tests may then be conducted to satisfy both the engineers and the building department.

Where piles are designed for working loads in excess of 40 tons, a test pile and load test program may be carried out in advance of production pile driving. Otherwise, detailed soil tests and static analysis methods are required to select pile penetration to develop the design load capacity.

The number of test piles to be driven depends on the code requirements, the size of the site and soil conditions. Test piles are usually driven in pairs and should always be located close to test borings. At least one pair of test piles should be driven in the area of poorest soil conditions. Pile load tests are performed on a selected number of the test piles. Test procedures usually conform to an accepted standard, such as ASTM D 1143-63T.

Pile load tests can be simple and straightforward or they can become field research projects involving special devices to measure the movement of the tip of the pile as well as the settlement of the top. Field personnel should be made aware of the importance of meticulous care in record keeping, including temperature readings affecting the gauges. On important work, separate settlement readings with surveying instruments are insurance against misreading or malfunction of the gauges. Field personnel in their well-intentioned zeal sometimes feel an urge to overdrive the test pile, "just to make sure." Since the piles have to be driven to the same final depth and resistance as the tested pile, this practice should be discouraged as it can backfire to everyone's disadvantage. Much has been written in engineering literature on the subject of pile load tests and the evaluations of the results (see Refs. 34 and 35).

Several criteria must be met for a load test to be considered satisfactory. Loading is increased in increments to a total of 200% of the working load. Unloading in increments is usually required. Generally the maximum permissible settlement under 200% loading is 0.01 in./ton of applied load (gross settlement). Many codes, however, limit the gross settlement to one inch or apply some other limiting factor. In many codes the gross settlement is not limited, but the maximum net settlement (after unloading) is specified. Nearly all codes require that there be no settlement under full load for periods ranging from 6 to 48 hr.

Experience has shown that the requirements of 1-in. net and 0.01 in./ton of load for gross settlement usually have resulted in satisfactory pile foundations. More restrictive provisions generally are not required, unless there are severe limits on settlement or some other performance criteria.

16.5   Verification of Estimated Pile Lengths and Bearing Values

In preparing estimates for pile foundations, contractors must review the soil data, the driving specifications, and the test pile and pile load test program to arrive at independent conclusions as to the average length of the piles compared with the lengths on which the bid is based, difficulties anticipated in fulfilling the driving specifications, and any risk of failure of the pile load tests.

In considering the probable pile lengths, some of the factors are the compaction of the soil where there are a large number of piles in groups, the presence of mica or silt which act as lubricants in granular soils, and the relief of overburden pressure due to removing the soil from deep excavations.

Driving requirements for purely friction piles seldom involve more than meeting a fixed length, a final driving resistance, or both. Where a specified bearing stratum must be penetrated, difficulties can arise. The top of the stratum may be defined clearly at each boring location. Between borings, however, the assumption of straight-line interpolation of its surface may result in considerable over-driving to reach the assumed tip elevation. When high capacity piles must be driven to rock, and rock exists at some elevation higher than the interpolated elevations, efforts to demonstrate that rock has been reached can involve overdriving and possible damage to the pile and to equipment. Also, there may be the time and cost of additional borings to verify the rock surface.

Should it appear that the bearing capacities are critically high for the soil conditions, the load tests may fail. The consequences must be considered, as well as alternatives available to the engineers. Not only the estimate of cost but also the selection of equipment must take such possible problems into account.

Frequently, soil conditions at a site turn out to be different from what was expected. This may be due to meandering streams with varying deposits of sand and silt, an erratic surface of rock or hard material overlain by more recent softer material, or the presence of sink holes in underlying limestone rock.

As a result, driving of piles is very confusing. The pile lengths vary considerably from one pile to the next. The driving record also may vary considerably from one pile to the next. How can the contractor decide on the proper pile length and the capacity of the pile?

These questions cause delays. Also, there are additional costs for making some piles longer or possibly even abandoning some piles.

In such cases, borings drilled at a site may have been located in such a way as to encounter firmer soils or to hit the bedrock or hard material at the higher elevations. In between, the rock is deeper or the soils are softer. Almost always, the only reasonable way to solve the problem is to obtain additional information. Additional borings should be drilled. Generally a considerable number of additional borings are drilled to make sure that the conditions are clearly identified.

Where additional pile lengths are required, who should pay? If the true soil conditions had been known in the beginning, the longer pile lengths would have been bid originally and would have been paid for by contract. The soil conditions did not change—they were a part of the site and belong to the owner. Therefore, in almost all cases, the cost of additional pile lengths is paid by the owner.

16.6   Pile Hammers and Equipment

Table 16.1 describes the pile driving hammers in general use for foundation piling and other construction uses. The types, energy ratings, the manufacturers, and such are listed. Manufacturer's catalogues are available and may be consulted for more details.

Table 16.1 is not all-inclusive. There are lighter hammers available for driving timber sheeting and other uses and heavier hammers for special uses, such as marine construction.

Hammers with energy ratings less than 15,000 ft-lb are employed mainly for driving steel sheet piling and soldier beams in short lengths (under 25 ft) and for easy driving conditions. Lightly loaded timber piles under 25-ton capacity have often been successfully driven with hammers rated at 12,000 ft-lb of both single acting and double acting types.

The minimum energy rating permitted by most building codes for bearing piles is 15,000 ft-lb. For many years, the hammers available were limited to maximum ratings of 15,000 ft-lb. (A few heavier

Table 16.1 Pile Driving Hammers (Partial List)

Energy (ft-lb per blow)[a]	Manufacturer	Model	Ram Weight (lb)	Stroke (In.)	Steam/Air (lb./in.²)[d]
Single Acting Hammers					
7,260	Vulcan[b]	2	3,000	29	
15,000	Vulcan	1	5,000	36	
16,250	McK-T[c]	S5	5,000	39	
19,500	Vulcan	S6	6,500	36	
24,370	Vulcan	0	7,500	39	
26,000	Vulcan	08	8,000	39	
26,000	McK-T	S8	8,000	39	
30,225	Vulcan	or	9,300	39	
32,500	Vulcan	010	10,000	39	
32,500	McK-T	S10	10,000	39	
37,500	McK-T	S14	14,000	32	
Differential Hammers					
7,260	Vulcan	30C	3,000	12.5	120
15,100	Vulcan	50C	5,000	15.5	120
15,100	McK-T	C5	5,000	18.0	100
19,500	Vulcan	65C	6,500	15.5	150
24,000	McK-T	C826	8,000	18.0	125
24,450	Vulcan	80C	8,000	16.5	120
26,000	McK-T	C8	8,000	20.0	100
36,000	Vulcan	140C	14,000	15.5	140
Diesel Hammers					
8,100	Link belt[e]	180	1,725	37.6	
6,600/9,900[f]	McK-T	DE10	1,100	108.0 max.	
9,100	Delmag[g]	D5	1,100	n/a[h]	
15,000	Link belt	312	3,857	30.89	
12,000/18,800	McK-T	DE20	2,000	113.0 max.	
16,800/30,100	McK-T	DE30	2,800	129.0 max.	
22,800	Delmag	D12	2,750	n/a	
26,300	Link belt	520	5,070	43.17	
24,000/43,000	McK-T	DE40	4,000	129.0 max.	
39,700	Delmag	D22	4,850	n/a	

[a] Manufacturer's ratings.
[b] Vulcan Iron Works, Chattanooga, Tenn.
[c] McKiernan-Terry Corp., Dover, N. J.
[d] Pressure acting at the hammer.
[e] Link-Belt Div., FMC Corp., New York, N. Y.
[f] Mean striking energy/maximum striking energy.
[g] Made in Germany, consult United States dealers.
[h] Not available.

hammers were available.) During that period, the bearing loads on piles rarely exceeded 60 tons. As bearing loads were increased, larger hammers were developed, and concurrently the differential hammer was introduced. Engineering practice and the more modern codes call for the use of higher energy hammers for heavier pile loads. For example, the New York City code accepts 15,000-ft-lb hammers for piles up to 60 tons, and calls for 19,000 ft-lb for 70 to 90-ton piles. Over 90-tons capacity, piles must be driven with 24,000 ft-lb hammers.

Where the soil offers considerable resistance to driving, a high energy differential hammer, which hits twice as many blows per minute as a single acting hammer, will give greater production. But where the final driving resistance is high, the heavier hammers may cause damage to the tops and tips of the piles. This is an important consideration in selecting hammers.

Diesel hammers, as the name implies, use fuel oil pumped into the combustion chamber which, mixed with high temperature air under pressure, ignites and creates the energy for each blow of the hammer. The need for boilers or compressors is eliminated. The range of energies which diesel hammers provide makes them suitable for most types of piles and pile capacities.

Single acting diesel hammers operate somewhat slower than single acting steam hammers. Diesel hammers have to be started with a trip; thereafter their operation is automatic. In penetrating soils with little or no resistance, the trip may have to be used until some resistance to driving is encountered.

Vibratory pile hammers have been developed in relatively recent times. The hammers get their name from the high frequency of the vertical strokes developed by the driving mechanism. They are useful in driving and extraction of steel sheeting and soldier beams. They have also been used to a limited extent for bearing piles of low to medium load ranges. Claims have been made that vibratory hammers can drive timber and pipe piles successfully through soils containing obstructions and through which conventionally driven piles could not penetrate. While there is some evidence to support the claim, more proof is needed and may come in time.

Resonant (so-called sonic) drivers impart vertical high frequency vibrations to the pile from a self-contained "driver" mounted on the front of the pile driver leaders. The vertical vibration of the pile reduces frictional resistance on the side of the pile so that nearly all the energy is transmitted to the pile tip. The energy is sufficient to break or dislodge boulders, penetrate obstructions, and pulverize ledge rock.

Most of the vibration caused by impact pile driving is eliminated. The noise generated by resonant driving is less objectionable than impact driving. Under most soil conditions, the time required to sink a pile is much less than for impact driving. Also, the piles are straighter. These units are especially effective in sandy soil and less effective in clay soil.

Resonant driving has been successful from an engineering and cost standpoint. However, further research is needed for the control of repair costs of the hammers to make this promising system more competitive.

Pile extractors are made by the major hammer manufacturers. Extractors may be double acting or single acting and rigged to drive upward. Vibratory extractors drive down or up and depend on vibration to break the friction and reduce the pull required to extract the pile. The vibratory driver-extractor appears to be the best for pulling steel sheet piling. For other piles, extraction depends on the pulling power of the crane aided by the friction breaking action of the extractor. The effective line pull of the crane is limited to the tension that the extractor can withstand and the grip on the pile. There is always the risk that the grip on the pile may let go. Precautions must be taken to provide some check to the boom against backward rotation if a break should occur.

Driving piles down an inch or two will often temporarily break the soil friction. In granular soils, a water jet may be all that is needed to loosen a pile.

The present generation of pile drivers are caterpillar mounted cranes. For special projects, whirleys mounted on bed sills which in turn move on rollers, permit a much greater radius for driving than crane drivers. Pile hammers are handled with a maximum of four parts of wire line reaved over sheaves at the top of the leaders. The leaders may be attached to the boom by a connection at the top in which case they rest on blocks on the ground during driving, or they may be connected so that the leaders extend well above the end of the crane boom. A frame or spotter can be adjusted in length so that piles may be driven on a batter either in or out. Special rigging is necessary to position the leaders to drive batter piles sideways.

16.7   Pile Driving

The process of pile driving is of interest primarily because so many things can go wrong. For instance, man made surface fills often contain broken concrete, rip rap, timber, scrap iron, and the like. Such obstructions can break timber piles, tear the casing of cast-in-place piling, and cause piles to drift from location. In natural deposits, obstructions consist of boulders, rock fragments, or gravel measuring 6 in. or larger. Excavations are often made at pile locations to insure good pile production through shallow obstructed fill. Holes can be dug with a backhoe. After discarding the obstructions, the hole can be backfilled with the remaining soil, and the pile can then be driven. Sometimes a mobile auger drill is used ahead of the driver to test for obstructions. Where there are so many piles that the pile caps almost form a mat, consideration should be given to excavating and backfilling the entire area.

Spuds are sometimes used where obstructions are located below the water level or are too deep for removal by inexpensive excavation. If the obstructions lie in loose or soft soil, they may be shoved sideways by driving some form of spud. The spud may be a heavy H-beam with the tip reinforced or a heavy wall closed-end pipe. It is often necessary to drive the spud more than once in a group of piles, since pushing the obstruction from one pile location may drive it to another. Where obstructions cannot be dislodged, it may be necessary to use the spud to locate unobstructed areas within the foundation area, drive the piles where they can penetrate, and redesign the pile cap for the piles as driven.

Predrilling is required frequently to get through firm soil layers or obstructions. In steel mill areas there are often slag fills up to 30 ft deep. Such fills contain "skulls," hardened rounded lumps of iron, or slag from the bottom of the ladles. Where the skulls cannot be spudded out of the way, it has been found necessary to drill auger holes at pile locations, and where skulls are encountered to blow them with dynamite.

The process of "casing off" may be used where sharp fragments will tear the casing of cast-in-place piles. An oversized casing is first driven and cleaned, and the pile driven through the casing which protects the shell of the pile after which the casing is withdrawn. Under some conditions, the casing can be driven with a loose fitting pan on the bottom, which must be driven off before the pile is driven through the casing.

16.8   Ground Heave and Displacement

Most types of piles are "displacement" piles; that is, they displace a volume of soil about equal to the volume of the pile. H-beam piles and open-end piles are considered "nondisplacement" piles. Actually, H-beam piles do displace some soil because a soil plug forms between the flanges and moves down with the pile as it is driven.

In granular soils, the displaced volume results in compaction of the soil surrounding the pile. Where granular soils are too dense for further compaction, the piles may have reached their bearing. If not, jets will be required to wash out the soil to permit further penetration.

In clay soils, driving displacement piles creates high stresses in the soil. Such soil is relatively incompressible during driving and can be relieved only by movement. The soil moves upward and also moves laterally away from the pile. The soil movements take time; thus the continuous driving of piles causes buildup of stress. On a level construction site, where the general excavation is shallow, the ground surface will heave upward by about the total volume of all piles driven. With 10 or more piles in a group, with pile caps which are close together, and with long piles displacing $1\frac{1}{2}$ yd³ or more, the whole area will heave vertically. The effect may be noticeable as it tapers off beyond the horizontal limits of the excavation. Utilities under adjacent streets may be displaced and heaved, and adjacent buildings may be affected. The driving sequence can have some influence on the heaving of piles. In a large group of piles, the sequence of driving should start in the center and work out toward the perimeter of the pile group. This permits more relief of soil stresses and reduces movement of driven piles. Should the site be located near the top of a deep cut or river bank, both vertical and horizontal movements may occur. Under extreme conditions, the whole soil mass may be set in motion so that pile groups already driven may move horizontally several inches or feet.

When shell type piles are driven, steps must be taken to verify the integrity of the driven piles. The usual procedure is to place a long piece of 3-in. pipe in the first pile driven in each group so as to establish the elevation of the tip and also the top of the pile. Where the tops of the piles heave, but the tips do not, and where no separation of the casing at any joint is observed, the piles may be concreted after all motion within the heave range has ceased. Any lateral motion must also cease. Added piles may be required to correct for eccentricity. Should the pipe telltale reveal upward movement of the pile tips, redriving (see Section 16.10) becomes necessary. To avoid inviting horizontal movements, it has been found advantageous to drive all piles from one level and make excavations for pits and partial basements after the pile work is finished. A cutting off tool can be used to cut pile casings below grade.

16.9   *Preexcavation and Jetting*

Lateral displacement within deep beds of cohesive soils (as described in Section 16.8) can be avoided by removing a quantity of soil at each pile location which represents all or part of the volume of the pile to be driven. The procedure is called preexcavation, preboring, or predrilling. The first attempt to do this was with a single tube preexcavator. It consists of a length of 14 to 16-in. pipe open at the bottom and closed at the top with a connection at the top to admit steam or compressed air. The preexcavator is driven into the soil at each pile location and withdrawn. The plug of soil is expelled from the tube by steam or air pressure. It should not be used in soft soils which flow back into the hole when the tube is pulled. It can be used in firmer soils but is limited to depths of about 30 ft maximum. In suitable soils, preexcavation may be accomplished with an earth auger operated by mobile drilling rigs. The augered hole must be able to stand open until the pile is driven. The success of preexcavation depends on close control of the actual volume of soil removed.

Ideally, the preexcavation should conform to the outside dimensions of the pile and remove 90 to 95% of the pile volume above the bearing stratum. Thus for piles over 50 ft long, dry tube preexcavation to a depth of approximately 30 ft will help reduce heave, but does nothing to relieve the stress and resultant soil movement below the 30-ft level.

Occasionally soil conditions are such that there is a reduction in pile driving resistance after pile driving is stopped. Where a pile has been driven initially to a specified final resistance of, say, eight blows to the last inch and after a pause of 15 min or more driving is resumed, the resistance may drop to three or four blows per inch. The previous final resistance has been partially lost. It may well take another foot or more of penetration to regain the specified resistance. Such a phenomenon has been called "relaxation of pile driving resistance."

Experience to date points to some shales and dense fine silt or sand as formations in which piles may behave in this manner. Loss of resistance has occurred in friable shales, particularly when inter-bedded with soft seams and in saturated fine silts and sands where the N value has been 50 or higher.

One proposed explanation is that pore water, unable to move rap-idly through dense fine soils, resists a large proportion of the hammer energy under repeated blows. The pore water pressure returns to normal during the pause in driving, permitting easier penetration when driving is resumed.

There is no single cure for this dilemma. One method has been to drive the piles initially to a resistance 50% greater than the specified resistance, and then, by redriving, determine whether the specified resistance has been retained. This system requires that every pile be redriven to prove its capacity. Also, additional pile load tests may be required (see Ref. 36).

To provide a reliable controlled method of preexcavation for piles of any length, especially in soft cohesive soils, "wet-rotary" preexcavation was developed. In this system, a hole is drilled to the desired depth by rotary driling methods. The hole can be straight or can be "shaped" by reamers attached at selected positions on the drill stem. Drilling mud is pumped through the drill stem and recircu-lated to a sump. The drilled hole is left full of slurry to prevent squeezing or sloughing of the walls. Thereafter the pile is driven into the hole displacing the slurry and developing intimate contact with the soil for the preexcavated lengths.

Jetting of piles, in a sense, is also preexcavation. Water jets are used to create a hole into which piles are driven, or to relieve piles of friction as they are being driven; this method is about as old as the art of pile driving. Although it is feasible to jet holes through sandy soils, it accomplishes little in clay soils. In sands, a typical setup is a 3-in. jet pipe with a nozzle on the end to jet or wash a hole into which the pile may be lowered and then driven. The presence of gravel in a formation often limits the effectiveness of jetting because the gravel tends to accumulate at the bottom of the jetted hole. Jetting alongside of the pile is probably more common. With a single jet, it is difficult to keep the pile on location. Therefore, more often piles are jetted with twin jets, one on each side of the pile, for greater effectiveness and better control.

16.10   Redriving and Tapping of Piles

The heaving of cohesive soils during driving frequently causes adjacent piles to lift with the soil. This will cause the tips to lift off the bottom. Possibly the piles will stretch and separate if the tips are anchored in a strong bearing stratum.

One piece piles such as timber piles, precast concrete, H-beams, and pipe obviously must heave as a unit. They can be "tapped" back to the original tip elevation and driving resistance by swinging the pile hammer back onto them.

In the case of shell piles, a telltale pipe inserted in the shell down to the tip will demonstrate the relative movement of the top of the shell and the tip of the pile. Evidence of movement of the tip calls for redriving. The mandrel must be inserted in the pile casing and the pile redriven to the same final resistance with the same energy hammer. Distortion of the casing, dog-legs, or bends in the casing can prevent the reentry of the mandrel. In such cases, redriving tools (consisting of a heavy walled pipe smaller than the mandrel, and fitted at the bottom to conform to the tip of the mandrel) are often used to redrive distorted piles. Mandrel driven cast-in-place piles, with corrugated thin shells, can stretch to some degree without separating before concrete is placed.

Where the bearing stratum is primarily clay soil, it may heave, carrying the entire pile with it. It has been demonstrated many times that the bearing capacity is not necessarily affected. This, however, has to be proven in each instance. The sequence of driving piles in a large group can influence the amount of ground heaving. It is best to start driving at the center of the group, and work outward.

More than one redriving or tapping may be needed to make sure that all piles in a group are seated properly. For cast-in-place piles, concrete should not be poured in piles until all heave has ceased and all piles are seated. Concreted piles may be redriven, but this involves some risk and is not good practice because of potential damage to the concrete.

16.11   Negative Friction on Piles

The preparation of a construction site may include raising the general grade by placing fill. When the fill is placed over a clay formation (including peat), the weight of the fill causes consolidation of the clay bed. The entire site settles, which may occur gradually over an extended period of time. Piles that are driven through the fill, the clay, and then into a bearing stratum derive most of their support from the bearing stratum. Some temporary support is contributed by friction in the fill and clay. As site settlement proceeds, the fill and the clay pull down on the piles and transmit load onto the piles. The piles may settle under this load (see Ref. 34). The negative friction or "drag-down" is in addition to the building loads. The amount of drag-down on the piles can be estimated as a function of the average strength of the fill and the clay. A technical soils analysis is essential for designing pile foundations under these circumstances.

16.12   Uplift Resistance

The ultimate capacity of a pile in tension is generally assumed to be measured by the shearing resistance of the soil surrounding it or the amount of adhesion between the pile surface and the soil, whichever is lower. There is evidence, however, to show that in some soils, moderately firm clays, for example, failure may occur below these values. Consequently, it is often advisable to verify uplift capacities by field testing. The usual procedure is to drive two reaction piles flanking the test pile. Then with a jacking frame, lift up on the test pile until failure occurs. By reducing the loading to zero at three or four points in the loading, the movement of the pile relative to the soil and elastic lengthening of the pile can be detected. The results are plotted in the same way as for a downward load test. From these data, and using an appropriate factor of safety, safe uplift load can be established. Generally, for friction piles the uplift load is the range of 50 to 75% of the downward bearing capacity. For end bearing piles, the uplift capacity may be small.

16.13   Piles Under Limited Headroom

Under low headroom conditions, piles have to be driven and spliced in short sections. Usually contractors select for this purpose closed-end 10¾-in. pipe piles with ¼ in. or slightly heavier wall thickness. The cost of splicing and corrosion possibilities operates against the use of H-beams in short sections. The conditions under which piles have been driven where headroom is restricted are so diverse that it is better to review low headroom problems by general categories.

Where headroom exceeds 14 ft, the piles are usually located under a ramp or overhead structure or in a high building or storage shed. The piles may be driven with a conventional driver with a short hammer, such as a McKiernan-Terry 9B3 mounted in outboard extensions.

If the headroom is over 25 ft, a light short boom crane with swinging leads and a light hammer may be used. For driving more than 50 piles where the headroom is too low for a crane, the best approach is to build a timber skid rig with timber leaders and a two-drum hoist. Steam or air can be supplied from a separate source.

Under headroom less than 14 ft, a specially built skid rig with open top leads is suitable where the working surface is unpaved and there is freedom to move the driver around the area. Where there is a good concrete floor slab, a fork lift truck with the hammer bolted to the front makes an efficient driver. The hammer should be attached so that it can be raised up to the ceiling. The load under the front wheels is considerable, so pier holes broken through the slab may have to be cut oversize to permit installing timber cribbing. By using rigid steel floor plates, the load of the front wheels can be carried by the timbers rather than the edge of the slab.

A few piles located in a confined area can be driven with a hammer handled with a chain hoist hung from a beam posted up against the ceiling by timber frames under each end. The rigging of the hammer cuts the headroom by about 3 ft. Excavation for the piles must be deep enough so that pipe sections can be added below the floor line, and the hammer must be able to follow the pipe into the pit as it is driven. Although slow and costly many piles have been driven this way. Operations in confined areas require that steam or air be piped to the hammer from outside. Condensation occurs in steam lines, so that a quick opening valve with a drain fitting is needed near the hammer.

Bearing capacities for piles where only light hammers can be used should be kept under 40 tons. It is seldom feasible to conduct pile load tests. It is important to plan the work so as to add sections of pipe in at least 4-ft lengths. The use of a No. 7 McKiernan-Terry hammer saves headroom. For pile capacities over 20 tons, a heavier hammer is needed. This can be done by driving all the piles in an area as far as possible with a No. 7, and then cutting the pipe off 1 to 2 ft above the pile top elevation, changing hammers to a 9B3, and finishing off driving.

16.14 Lateral Resistance of Piles

Several methods have been developed for estimating the lateral loads which can be put on piles. Generally, they consider the load which can be placed on a single pile. Four commonly used approaches are as follows:

Pole formula. Several pole formulas have been developed, considering basically how deep a flag pole must be embedded to keep it from overturning. The pressure on the faces of the pole are indicated in Fig. 12.8. It is necessary to know the soil allowable lateral bearing value to make the calculation. Pole formulas are given in some building codes, such as the uniform building code. A typical formula is given in Fig. 12.8. Allowable lateral bearing values are given in some codes, such as the uniform building code, or can be obtained from soils engineers.

Point of fixity.   In this method, it is assumed that the pile is fixed at some point in the earth and is a free cantilever above that point. Points of fixity are arbitrarily assumed. Commonly used depths of fixity are 5 ft below ground surface for firm or compact soil and 10 ft below ground surface for soft or loose soil.

Elastic analysis.   In this method, the soil elastic deformation is calculated. The result is a diagram of lateral deflection of the head of the pile for various assumed lateral loads. Since lateral deflection cannot be too much without damage to the structure, this establishes the allowable lateral design load on the pile. Soil testing and analysis are required for this method.

Load test.   A pole or pile can be driven and tested by applying a lateral load at the head of the pile. Usually, a lateral deflection of $\frac{1}{2}$ in. is the maximum allowable, with residual deflection after removal of load of $\frac{1}{4}$ in. or less. Also, the design load is usually 50%, or some other percentage, of the test lateral load.

Additional information on design can be obtained from Ref. 37.

16.15   Summary

The important points in this chapter are as follows:

FACTS: The risks of property damage should be realistically appraised and covered by insurance, including "extended coverage." Compilation of data supporting claims for extras can become a major undertaking. The adequacy of the soil information, and its inclusion or exclusion from the contract documents is important. Problems frequently result from the following:

1. Obstructions to pile driving.
2. Driving displacement piles through cohesive soils.
3. Negative friction on piles.
4. Lateral forces on piles.

WATCH OUT FOR: Potential damage to structures from pile driving. Soil information indicating erratic elevations of rock surface or the surfaces of bearing strata. Carelessness in driving test piles and conducting pile load test. Modified pile driving formulas resulting in damage to hammers and piles.

17

Timber Piles

The use of wood piles (often called spiles in early writings) goes back to antiquity. Where soil conditions are suitable and the column loads moderate, timber piles will provide an economical and adequate pile foundation.

17.1 Procurement, Tolerances, and Inspection

The southeastern states, from Maryland south into Georgia, produce Southern Pine piles and furnish the bulk of timber piling used in the eastern portion of the country. Piles up to 60 ft long are in quantity. Longer piles can be found in small quantities. The Great Lakes region, principally Michigan, provide mixed hard woods, white and red oak, some cedar, and other species. Available length is about 60 ft. The Pacific Northwest grows Douglas fir. This is the only source of piles in quantity in lengths from 65 to 90 ft. For lengths under 60 ft, the cost of transportation governs; thus fir is used on the West Coast and pine in the East. Untreated piles are sold with the bark left on, but long fir piles to be shipped to the East are peeled frequently to save freight costs. If the piles are to be treated, they are always peeled before shipment.

Timber piles are sold by the linear foot in brackets or groups with a variation in length of 5 ft. Thus piles in the 40-ft range may be furnished anywhere from 40 to 44 ft at the seller's option for a fixed price per foot. The next bracket runs from 45 to 49 ft. When a contractor orders, for example, 500 42-ft piles, the length delivered will usually average closer to 44 ft, which must be considered in estimating waste.

The responsibility for preparing an order list of wood piles may fall upon the contractor or the engineer, depending on the terms of the contract. Though rare today, in the past the piling contractor was paid for the length of pile hung in the leads. The order list was prepared by the engineer (or owner's representative) and the cost of the length of piles cut off was borne by the owner. Under present practice, contracts provide for payment to the contractor for the lengths of piles after they are driven and cut off. Here the contractor is responsible for the length ordered. In either case, test piles should be driven and each test pile should be driven alongside a test boring. The correlation of the soil data and the driving logs of the test piles are of great value in deciding the lengths to be ordered.

Specifications for timber piles are presented in ASTM D 25-70. This specification applies to round timber piles and establishes pile sizes based on intended use. For end bearing piles, the tip diameter is a controlling dimension. For friction piles, the butt diameter is a controlling dimension. *Note.* Previously used classifications of piles as class A, B, or C is eliminated. Specifications written into building codes reflect local usage, but do not vary greatly from ASTM. Engineers may call for an oversized pile tip for some particular project. Tips are seldom permitted less than 6 in. in diameter, which presents a problem only with very long fir piles.

Requirements for straightness usually state that a straight line from butt to tip falls within the body of the pile. This is not difficult with fir piles if they are carefully handled and stored, but pine piles do not grow with the same uniformity. Consequently, in securing quotations from vendors, exact copies of the specifications should be furnished to them. In addition, inspection of the piles in the woods by qualified inspection agencies is worth the cost to reduce the number of rejected piles. Even though the vendor must dispose of rejected piles, the cost of sorting, handling, and loading is borne by the contractor.

17.2   Storage and Breakage

Wood piles 50 ft in length and longer are slender, fragile units. The location and layout of the job will determine how long and how many times a pile must be handled before it is driven. Experience indicates that it is wise to allow from 1 to 2% for breakage. Often overlooked is the effect of long periods of storage on timber piles. Direct sunlight may cause piles to become dehydrated, sometimes unevenly. Piles which have passed inspection on delivery for straightness may become so curved as to be unacceptable. Piles in storage more than a month or two should be examined and restored. Dehydrated piles become brittle and break more readily in driving.

17.3   Treated Wood Piles

Untreated timber piles may be considered permanent only where the entire pile length will be below the ground water level in permanently saturated soil.

Occasionally the water level in the ground is below the pile caps. In some cases, it will pay to lower the pile caps by deeper excavation so that untreated piles can be used. In many situations, the water level is too deep, and the piles will develop bearing capacity in dry soils. For these conditions, timber piles must be treated in order to be permanent (also see Section 17.7).

The practice of treating wood piles is to impregnate them with creosote oil. Peeled piles are placed in long cylindrical tanks where they are steamed, subjected to a partial vacuum, and then immersed in hot creosote oil under pressure until the full length of the pile has absorbed a predetermined weight of oil per cubic foot. This is known as the full cell process. ASTM specification D is one recognized standard. Specifications may call for a retention of from 8 to 12 lb/ft^3, depending on the service anticipated. Piles are inspected for size and straightness at the plant before processing. More care is required in handling treated piles because they are more brittle and because cable slings may abrade the treated surface, exposing untreated wood. The protection against dry rot is provided by a rather thin outer layer of treated wood so that care must be taken to preserve it. After a pile butt has been cut off, the top should be given a coat of oil.

17.4   Driving Limitations

Wood piles are fragile and can be broken or "broomed" by overdriving. If an obstruction is encountered, they can be broken under normal driving. When a pile is broken during driving, the penetration suddenly increases. For instance, from a penetration of 1 in. per blow it may jump to 3 in. per blow. If a blow-by-blow driving log is being kept by an inspector, this will be detected. Otherwise, it is likely to pass unnoticed, except by the pile driver foreman. He should be repeatedly cautioned to report every such occurrence. "Brooming" of the tip of the pile may cause some increase in the penetration rate, but more often can be detected by rebounding of the butt of the pile and a generally "rubbery" behavior under driving. Splitting or other damage to the pile butt is, of course, directly observable.

To minimize damage to timber piles, the first step is to follow good pile driving practice. Piles should be driven in fixed leaders that are kept plumb (and continuously checked for plumbness). Also, it is important to make sure that the hammer is hitting squarely on the pile. All this can be done without sacrificing progress (except when worrying a pile down through obstructions). Points of wood piles should be cut square, not pointed, for straight driving.

Selection of the appropriate hammer for the length of pile and soil conditions needs careful consideration. The greater the energy of the blow, the greater the risk of damage. Single acting hammers are safer to use than those delivering more blows per minute. Hammers developing 15,000 ft-lb of energy per blow usually are the upper limit. For piles under 25 ft long, 12,000 ft-lb hammers are safer. Using hammers with energies less than 8000 ft-lb is unwise, except for short and lightly loaded piles. The use of a lower energy hammer on long piles may give resistances which by formula appear adequate but may fail under the load test. Hammers of 8000 to

10,000 ft-lb are considered the lower limit. The risk in the use of high frequency hammers is that they cannot be stopped as quickly as the single acting hammer when refusal or an obstruction is encountered.

There is a limit to the final driving resistance that a wood pile can stand without real risk of damage. The building code or the specifications usually establish the resistance to which the piles are to be driven. In the 1930s pile loads were limited to about 20 tons. Pile loads have increased; 30-ton capacity have been written into certain codes and some specifications have called for even higher loads. In the 1960s, many piles were driven for loads of 40 and even 50 tons. A startling increase in the risk of damaged piles has thus developed. This is not to question the structural capacity of timber piles driven perfectly to sustain loads, but to point out that as loads increase, there is less leeway for a few damaged piles. The percentage of damaged piles must decrease in each group of piles if the safety factor is to remain the same. Recognition of the increased risks inherent in higher loads is found in the 1967–1968 revision of the New York City building code. Eight-inch tips are required for all piles loaded from 25 to 30 tons (maximum allowable), and where piles are to be end-bearing, the personal supervision (not just inspection) of an architect or engineer is required.

The estimated economy from the use of higher loads carries with it increased costs of inspection and an increase in the number of rejected piles.

On any particular project, the risk of damaged piles must be evaluated by a study of the soil conditions and the final resistance to which the piles are to be driven. Where timber piles are endbearing and driven through soft and loose formations to an impenetrable stratum, the "take-up" of the piles will be sudden. After the first bounce of the hammer, it should be stopped. Further blows will broom or break the pile. While steel shoes may prevent brooming, they do not reduce the chance of breakage. Under such conditions, pile driving formulas should not be used. The purpose is to seat the pile with one final blow. There is also a risk that piles first driven may heave up off the bearing stratum as later piles are driven. Where level readings indicate heave, the piles should be retapped to reseat them.

Where the bearing stratum is moderately dense or stiff, free of boulders, cobbles or large gravel, the risk of damage is slight. Under such conditions, 30-ton loading may be justified. Using a 15,000 ft-lb hammer, experience shows that three blows per inch is a safe limit for long piles driven through soft soils. Four blows per inch is a safe limit for piles up to 50 ft in length.

Boulders or other obstructions in the soil present problems in driving timber piles which can be virtually unsolvable. Much depends on the depth below the excavation to the bottom of the obstructions. Where a layer of man-made fill of boulders, timber, or bricks exists to a depth of approximately 6 ft, the following solutions should be considered. Where there are no more than four or five piles per pier, a heavy steel spud may be able to penetrate or displace the obstructions. The pile should be driven in each spudded hole immediately after the spud is removed. For larger groups of piles, it may be cheaper to remove the fill in each pile group area and backfill to grade with suitable soil.

It may pay to cut the bad fill off the entire building site and replace it with selected fill.

A loosely deposited layer of sand and gravel above the bearing stratum is a potential source of trouble. The test borings also may have missed possible cobbles or boulders. Jetting should never be used, because it only washes out the sand, and all the coarser material then collects just where the pile is to be driven. Any cobbles as large as the pile tip will be difficult to dislodge by driving. There are two expedients which may help to solve the problem or at least reduce the number of damaged piles. Steel shoes will help to punch through. Also, short stroking the hammer and hitting the pile with reduced energy may dislodge and drive by the cobbles.

17.5 Lagging Timber Piles

The term "lagging," as used in pile driving practice, refers to an increase in the size of a pile at its lower end to increase the frictional resistance and the displacement of the pile. Where piles do not quite meet the driving requirements or satisfy the load tests, lagging may produce good results. Two 4 by 6 in. timbers long enough to equal the anticipated penetration into the bearing layer are bolted to the lower ends of the piles. Lagging is an expensive procedure, but may be justified to make use of the piles already on hand. This expedient is not limited to timber piles.

17.6   Driving Butt First

Occasionally, the soil formation may contain a layer of granular soil thick enough to spread the load from a group of piles so that a softer deposit below it will support the reduced loads satisfactorily, yet not so dense as to keep the piles from punching through. In a number of instances good results were obtained by driving the piles with the butt end down. A 14-in.-diameter butt has four times the area of a 7-in. pile tip. Stopping the pile high in the sand layer helps to prevent overstressing the softer soil below the bearing stratum.

17.7   Composite Piles

Timber piles which have top extensions in the form of cast-in-place concrete piles are called composite piles. The composite pile was developed to meet the situation where the permanent ground water level is too far below the pile cut off to lower the concrete cap economically. On the other hand, the water level must not be so far down as to make creosoted piles more economical. As a very rough guide, when the water level lies from 6 to 25 ft below the cut off, composite timber piles may prove economical. They are subject to the same loading and driving limitations as wood piles.

The joint between the wood section and the concrete section is the most important feature of any composite pile. It must perform three functions. It must be reasonably watertight so that placing concrete can be done properly. It must hold the two sections together so that the concrete section cannot be forced upward causing a separation. It must have enough strength in bending to stand lateral forces. Many patented devices have been developed for joining composite piles.

Where the joint may be subject to bending, the most common method is to form a tenon at the top of the wood section at least 8 in.

in diameter and at least 14 in. long. The pipe or casing for the upper
section should be equipped with a sealing ring which will drive
against the shoulder of the tenon and provide an annular space surrounding the tenon so that good concrete can be assured at the joint.
A rod fastened in the tenon and extending through the concrete section should be used. There are other methods of accomplishing these
results. The literature of the specialty contractors in the field should
be consulted.

17.8 Summary

The important points in this chapter are as follows:

FACTS: Timber piles may break or broom during driving.
Piles should be inspected "in the woods." Timber
piles may need to be creosote treated to prevent
decay of the wood. Composite piles, combinations
of timber, and concrete piles are useful under certain ground water conditions.

WATCH OUT FOR: Sudden increase of penetration during driving.
Rubbery action of piles during driving. Hammer
energies too low or too high.

18

Steel Piles

18.1   H-Beam Piles

The use of structural steel beams for foundation piling came into general use in the United States in the early 1930s. Special H-sections designed for use as piling are rolled by the major steel companies. H-beam piles are usually used for heavy loads, where they can be driven to rock or into a dense formation such as hardpan. They are often considered as nondisplacement piles, because they do not usually displace as much soil as solid piling. Under certain soil conditions, this feature may be very helpful. A structural steel pile of heavy cross-section (over 100 lb per lineal foot), properly reinforced, and driven with a big hammer, can be driven through almost any soil formation other than rock.

18.1.1   Order Lengths

H-beam piles may be ordered in any length up to 65 ft long and are quoted at a base price per pound. Lengths over 65 ft, up to about 120 ft, are rolled. However, a "length extra" must be paid for the full length.

18.1.2   Splicing and Reinforcing

The specifications for a project stipulate the type of splice either by detailing the splice to be used or by requiring that the contractor provide splices which will develop a certain percentage of the strength of the H-beam in axial compression and in bending. There are several types of splices, such as (a) joining sections by full butt welding, (b) welding steel plates to the outsides of the flanges and to both sides of the web, and (c) using patented slip connections. In splicing of structural members, it is important to maintain precise alignment of the sections; this is difficult and time-consuming.

By splicing beams to the full length needed, the piles may be driven in one piece. Otherwise, piles are spliced during driving. This means a delay and is more costly. Where splices are made in the leads, it is often necessary to trim the top of the driven section to get full contact between the sections.

In comparing the costs of field welding of H-beams with the extra costs of ordering beams full length, the problems of transporting long beams through city streets (often permitted at night only) and of unloading and handling need careful consideration.

When H-beams are to be driven through soils containing obstructions, stiffening plates are often welded on the outside of the flanges to reduce twisting and warping of the piles. To secure end-bearing on sloping rock, the webs may be reinforced and the corners of the flanges burned off at an angle. Since the design load on H-beams is usually high, the driving requirements are proportionately severe. Under prolonged hard driving, H-beams tend to twist. A circular follower or bonnet is preferable to a square shape so that the beam is free to twist in the follower. Twisting of H-beams for building foundations is not serious because the tops are covered with a concrete cap. However, where the upper ends are exposed as, for example, pile bents for a trestle, misalignment and rotation will not pass inspection. If the design calls for concrete encasement above the ground line, the cross-section of the concrete may have to be enlarged to solve the problem.

Under hard driving in disintegrated rock, hardpan, large gravel, or boulders, H-beam piles suffer curling of the tips and drifting off location. Numerous cases of extracted piles show this to be so. In one case, pile A had reached rock at a depth of 136 ft. Pile B, 4 ft distant, drove 156 ft, at which time pile A began to rise. Redriving pile A caused pile B to come up. To correct this problem, it was necessary to reinforce the tips. Difficulties of this nature arise usually because the weight per foot of the H-beam is too light for the driving requirements and the soils or rock conditions. During estimating, a contractor should weigh all these facts and the obligations for damaged piles that he will assume under the contract.

18.1.3 Driving

Where the borings reveal the presence of sound rock below a glacial till, H-beams are often selected on the expectation that they can be driven to the rock for relatively high bearing capacity. If, however, it turns out that a substantial number of the piles cannot be driven to the sound rock, but instead stop in glacial till (a situation that has often occurred), serious problems develop. Most building codes limit the allowable load on piles that are driven into till or disintegrated rock to lower values than on piles that bear on hard rock. No matter how hard the piles are driven in the till, the fact is that they cannot qualify for sound rock loads. Much depends on the accuracy of the conclusion that the piles have not reached rock. Interpolation of rock surface elevations, on the assumption that the rock slopes uniformly between widely spaced borings, can be challenged. A few check borings may show that rock elevations are higher than expected. In this case, some rational basis for accepting piles that do not quite reach the interpolated grades may be agreed upon. Where there is no doubt that the piles have failed to reach rock, successful pile load tests may satisfy the building department and the engineer. Pile load tests for high capacity piles, however, are expensive and time-consuming, and they may fail. Under these circumstances, consideration should be given to experimenting with test piles. Rock might be reached using reinforced pile tips, and the heaviest hammer the H-beam section can stand. Also, beams of a heavier section could be tried. To get good piles it may be necessary to stiffen the ends of the piles with plates so they will bite into the rock and not slide.

There is a limit to the hammer energy which H-beams can stand without buckling at the top. For example, a 12-in. 53-lb beam cannot be expected to withstand hard driving with greater than a 22,500-ft-lb hammer. However, a 14-in. 89-lb beam can stand up under a 30,000-ft-lb hammer.

Where a foundation design is based on piles reaching or penetrating a given formation, the specifications make the contractor
fully responsible for doing so. While such requirements may apply
to any pile type, H-beam pile foundations are required to reach fixed
elevations more often than other types. The pile contractors should
have no illusions about what will be expected of him if normal pile
driving methods cannot drive the piles deep enough. Heavier hammers may be demanded; the cost of changeover and of the hard
driving usually is borne by the pile contractor.

The use of H-beam piles as friction piles is rare. They are not well
suited for this purpose. Other types of piles are better able to develop
frictional resistance and are more economical.

H-beam piles are often employed where a penetration of 5 to 10 ft
into a dense formation will develop bearing capacity through friction
and end-bearing. Verification of the bearing capacity by test piles and
pile load tests is standard procedure. In estimating such work, a
contractor must weigh the chances of load test failures. When this
happens, additional and longer test piles are usually driven, and
extra tests are performed. While specifications may include payment
for the longer lengths and splices, the contractor must be sure that
his equipment is tall enough to take longer lengths in one piece, that
his price for load tests will cover delays to the work, and that he can
pay warehouse prices for the longer beams.

Often it is desirable to drive from a general excavation level considerably above the pile cut-off elevations. In such cases, it is necessary to drive H-beams (or any pile) with a follower. A follower must
be of heavier section than the pile and be rigid enough so that the
full energy of the hammer will be delivered to the top of the pile. It
must be realized that the tolerances as to pile location at cut-off need
to be increased substantially. Furthermore, remedial measures to
correct for pile eccentricities should be anticipated and payment
therefore predetermined.

Specifications sometimes call for driving piles to "refusal." While
this method is not confined to H-beams, it occurs often enough to
call for comment. Literally, this means that under successive blows
of the hammer the top of the pile does not move appreciably. Driv-

ing on a pile in this fashion may damage the point of the pile, and there is the possibility that the pile will be broken, deformed, or injured in a way to reduce its carrying capacity. A better definition of refusal is that "when resistance to driving causes the ram of the hammer to bounce, refusal is indicated and driving shall stop." Refusal is a misunderstood term and should be defined in the specifications. Rather than prolonged driving to satisfy the criteria of so many blows per foot, or per inch, the specifications should permit stopping at a lesser number of blows when the pile has completely stopped.

18.1.4 Corrosion Protection

Potential corrosion of steel H-piles is an engineering matter. The contractor's responsibility lies in furnishing and installing such protection as it is called for. The subject of corrosion of steel piles is controversial, and contractors are well advised to be familiar with the literature on the subject (see Ref. 38). Since contractors must warrant their workmanship and materials for a period of time, it is only prudent to consider carefully the need for protection, the means specified, and the duration of the warranty.

It is generally agreed that steel piles are subject to corrosion for the length extending above the permanent ground water level. Rust which forms on the surface of the steel forms a protective coating which arrests further loss of cross-section. An allowance of $1/8$ in. is usual. However, any physical scouring action, such as windblown particles and waves, may erode the protective coating. More positive protection is necessary. Chemical wastes or drainage therefrom or fills containing cinders or granulated slag will bring about progressive corrosion (unless such fills are old enough to be leached out and inert).

Stray electrical currents from power plants and generating stations and from third rails of transportation systems are considered causes of corrosion, both above and below ground water levels. Dissolved gases carried in water-bearing strata may also cause corrosion, even at considerable depth in the soil. In soils above the water level, the more oxygen present the greater the rusting action. Thus corrosion is proportional inversely to the soil density.

One positive method of protection, often specified, is the application of an asphaltic emulsion to the length of pile above ground water. Sandblasting to remove mill scale is required, and the emulsion is brushed or sprayed on, usually heated. Piles so treated must be driven in such a way that the friction of driving does not abrade the coating. In soils that might abrade, one solution is to spud a hole slightly larger than the diagonal of the H-section. The space in and around each pile should be backfilled. Where the sides of the hole will not stand up, a temporary casing may have to be driven. After the pile has been driven, the casing is withdrawn as the backfill is placed. A flight auger can also be used. It loosens the soil so that the pile can penetrate easily. Where the soil is free of gravel or coarser particles, jetting with air or water may prove successful.

To counter corrosion from electrolysis and stray currents, pile groups may be grounded by attaching copper wire to one pile in each group and arranging the reinforcing steel in the pile cap to connect all the piles. Cathodic protection is of dubious value above the ground water level and is rarely used on building foundations (see Ref. 38).

18.2 Pipe Piles

Pipe piles fall in the general category of cast-in-place piling. After being driven, they are usually filled with concrete. The term implies that the wall thickness of the pipe is sufficient to withstand the driving forces without internal support (as by a mandrel). In certain cases, where sufficient wall thickness is specified to allow for both external and internal corrosion, piles are not filled with concrete. They may be left empty and capped, filled with granular material or partially filled with concrete or sand and capped.

Closed-end pipe piles designed for friction or end-bearing, usually are 10- and 12-in. I.D. pipe. Occasionally 8-in. I.D. pipe has been employed. Ten- and 12-in. piles frequently are designed for loads on the order of 50 tons. Provided soil conditions are suitable and the wall thickness is adequate, 10- and 12-in pipe piles sometimes are designed for loads up to 100 tons. For closed-end pipe piles, larger diameters are seldom required unless the piles are subject to bending moments or are extended above the ground level.

Open-end pipe piles commonly are 14- to 20-in. O.D. pipes. These open-end piles usually are driven to rock. The design loads on such piles range up to 250 tons, and so require the larger sizes and the thick wall sections. Although rarely used for building foundations, pipe piles with diameters from 24 to 48 in. are used for special applications, such as offshore drilling platforms. These large sizes are discussed in Chapter 21, Section 21.7.

18.2.1   Materials, Points, and Splices

Pipe suitable to stand up under driving is made either from seamless steel tubing or steel plate which is spirally rolled and welded to the required size. Lap-welded pipe, whether seams are straight or spiral, is suitable for piles. The material must comply with ASTM Des.A-252, grade 2 or 3 or API specifications, class 2 or 3. The ability of steel pipe to withstand driving forces without permanent deformation is a function of the carbon content. Mill tests showing the carbon content should be demanded for all shipments. For grade or class 2 pipes, the content should fall between 0.2 and 0.3%. For grade or class 3 pipe, it should be about 0.35%. Such material is weldable, but where the carbon content exceeds 0.35%, special techniques are required.

Pipe is ordered either in single random lengths, 18 to 22 ft in length or in double random lengths of 36 to 44 ft. By special order, one and one-half random lengths may be procured which usually involves a butt weld made at the mill to produce the longer length. Spirally welded pipe may be ordered in any length which can be handled and transported. The ends of each section of pipe are cut at right angles to the axis of the pipe, but may be ordered bevelled when pipe is to be spliced on the site. For special services, the ends may be ordered "milled" (ground to a precise plane).

The nominal diameter of pipe up to and including 12 in. is the inside measurement. Over 12 in., the outside diameter is the nominal size. Thus 12-in. pipe with a $3/8$ in. wall thickness will measure $12\frac{3}{4}$ in. O.D., while 14-in. pipe of the same thickness will be $13\frac{1}{4}$ in. I.D.

The lower end of closed-end piles may be fitted with conical cast steel points or flat steel plates. Cast steel points have a shoulder and tapered sleeve providing a drive fit into the pipe as shown in Fig. 18.1. Circular flat steel plates welded to the ends of the pipe are also shown. Where piles are to be driven as friction piles, the method illustrated in which the plate does not extend beyond the outside diameter of the pipe is preferable. The thickness of the plates is usually left to the contractor. For 10-in. pipe, 5/8-in. plate is customary. For 12-in. pipe, 3/4-in. plate is customary. The choice between points and plates depends on several factors. While points cost more than plates, the pile driver crew can attach them without the services of a welder. Points are not always watertight. Under hard driving on boulders or rock, points may break. Plates need welding services, but are watertight and usually drive straighter. Where welding services are not otherwise needed and soil conditions are favorable, points are economical and satisfactory.

Splices joining sections of pipe are made either by sleeves or by welding. Figure 18.1 illustrates a typical sleeve splice and details of welded splices. Both the short and long sleeve splices are shown. The advantage of the long sleeve splice is that it provides a stiffer joint. Where splices will end up more than about 30 ft below grade, the extra cost of long sleeves may be more than offset by fewer piles rejected for bends and dog-legs, not to mention greater watertightness. Above a depth of 30 ft, short sleeves should be acceptable, except for leakage. In ordering sleeves for pipe over 12 in. in diameter, care should be taken to specify the inside diameter of the pipe as this changes with the wall thickness. The advantage of the use of sleeves is that they do not delay the driving operation. The disadvantage is that sleeves are not always watertight. For this reason, specifications call occasionally for a sleeve splice to be welded to both sections of pipe. This may be impossible to accomplish in the leads. With tight-fitting sleeves, the joint may not "make-up" before it is driven below grade. If it is welded before it makes-up, the driving will break the weld.

Sleeve splices create an obstruction on the inside of the pipe. External sleeves are available (Fig. 18.1) to leave the inside of the pipe full diameter.

While sleeve splices have their place, welded splices are better structurally, and they are watertight. In welding, the end of one piece of pipe should be bevelled at 45 degrees and the other cut square. With a backup ring tacked to the inside and a space approximating 3/16 in. left between the pipe ends, a full penetration weld can be assured. Figure 18.1 also shows the arrangement.

Care must be taken to stress-relieve and cool the weld (particularly if single pass welding is used) before driving is resumed. Otherwise, the weld may crack when driven below the ground water level.

18.2.2 Driving Closed-End

A closed-end pipe pile must have sufficient rigidity and wall thickness to stand up under the energy delivered to it by the pile hammer. In practice, a wall thickness of 0.18 in. is the thinnest section practical to use. Such thin wall pipe should be limited to 10-in. pipe, to loads not exceeding 50 tons, and to driving not exceeding seven blows per inch with a single acting 15,000-ft-lb hammer. For 12-in. pipe, the minimum thickness should be 0.219 in. for loads in excess of 40 tons. As a general rule, pipes with wall thicknesses under $1/4$ in. should be used only as friction piles for loads up to 50 tons and where there is definite limit on hard driving. Pipe piles driven for end-bearing, or a combination of friction and end-bearing, should have minimum wall thicknesses of 0.279 in. for 10-in. pipe and 0.312 in. for 12-in. pipe.

Difficult driving conditions, such as fill containing timbers, concrete, boulders, rock fragments, or sloping rock surfaces present seri-

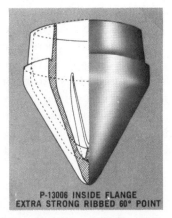
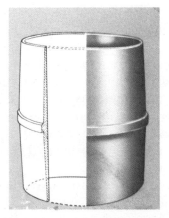

P-13006 INSIDE FLANGE
EXTRA STRONG RIBBED 60° POINT

Fig. 18.1 Typical pipe pile point and sleeves, welded bottom plates and welded splice.

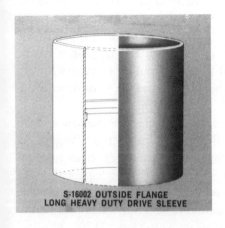

S-16002 OUTSIDE FLANGE
LONG HEAVY DUTY DRIVE SLEEVE

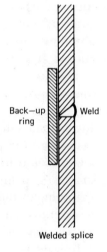

Back—up ring

Weld

Welded splice

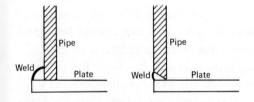

Fig. 18.1 *Continued.*

221

ous problems, more or less as they do for all pile types. Obviously, pipe piles can be driven through rough fill and compact soil layers which would stop or break wood piles or stop precast concrete piles.

In comparing pipe piles with H-piles under difficult driving conditions, experience shows that pipe is superior to beams of similar weight because the pipe is more rigid. On the other hand, 12-in. 53-lb and heavier H-piles will punch through better than pipe. Unfortunately, the alignment of the H-pile and its condition after driving through obstructions cannot be determined.

It is particularly important for contractors to realize that the widely proclaimed advantage of a "pile which can be inspected" (a claimed advantage of all cast-in-place piling) is a two-way street. Because they can be inspected, out of plumbness, sharp bends (dog-legs) and leakage of water or mud can be observed and be the cause of rejection. Also, there is the added expense in efforts to seal out water and delays awaiting decisions about acceptance or rejection. With H-piles, plumbness and deflections cannot be observed. They exist but are not known. It is incumbent upon the contractor to conduct his work so as to minimize these troubles, thereby reducing the percentage of rejected piles.

The pile driver leads must be plumbed when the pile is started and any tendency for the pile to drift or slope should be countered by "bucking" the pile with the leads back into position. The pile follower should have a snug fitting projection into the top of the pipe so that the hammer blow is evenly distributed on the top of the pipe. Crimping or bulging below the follower calls for the damaged end to be carefully cut off at right angles to the pile axis. Crimping can occur with no damage to the completed pile (See Fig. 18.2).

In waterbearing soils, welded end plates and welded splices should be used. In spite of all precautions, piles will not always be plumb and straight or dry. Where piles have to be overdriven to get them down and where high bearing capacities call for high final driving resistance, the number of piles which fail to meet the specified tolerances will be greater than for piles driven as friction piles for lower final driving resistance (See Ref. 40). Estimates should include the cost and time for replacement piles.

Back pressure from cohesive soils usually has no effect on pipe piles because of the strength of the pipe. In deep beds of clay soils and in

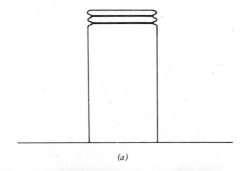

(a)

(b)

Fig. 18.2   Crimping or bulging at the top of a pipe pile under hard driving.

thick beds confined under a layer that acts as a crust, the displacement caused by the introduction of the piles results in heaving of the clay and the development of intense lateral forces. Where the clay is confined, the stresses are most severe. Generally pipe piles can resist these stresses. Sometimes, however, it may be necessary to predrill or to fill the pile with water during driving. The built up pressure also may cause upward movement of the clay or heave. The piles might be lifted from their driven depth. A discussion of pile heave will be found in Chapter 16.

Closed-end pipe piles when driven as friction piles seldom present difficulties (except for obstructions and boulders) so far as driving is concerned. The failure of such piles under pile load tests has occurred with sufficient frequency so that contractors should consider such a possibility when bidding. Pipe piles driven as friction piles in granular soils depend for their carrying capacity on a nominal amount of end-bearing (a few tons) plus friction between the smooth surface of the steel and the soil. Such a friction value is not likely to exceed 1000 to 1200 lb/ft^2, although the frictional value of the soil itself may be much higher. In cohesive soils, the situation is quite different. The adhesion between clay soils and the pile surface equals or exceeds the shear value of the clay itself. When piles are extracted from clay, it is usual for slabs of clay to adhere to the pile and come out with it. Thus the adhesion between the soil and the pile is greater than the soil strength. This relationship has limitations. The ultimate bearing capacities of piles driven into normally consolidated clays can be approximated from the shear strength of the clay. This has been demonstrated for piles driven into the clays in the Great Lakes and Gulf of Mexico. Where the clay is very stiff (N exceeds 15), such a relationship is no longer dependable. In the moderately stiff clays (above $N = 15$), the adhesion between pile and soil is often less than one-half the shear strength of the clay. In such formations, neither the driving resistance nor the strength of the soil is a measure of the pile capacity. This applies to straight-sided piles. It requires extensive study by experts in this field, supplemented by pile load tests, to assign safe bearing capacities to piles under such conditions.

When pipe piles designed as friction piles fail under load test, the engineer may reduce the design loading. This means adding piles to the job, or driving the piles harder and deeper. The payment clause may take care of added piles or longer lengths, but rarely takes care of harder driving. For friction piles this may mean appreciably more driving time per pile. If the piles were long in the first place, the leads may not be tall enough to handle the longer lengths in one piece. This requires that a splice be made in the leads, instead of in the welding yard. In such cases, records should be kept of the extra time required to reach the revised driving resistance, to provide back-up for a claim.

18.2.3   Driving Open-End

For many years pipe piles have been driven open-end to bear on rock. The piles are then cleaned out and filled with concrete. They are designed to carry substantial loads, from 150 to 300 tons per pile, depending on diameter and wall thickness of pipe. The use of open-end piles has declined in recent years because of the higher loads permitted on other pile types and the difficulty of estimating the cost of installing open-end piles. However, there are conditions under which they are the best engineering solution. The foundation piling of the Vertical Assembly Building at Cape Kennedy, Fla., is a case in point.

It is assumed that the pile load is distributed onto both the concrete and the steel pipe. To transmit this load into the rock, the full circumference of the pipe and area of the concrete filling must be in intimate contact with the rock. The lower end of the pipe usually is protected against curling by an exterior collar. In driving, great attention has to be paid to keeping the pile plumb. Overdriving has to be avoided to prevent damage. As the pipe is driven, soil accumulates inside which from time to time must be removed to reduce resistance to penetration and possible drifting of the pile. When boulders or obstructions are encountered, overdriving again must be avoided; other means must be found to break up or dislodge the obstruction. If spudding fails, a churn drill can be used to break up the obstruction. When the cutting edge reaches rock, it must be seated completely to seal out soil and to reduce the inflow of water to acceptable amounts.

18.2.4   Excavating Open-End

Many ways are used to excavate the soil inside of open-end piles. Well driller's bailing buckets, augers, water jets, and air jets have all been used. An effective method is the use of a jet which combines some water with a large supply of compressed air. Both are introduced at the same pressure. The water helps to loosen compacted soil and to wash the insides of the pipe clean. Precautions must be taken to keep the debris and mud blown out from affecting adjacent buildings, streets, cars, and the public.

Specifications require that after a pile has been driven to rock and cleaned, it shall be redriven and cleaned again to assure a clean surface on which to place the concrete and to cut off the inflow of water. In practice these operations may have to be repeated several times to produce the specified results. Three times is not unusual and five or six times may be needed. A careful study of the rock cores from the site is necessary to evaluate the seating problem.

18.2.5   Inspection

The inspection of materials is routine. Pipe dimensions and physical properties as certified by mill test reports have to be verified. An important part of inspection, almost always left to the contractor, is the checking of the fit of pipe pile points and sleeves.

Inspection of piles as driven must include the measurement of the deviation of the center of the pile at the cut-off elevation with reference to the "plan" location. The critical operation is the inspection of the interior of the pile to determine plumbness and straightness.

Most specifications permit a deviation of 3 in. from the plan location of the head of the pile. Except in badly obstructed soils, piles can be driven within a 3-in. tolerance provided that good pile driving practices are followed. Every effort should be made to have such measurements taken upon the completion of each pile group so that any extra piles needed to correct for group eccentricities can be driven without having to bring the driver back from other parts of the site. Where deviations occur all in one direction, the driving is not likely to be the cause. The pile stakes may have been offset by an error in layout or lateral movement of the soil mass may have taken place. Pile stakes which have been in place for a week or more should be checked. Stakes get knocked over, and when replaced by anyone who happens to come along, they are almost always reset off location.

Certain soils heave during pile driving with lateral as well as vertical movement. With large groups of piles closely spaced, movements become cumulative and the situation can get out of hand (see Chapter 16).

The phase of inspection which causes the most controversy is the verification of the plumbness and straightness of the piles. Specifications are usually definite as to the deviation from the vertical which will be permitted. However, these tolerances vary widely. They range from $1/4$ in./ft. (which is about 1 : 50) to 1 : 100. Probably 1 : 60 is the most common. As to straightness, specifications usually state that some portion of the tip of the pile must be visible from the top. Less specific criteria concerning bends, reduction of area, and water inflow are also included.

Deviation from the vertical is difficult to determine without the time-consuming and expensive use of an inclinometer or well-logging device. It becomes a matter of judgment. In general, a slope of 1 : 60 is reasonable. However, for long piles tolerances more severe than 1 : 60 may be required. Also, the tip of the pile may not be visible. The result can be a high percentage of rejected piles, no matter how carefully the piles are driven. For pipe piles, reduction of area is rarely a problem. Although wet piles are seldom experienced with welded pipe, piles with points and sleeves often are wet. Salvaging wet piles is discussed in Chapter 19.

Sharp bends (dog-legs) and long sweeping bends can occur no matter how carefully the piles are driven. Whether to accept or reject such piles is a matter of experience and judgment. Contractors should be familiar with the literature on this subject (see Ref. 40).

A better approach is needed for evaluation of piles which exceed tolerances as currently specified. Some piles end up out of plumb, and yet are straight enough so that some part of the tip can be seen. Such piles are "batter piles" and are competent to carry their loads. The small amount of horizontal force which they exert on the pile cap is seldom significant in groups of five or more piles. With groups of only two or three piles, however, the lateral force might be unbalanced. In such cases, remedial measures may be required. The second problem relates to piles which have bends and the tip of the pile cannot be seen. The first requirement is assurance that the pile is not ruptured and is reasonably free of water or mud. This can be verified with a bailing bucket. The difficult question is to determine the degree of bending which is acceptable, and to measure it. A bailing bucket of a certain outside diameter and length can be built which cannot pass a sharp bend in the pipe.

18.2.6   Placing Concrete in Pipe Piles

The importance of placing concrete in piles properly cannot be over-emphasized. A pile is not a pile until it is concreted. Using care and proper methods add so little to the cost that there is no excuse for slighting so important an operation. The first consideration is how to pour the concrete without segregation of the concrete and without arching and plugging so that voids are left in the casing. Generally, the specifications require tremie pouring or pouring through a down-spout set in the center of the shell of the pipe. It is most common to use a hopper with a downspout of at least 18 in. long centered in the shell. The downspout directs the flow of concrete straight down the center of the pile.

The second major consideration is the slump of the concrete. For piles up to 12 in. in diameter, the slump should not be less than $3\frac{1}{2}$ in. nor more than 5 in. For larger piles, the slump should be $2\frac{1}{2}$ to 5 in. There is a tendency for low slump concrete to form an arch at any restriction, such as an internal sleeve or at a bend in the pile. Dry concrete also tends to adhere to the sides during an interruption in a pour. When arches form, a void in the concrete may develop. When low slump concrete must be used, there are precautions which should be taken. One or two wheelbarrows of rich grout poured into the pile will coat the sides and help the flow of the concrete.

The use of a sash weight on a line worked up and down will break up an arch. A piece of reinforcing steel can be similarly used. Some specifications call for the use of vibrators. They will prevent arching; however with 4-in. or more slump, they tend to increase segregation. Although rarely used in pipe piles, the presence of a cage of reinforc-ing steel required special attention. Coarse aggregate should be lim-ited to $\frac{3}{4}$-in. size and high-strength high-slump concrete should be used. The use of a vibrator will also help. For piles over 60 ft long, the use of several cubic feet of grout to coat the inside of the pile is recommended.

For open-end piles, the same procedures and slumps are advised, but here the usual problem is to overcome an inflow of water. Where leakage is minor, one or two sacks of dry cement are dropped in the bottom of the pile, followed at once by the concrete. Thereafter, the concrete should be placed as fast as possible without delay. Until the concrete in the pile has been poured to a point above the ground water level, water infiltration will continue. Where the inflow of water is too great to be handled in this way, placing concrete under water is a better method. First, the pile should be filled with clean water from the top (not by ground water from the bottom) to a point higher than the ground water level, and then the pile should be flushed out with a water jet until all soil has been cleared. There are several ways to do a good job of underwater concreting. Probably, the best way is to use a concrete pump. If an interruption of the concreting takes place, it is important that the discharge end of the hose be buried into the previously placed concrete when pumping is resumed. The least expensive way (where only a few piles are involved) is the use of a bottom dump bucket. Great care must be taken to prevent premature dumping of the bucket. The holding line must have plenty of slack and no strain taken on it until the bucket has settled into the previously deposited concrete. A self-tripping bucket reduces the risk of premature dumping. A conventional tremie pipe can be used, but it is awkward except for short piles (50 ft or less). The closure should be a steel plate and gasket which can be left in the pile. The tremie has to be filled as it is lowered, which requires extra head room. If the closure plate and gasket are not watertight, the concrete may be destroyed. Placing concrete in piles by tremie should be attempted by only highly experienced personnel. The amount of concrete which a pile requires can be closely estimated. No matter which method is used, if the pile takes less than 90 to 95% of the estimated amount, segregation is almost certain. A core boring should be made to check the quality of the concrete.

The usual practice is to place underwater concrete only high enough so that when the concrete has set and the pile is unwatered, the plug will stand the hydrostatic uplift. Laitance found on the top of the concrete has to be removed. It can be broken up with a chopping bit and removed with a well driller's bailing bucket or blown out with air and water. An eductor type pump is useful for cleaning off laitance. Also, it can be used to clean off the rock surface.

18.3 Summary

The important points in this chapter are as follows:

FACTS: Steel-H beams are usually economical when driven to end bearing on rock for high bearing capacity. Closed-end pipe piles are best suited for driving into dense bearing strata or end bearing on rock designed for moderate to high bearing capacity. Open end pipe piles are employed for end bearing on rock. They may be designed for very high loads. They are expensive and only justified by unusual soil conditions and other criteria.

WATCH OUT FOR: Erratic rock elevations cause confusion and delays in driving piles for end bearing. H-beam piles can suffer damage and drift off location during prolonged hard driving. Pipe piles with sleeves for splices often develop leaks below water level. They may deflect at a splice and become "dog-legged." Open-end piles may have to be redriven and cleaned out several times before securing a seal in the rock. Driving or installing open-end piles to rock involves many uncertainties. Such work cannot be estimated closely.

19

Cast-in-Place Concrete Piles

19.1 Introduction

Developed for economy, "cast-in-place" concrete piles comprise a pile system in which a light gauge steel shell or casing is dressed over a mandrel and the assembly is driven into the ground. The mandrel is withdrawn, and the shell is filled with concrete forming a concrete pile. Two important exceptions do not make use of a mandrel: pipe piles, discussed in Chapter 18, and monotubes, discussed in Section 19.3.1.

The steel casing acts only as a form to receive the concrete and contributes nothing to the bearing capacity of the piles. The full load is carried by the concrete.

Cast-in-place piles are almost always installed by specialty pile driving contractors on a subcontract basis. A high degree of expertise is needed for selection of equipment and materials to fit given soil conditions. Consequently, it is rare for general contractors to drive these piles. Piling contractors who do such work can be found by contacting local construction, public works, or engineering organizations, or can be found in the yellow pages of the telephone directory.

19.2   Mandrel-Driven Piles

The mandrels or cores, as they are commonly called, are designed to provide internal support for thin wall casing and to withstand the energy of the hammer as the mandrel and shell are driven down together. They differ in shape and construction and in their capacity to transmit the hammer energy into the soil bearing stratum.

The rigidity of the mandrel has a direct effect on the amount of hammer energy which does useful work in displacing the soil during driving. A portion of the energy is used up in the elastic deformation of the mandrel under each blow. Thus, a stiff mandrel absorbs less driving energy than a limber one, even if the weight per foot were equal. For example, a 10¾-in. pipe, 0.365-in. thick, will absorb more of the driving energy than a 12¾-in. pipe with a 0.312-in. wall thickness, although the two sizes have about the same weight per foot. Thus, the efficiency of a mandrel is proportional to its stiffness or rigidity. Where final driving resistance is used as a measure of the bearing capacity of a pile, the maximum design load of the pile may be limited by the flexibility of the mandrel.

19.2.1   Uniform Diameter Cast-in-Place Concrete Piles

Piles of this type are often referred to as "Cobi" piles, being named for the inventor of the Cobi mandrel. Other types of mandrels for the same purpose are available.

The steel shells are corrugated helically and are placed on a mandrel. The mandrel can be expanded to support the shell during driving and later retracted for removal of the mandrel. Armco Steel Company and Republic Steel Corporation manufacture helical corrugated casings for this purpose. The thickness of shells varies from 14 to 18 gauge. The shells are held in cylindrical form by a lock seam which follows the root of the corrugations. The lock seam may be welded to prevent the inflow of water. Casings may be ordered in any length up to 64 ft and can easily be spliced by brazing or welding. Cut-off sections of shell may be welded together to reduce waste.

There are several types of expandable mandrels currently in use.

The Cobi mandrel is expanded and contracted with pneumatically operated rubber bags. Contact with the inside of the casing is made by corrugations on the core segments mating with the shell corrugations. A mechanically expandable core known as the Hercules core is made by Vulcan Iron Works.

Another type of core, made by Chandler-Rusche of Detroit, Mich., is composed of a heavy wall pipe with oval openings through which shoes with corrugations may be expanded to engage the shell corrugations. It is the most rugged of the expanding cores and absorbs less of the driving energy than the others.

Although 60 ft is the maximum length usually employed, cores can be made longer by welding segments together.

A number of individual piling contractors with cores of these types offer their services in various parts of the country (see Section 19.1).

19.2.2   Raymond Concrete Piles

The Raymond Concrete Pile Division of Raymond International Inc., furnishes and drives three general types of cast-in-place concrete piles.

1. The "standard" pile is tapered uniformly and driven with an expanding mandrel. The pile tapers 0.4 in./ft. The tip diameter is 8 in. and the maximum length is 37 ft and 6 in. The butt diameter can be as much as 23 in. The mandrel has two leaves and is operated mechanically. The shells are made from steel sheets ranging from 14 to 24 gauge.

The standard pile's main use is as a friction pile in moderately dense granular soil. The wedging action of the heavy taper compacts the soil around the pile. Therefore, the pile develops capacity with less penetration than a straight pile. Standard piles are limited in the bearing capacity that they can develop because the core cannot be driven for high loads. In general, 30 tons is the maximum load for a standard pile.

2. The "step-taper" pile tapers at the rate of 1 in. per 8 ft. The pile is virtually (though not quite) straight sided for a distance of 8 ft, then it increases by 1 in. in diameter which is constant for the next 8 ft and so on. The core is made of heavy wall pipe welded together in 8-ft lengths of increasing diameter or made up of two core sections

joined together with a tenon and pin to provide the desired core length. Thus cores up to about 90 ft can be assembled.

Alternately, cores and shells which taper in steps of 1 in. per 12 or 16 ft are available. The shells are corrugated and produced in lengths and diameters to fit the several types of cores. Gauges vary from 12 to 18. Each shell section is fitted at the bottom with a steel ring and sleeve. The ring fits against the shoulder formed by the "step" of the core and the sleeve extends downward to form a screwed joint with the section below. The closure at the tip of the pile is a welded flat plate. The tip of the pile ranges from 8 in. up. However, 8 to 12 in. are the most common point diameters. A drawing of this pile is shown on Fig. 19.1.

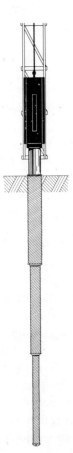

Fig. 19.1 Raymond step-tapered pile. Courtesy of Raymond Concrete Pile, a division of Raymond International Inc.

3. The constant section Raymond pile is similar to those described in 19.2.1.

The step taper pile, while under certain soil conditions may be used as a friction pile, is primarily an end-bearing pile or combination friction and end-bearing pile. The cores can withstand hard driving, and the casings have moderate resistance to tearing and abrasion. For extreme lengths or where driving conditions at the bottom are severe, the pile can be extended with a section of closed-end pipe; such a combination is called a "pipe step tapered" pile.

19.2.3 Other Mandrel Driven Piles

A method widely used for many years consists of driving a heavy wall pipe with a loose fitting steel boot to desired length. Then a corrugated casing is lowered inside the pipe. Concrete is deposited in the casing, and then the pipe is withdrawn.

Another method is to drive a core and the outer pipe together. The core is pulled and a corrugated casing is inserted and concreted. The core is then placed on top of the concreted pile to hold it in place as the outer pipe is withdrawn. The closure at the bottom may be a steel plate or a precast concrete point with a shoulder over which the shell is slipped for a seal. Piles installed by this method are end-bearing. Relatively light gauge shells may be used. The heaving of previously driven piles in which the concrete is partially set may become a problem in some soil conditions.

19.2.4 Advantages and Disadvantages

When driven as friction piles, light gauge corrugated casing offers certain advantages. In granular soils, sand becomes packed into the roots of the corrugations. Thus, the bearing capacity must be at least the shear strength of the soil. Consequently, such piles will sustain greater loads than smooth wall pipe piles or H-beams of the same length and diameter. Similarly, corrugated shells will develop the required resistance to driving with less penetration into the bearing stratum.

Corrosion need not be considered, since the shell is only a form for the concrete.

The corrugated casing is less expensive per lineal foot than either pipe or H-beams. In addition, it offers economical splicing so that adjustment in length can be made readily. The cut-off waste can also be minimized.

Comparing the types of light gauge mandrel driven piles, experience demonstrates that heavy taper piles will develop higher frictional resistance in sandy soil than will straight sided piles for piles of equal penetration. No difference is apparent in silt or clay soils.

Conventional design loads on friction piles range from 30 to 60 tons. The expandable mandrels used for straight sided piles can take the driving required for this load range. The standard Raymond core cannot be used for the heavier loads.

Where soil conditions are suitable for a combination of friction and end-bearing, or end-bearing alone, pile loads from 60 to 80 tons are feasible. Large pile hammers with more energy per blow than 15,000 ft-lb are generally required. The main limitation is that expanding mandrels may not stand up under hard driving. More rugged cores will no doubt be developed. Until then, loads over 60 tons are a strain on the cores and casings.

The principal disadvantage of the mandrel driven pile lies in the vulnerability of the light gauge casings. They may be torn by obstructions, boulders, and gravel. Foot after foot of driving through sharp sand may wear away the outer ridges of the corrugations. Rupture of the casings brings on a series of difficulties. After the core is withdrawn, the pile may fill with water and mud. Sand may work into the pile during driving and pack around the mandrel causing a stuck core. By the time the core is jacked loose, the pile is usually lost. Specifications normally obligate the contractor to provide, at his own expense, casings strong enough to overcome these difficulties. There is a practical limit to the thickness of steel sheets which can be fabricated into shells. Particularly with high capacity hard driven piles, where experienced pile contractors would use heavy gauge shells to start with, there is no "out" when the heaviest gauge shells tear or wear through or collapse.

Cast-in-place piles are displacement piles. The soil displaced by the pile has to go somewhere. In granular soils, densification and lateral displacement take place as the piles are driven and any buildup of pressure dissipates rapidly. However, where piles are driven through cohesive soils, even in so thin a layer as 6 ft, back pressure can be serious. For deep beds of such soils, heaving will also take place (see Chapter 16). During driving, the mandrel supports the casing so that it cannot collapse from back pressure. On removal, the casing may squeeze or collapse completely. Even heavy gauge casing may be squeezed in from extreme back pressure. Often piles which show no deformation when the core is pulled collapse later as the pressure builds up from the driving of adjacent piles. Corrective measures for straight sided piles are limited, because a severely deformed pile cannot be reentered with the mandrel. If the deformation is small enough, the core in its retracted position can be lowered into the pile, and the pile can be enlarged by redriving so as to pass inspection.

When step taper piles collapse, a new set of shells can often be driven inside the first set to salvage the pile. In extreme cases where partial collapse is affecting many piles, "dummy cores," such as lengths of pipe which will fit into the piles, may be set in each pile as the mandrel is withdrawn and left there until all piles in a group are driven. Then the dummy cores are pulled, and the piles are concreted one at a time. Frequently, the pile casings will be deflected out of line at the level of maximum back pressure. Where such piles cannot pass inspection, reentry with the core (where possible) may help to make them acceptable. There is a risk, however, of tearing the shell and letting water in.

A case can be cited where in a deep bed of soft clay all the piles driven on a shift were rejected, because they were "bowed." Next morning they were reinspected and were found to have straightened out enough to be acceptable and concreted. The same phenomenon took place again. With concentrations of piles, soil movements occur which can continue after driving ceases.

It is possible to judge from a careful study of the soil profile, as it will be after the general excavation has removed the overburden, whether heave of the soil is free to take place. Where it is, back pressure can relieve itself. If not, special steps to relieve it will almost certainly be needed. The use of predrilling and similar methods are described in Chapter 16, Section 16.8.

When piles have collapsed or are torn and filled with water beyond repair, they must be abandoned. The procedure for abandoning piles should be agreed upon prior to starting work. Abandoned piles usually are backfilled, using lean concrete or sand or sand cement grout pumped into place. If the casing is completely collapsed in the clay zone, it may be impossible to fill the portion below the clay zone. What happens then? Will the specs permit backfilling only the upper part of the pile? Usually, this is the only practical thing to do. After backfilling, the piles usually are cut off below the bottom of the pile cap.

When a general contract includes a subcontract for piling of any type, it is most important that the general contractor clearly understands what, under the specifications or building code, constitutes a satisfactory and acceptable pile. The troubles, which may cause the rejection of piles such as out-of-tolerance, torn or collapsed casings, and wet piles, have been discussed in this and other sections. Even though the subcontractor bears the cost of rejected piles, the general contractor has several responsibilities:

1. To see that inspection is prompt and efficient. For instance, the extension cord with a guard-protected light bulb is better than depending on light reflected from a mirror. Dust in piles can delay inspection and is often caused by failure to keep casings and mandrels clean.

2. To see that abandoned piles are cut off below the pile cap after backfilling.

3. To make sure that the pile stakes are in their proper location *at the time the piles are driven.*

4. To ascertain *in advance* that an equitable arrangement is made for payment of the costs of redesign and for correction of eccentricities of pile groups. Where many piles on a job are lost or rejected, the time spent by the subcontractor in efforts to salvage and to drive replacements may seriously delay his operations.

19.3   Monotube Piles

19.3.1   Monotube Piles

Monotube piles are manufactured by the Union Metal Manufacturing Company of Canton, Ohio. The pile shells are often called "fluted" piles. After the shells have been rolled and welded into tapered or uniform diameter form, they are fluted by cold rolling. The arches of the flutes are formed inward similar to an Ionic column. The cold rolling increases the strength of the steel plate and also increases the section modulus, hence the rigidity of the shells. Because of their stiffness, monotube shells withstand the energy of the pile hammer without the need for support from a core or mandrel.

Monotube shells may be ordered tapered their full length or tapered at the bottom with constant diameter at the top. The rate of taper and maximum lengths available are as follows:

One inch in 7 ft, up to 75 ft long.
One inch in 4 ft up to 40 ft long.
One inch in 2½ ft up to 25 ft long.

The points are 8 to 8½ in. in diameter. The straight sided extensions vary from 12 to 18 in. in 2-in. increments. Variations in wall thickness range from 3 to 11 gauge, by increments of 2 gauge numbers. The closure at the tip is formed with a factory welded conical point (see Ref. 41). Driving heads fitting most pile hammers are available.

By telescoping one section within another, welded splices can be made. Thus piles may be extended by welding sections to those already driven, or full length piles may be assembled in a job welding yard and driven in one piece.

Monotube piles offer certain advantages over mandrel driven cast-in-place piles. Relatively light equipment with simple leaders can be used. Where taper is an advantage in developing driving resistance, three tapers to suit soil conditions are available. A pile shell that has a tapered lower section and a straight sided upper section puts the taper where it will do the most good.

An illustration of this advantage is shown in Fig. 19.2. A pile, tapered for its full length and driven under the soil conditions illustrated, will take up in the granular stratum which starts at −25 ft. But due to the wedging action of the taper, it will build up appreciable resistance in penetrating the layer of fill at the ground surface. Whereas a pile which has constant cross-section for its upper 10 ft will develop virtually all of its resistance in the bearing stratum. Under load tests, both piles probably would meet the usual requirements. If both were loaded to failure, however, the pile with the

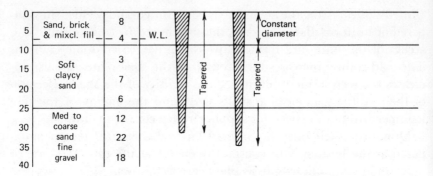

Fig. 19.2 Comparison of pile penetration between pile tapered full length and pile with tapered lower section but constant diameter upper section.

constant diameter upper length would sustain the greater ultimate load. Due to the welded construction and heavier gauges of the casings, wet monotube piles are rare. Also, loss from abrasion and tearing is greatly reduced.

Because of the stiffer cross-section, shell collapse and deformation is less with monotubes than with thin wall casings. However, the problems with obstructions and out-of-tolerance piles are the same as with other cast-in-place piles.

The stiffness of the monotube shell, the ease with which it can be extended, and its appearance make it particularly useful where piles must be extended above ground level as for the support of ramps, trestles, and pile bents of bridges.

Monotube piles can be driven with equipment which is lighter in several ways than that required for mandrel driven piles. Because no "shelling up" headroom is required with fluted piles, the leaders can be shorter. The pulling power needed to lift a heavy core makes the use of smaller crane drivers possible. The hammer line does not have to be reaved with so many parts of line, thus speeding the operation of lifting the hammer (see Ref. 41).

19.4   Reinforcing in Cast-in-Place Piles

Frequently the design requires a cage in the upper 10 to 15 ft of a pile. Occasionally, the reinforcement must go down the full length.

When reinforcing steel is called for, the problems which the operation presents and the costs involved need realistic analysis and pricing. In the first place, setting the cage interrupts the placing of concrete. After the cage has been set, centered, and tied-off, a vibrator or other device should be used during placing of concrete in the reinforced portion. Since the cage always projects above the top of the pile, concrete may have to be shoveled into place, or a conventional hopper and downspout may have to be fitted to drop the concrete down inside the cage.

Reinforcing cages are made up with hoop ties or spirally wound bars. A cage with horizontal hoops 4 in. or more on center does not present any difficulty in placing the concrete if the concrete has sufficient slump (see Chapter 18, Section 18.2.6). A vibrator can work the concrete through the cage. Spiral wire on 3-in. pitch makes for trouble. The coarse aggregate tends to arch on the inside. Therefore, small size aggregate and high slump high cement concrete can be used, but at extra cost. A possible alternate is to substitute tied cages with larger ties at wider spacing. This will assure a better job of placing concrete.

19.5   Pouring Concrete in Cast-in-Place Piles

Note: This procedure has been discussed in Chapter 18, Section 18.2.6.

There are occasions when concrete must be placed in piles where the cut-off elevation is below the hydrostatic head of the water in the ground. Where a small inflow of water into a pile would (if the pile were allowed to fill up) flow over the top of the casing, the height to which the water will rise should be determined. The casing should be built up to just above that level. After the pile has been dewatered, concrete should be placed as rapidly as possible to cut-off. The extended casing should immediately be filled with water to balance the head.

The formation of an appreciable amount of laitance at the top of the pile is an indication that water is flowing upward through the fresh concrete. If the inflow of water is more than a trickle, piles should be filled with clean water high enough to balance the head until the pile is concreted.

19.6   Uncased Cast-in-Place Piles

19.6.1   Drilled Piles

Holes drilled into the ground and filled with concrete are used regularly in many parts of the country and are called drilled piles or caissons. The drilled pile develops its bearing capacity by transmitting the load into the soil surrounding the pile by friction. The area of the tip contributes little in most cases. Such piles generally range from 12 to 24 in. in diameter, but have been constructed up to 48 and 60 in. in diameter.

Soil conditions suitable for the installation of drilled piles must meet certain criteria:

1. The soil must have sufficient cohesion so that it will stand open during drilling, inspection, and the pouring of concrete.
2. The soil must be free of large pockets or lenses of sand which will cave into the drilled hole.
3. The soil must be free of water seepage.
4. Where fill overlays the natural soil, an oversized hole may have to be drilled and cased through the fill to avoid sloughing of the fill.

The bearing capacity of drilled piles is predetermined by a static analysis. The capacity also may be verified in the field by load tests. From laboratory tests on undisturbed soil samples, the ultimate shearing capacity of the soil may be determined. Where the soil is uniform, this value may be applied to the total surface of the pile to determine the ultimate capacity. The ultimate capacity is divided by a safety factor (such as two or three) to obtain the design load. In stratified soils, the analysis can be quite complicated, since the softer layers cannot develop their shearing resistance until the stiffer layers deflect.

Holes for drilled piles may be excavated with flight augers or bucket augers. Cobbles and boulders present difficulties.

In bidding a drilled pile foundation, the contractor should be satisfied that a thorough soil investigation and analysis have been performed and that the difficulties mentioned above are minimal. The design should be verified prior to construction by auger borings left open long enough to detect problems with water or caving.

In some cases, drilled piles have been installed in soft ground below water level. A complex arrangement was used, consisting of temporary casing and thick, heavy drilling mud. The concreting was done by tremie pipe. The casing was removed during concreting (see Ref. 42).

19.6.2   Grout Injected Piles

Methods and equipment have been developed for the installation of drilled piles in loose, caving, and waterbearing soil formations. The essential difference is that cement grout is used instead of concrete and that continuous flight augers are used.

Predetermination of bearing capacity is made in the same way as for drilled piles described in Section 19.6.1.

The use of a continuous flight auger offers support to the sides of the hole as it is drilled. When the drilling has reached the required depth, cement grout produced by a grout mixer and grout pumps is forced under pressure through the hollow drill stem of the auger. The pressure is maintained as the auger is withdrawn, leaving a column of grout which constitutes a pile. During drilling, the hollow drill stem is closed at the lower end with a plug or other arrangement which prevents soil from entering the opening. The closure device has to be removed or opened when grouting begins. The most important control is the pressure at which the grout is pumped. Excess pressure may force the grout out laterally into gravel seams or up and around the auger. Thus voids may be left into which soil and water may flow. Too little pressure may permit loose soil or soil under hydrostatic head greater than the grout pressure to reduce, distort or cut off the column of grout. Pressure gauges and volume measuring controls are used to monitor the operation, but the experience and judgment of the operator are important factors.

Coarse gravel, cobbles, and boulders cause serious trouble, often causing the loss of piles drilled into such formations. In porous or caving soils, overrun of the quantity of grout takes place. This is expensive, difficult to control, and hard to estimate. Grout piles cannot be inspected, which creates uncertainties.

There are many applications for the grout injected pile. It can be installed on a batter in soils with some cohesion. These piles may be used near existing footings in unstable soil, since the lack of vibration results in minimum risk of loss of ground under adjacent foundations. They can be placed in a continuous line of slightly overlapping piles to form a retaining wall.

In predetermining the bearing capacity, engineers need to consider the changes in soil density brought about by the construction operations and should verify the calculations with load tests.

19.6.3   Piles with Enlarged Bases

This class of foundations may be called piles, caissons, or pressure injected footings. This type of foundation is included under piles, because the most commonly used foundation of this type uses a pile driving rig and a drive weight to form the enlarged base. It is included under "uncased" piles because the casing used is temporary and is not left in place. Currently, however, there is more frequent use of a permanent casing for part or all of the shaft.

The Franki Pile Company has pioneered this type of foundation for many years in Europe, Canada, the United States, Mexico, and South America. Others active in this field are Western Caissons, Ltd. and Bermingham Construction Co., Ltd. in Canada, and Raymond International Inc. in the United States.

To install Franki Foundations, a charge of very dry concrete is placed in the bottom of a heavy walled casing. A 7000-lb drop weight is used to compact the concrete so as to develop friction against the inside of the casing. By varying the height of the fall of the drop weight, the casing can be dragged down into the ground. When the desired depth has been reached, the casing is held at the top to prevent further penetration and small charges of dry concrete are added and driven out to form the bulb or enlarged base. Usually, about 5 ft³ of concrete is added and the stroke of the drop weight is increased to 20 ft. Ten blows of a 7000-lb weight falling 20 ft is considered a measure of the base forming operation. This represents 140,000 ft-lb per blow.

When a permanent casing is used, corrugated casing is dropped on top of the concrete in the base and a few cubic feet of concrete deposited in the shell. The concrete in the casing is then tapped gently to seal the shell and the base. The outer casing is then withdrawn. When no permanent casing is left in place, successive charges of concrete are placed and driven with the drop weight as the casing is pulled. Full length reinforcing steel can be inserted in the shaft where required. Batter piles can be installed by this method.

The operation of driving the concrete out to form an enlarged base accomplishes two purposes: *(a)* As an end-bearing pile, it increases the area of contact with the soil. *(b)* The high energy impact compacts (densifies) the soil below the bulb. It is assumed that in uniform soil formations, the enlargement of the base will be reasonably uniform in dimensions.

Since pressure injected bases tend to compact the soil underlying the base, settlements of such foundations are small, even for heavy loads. Gross settlements of $\frac{1}{4}$ to $\frac{1}{2}$ in. for 120-ton loads on sandy soil are typical.

Such piles may be employed for relatively high design loads on hardpan or other dense formations. The ideal application is in loose granular soil strata. By distributing the pile load over the area of the enlarged base and by increasing the density of the soil below the base, substantial design loads are obtainable. By contrast, conventional piles cannot develop appreciable resistance in such a layer and must be driven to greater depths to reach firmer supporting soils or rock. Boulders are not a serious problem as with other types of piling. The heavy drop weight can displace or demolish boulders.

Piles with enlarged bases have certain limitations in use and present certain problems. They are used in sand, silty sand, gravel, hardpan, and such. They are not used as friction piles in silt or clay soils or cohesive soils. Inspection of this pile is difficult, since the driving action takes place down in the casing where it cannot be observed or inspected. No matter how well compacted, the adequacy of very dry concrete to withstand the inflow of ground water for the time it takes to drive all piles in a group is open to question. Pile spacing has to be greater. Usually these piles are spaced 4 ft, 6 in. on center, which affects the size of the pile caps. By contrast, conventional piles are spaced 3 to 4 ft on centers. Such piles are displacement piles. Uncased shafts may be displaced laterally in beds of clay by the driving of adjacent piles. Also, the shafts may suffer separation from their

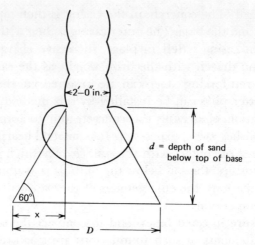

Fig. 19.3 Stress distribution in soil below pressure injected footing, per Boston Building Code, Section 2909 (g) 2912 (d).

$$\tan. 60° = 1.73 = \frac{d}{x},$$

$$x = \frac{d}{\tan 60°}$$

$$D = 2x + 2'\text{-}0$$

$$A = \frac{\pi D^2}{4}$$

$d = 4'\text{-}0$	$x = 2.31$	$D = 6.62$	$A = 34.3$ sf
$d = 5'\text{-}0$	$x = 2.89$	$D = 7.79$	$A = 47.8$ sf
$d = 6'\text{-}0$	$x = 3.47$	$D = 8.94$	$A = 62.0$ sf
$d = 7'\text{-}0$	$x = 4.05$	$D = 10.10$	$A = 80.0$ sf
$d = 8'\text{-}0$	$x = 4.63$	$D = 11.26$	$A = 99.5$ sf
$d = 9'\text{-}0$	$x = 5.20$	$D = 12.40$	$A = 121.0$ sf
$d = 10'\text{-}0$	$x = 5.78$	$D = 13.56$	$A = 144.0$ sf
$d = 13'\text{-}0''$	$x = 7.52$	$D = 17.04$	$A = 228.0$ sf
$d = 14'\text{-}0''$	$x = 8.10$	$D = 18.20$	$A = 260.0$ sf
$d = 15'\text{-}0''$	$x = 8.67$	$D = 19.34$	$A = 294.0$ sf
$d = 4'\text{-}6''$	$x = 2.60$	$D = 7.20$	$A = 40.7$ sf
$d = 5'6''$	$x = 3.18$	$D = 8.36$	$A = 54.9$ sf
$d = 6'6''$	$x = 3.76$	$D = 9.52$	$A = 71.1$ sf
$d = 3'\text{-}0''$	$x = 1.73$	$D = 5.46$	$A = 23.4$ sf
$d = 3'\text{-}6''$	$x = 2.02$	$D = 6.04$	$A = 28.6$ sf

bases where heaving of soil takes place. Piles are usually limited to depths of 50 to 60 ft, except for very large projects on which very large equipment can be used.

The equipment for installing piles with enlarged bases is highly specialized and is available only from specialty contractors such as Franki.

The predetermination of bearing capacity is based on a static analysis, rather than on pile driving formulas (see Fig. 19.3). Two assumptions are made: the size and shape of the bulb and the extent and amount of the consolidation of the soil below the base. These are matters of judgment; therefore an adequate soils investigation is essential. Pile load tests usually are performed. The building codes of Boston, New York, and other cities consider the unusual character of these foundations and make provisions for their use and construction. A typical method of estimating the stress distribution in soil below pressure injected footings is shown on Fig. 19.3. In addition, typical methods are available for groups of such foundations (see Ref. 43).

19.7 Summary

The important points in this chapter are as follows:

FACTS: Tapered piles have certain advantages over straight sided piles. Cast-in-place piles driven without a mandrel have advantages. Reinforcing steel in cast-in-place piles can be a problem. Uncased drilled piles have limitations. Piles with enlarged bases or "bulbs" have certain applications.

WATCH OUT FOR: Soil and water flow into piles from torn casings. Tapered piles develop resistance in compact upper layers, resulting in insufficient penetration of the bearing layer. Piles having cut-offs below ground water level. Special methods for placing concrete may be necessary.

20

Precast and Prestressed Concrete Piles

20.1 Introduction

Concrete piles, cast in wood or metal forms and reinforced with standard reinforcing steel, are known as precast concrete piles and have been in use for many years. They have been principally used for marine and waterfront construction, and are competitive in cost with other types of piling for use in building foundations in certain areas served by a central casting yard.

The application of the principle of prestressing concrete to the design and manufacture of prestressed concrete piles offers a superior pile that is competitive in several areas. These piles are cast in various shapes, such as triangular, square, octagonal, and round.

20.2 Casting and Curing

The precast pile, with its reinforcing bars, has the inherent weakness of hair line cracks resulting from the contraction of concrete during curing. Even when such cracks do not affect the structural strength of precast piles, they permit moisture to penetrate to the steel where, above the water level, corrosion of the steel can result in spalling of the concrete. Crazing or cracking may be caused by too high a cement factor, the placement of the reinforcing too close to or too far from the face of the concrete, uneven or interruptions in curing by wetting, and too short a curing period in the forms. On the other hand, prestressed concrete piles eliminate most of these problems, since the concrete is in compression and all tendency to crack is offset. Furthermore, controlled curing in modern plants assures consistent results.

The amount of compressive stress induced by the tension in the wires or bars depends on the cross section, length of the pile, and the number of pickup points.

20.3 Handling

Handling of heavy concrete piles is critical in avoiding bending and cracking of the piles.

Either precast or prestressed concrete piles should be handled from the forms to storage and out of storage with a minimum of two lifting slings. As a general rule, the pickup points should be 0.2 times the pile length in from each end.

The lengths of precast or prestressed concrete piles which may be transported from the plant to the job site may be limited by local regulations and widths of streets. Handling on the job has to be performed with adequate equipment. Piles should be inspected periodically to see if they are being damaged. Such piles cannot be "snaked" to the driver as can steel or wood piles. Prestressed piles, up to about 40 ft long can probably be lifted into the leads with one sling whereas precast piles need to be lifted clear of the ground with two slings at least.

20.4 Driving and Jetting

In driving concrete piles of either type, it is customary to use a follower with a wood cushion block 2 to 4 in. thick on the head of the pile. The alignment of the hammer and pile is most important. Unless the hammer delivers its blow squarely, a concrete pile may be shattered at the top and it cannot be trimmed like a steel pile.

A concrete pile with a volume of 1 ft³ per foot of length weighs about 150 lb/ft. With few exceptions, such piles are heavier than any other type of pile driven for building foundations. Because of the inertia which the weight represents and the extra cushion block, measures have to be taken to assist the penetration besides the hammer energy. There are soil conditions, such as soft or loose materials, through which precast or prestressed piles may be driven to end-bearing unassisted. In many cases, however, water jets, spudding, or preexcavation is necessary. These methods are described in Chapter 16, Section 16.9. Pilot jetting in advance of driving may be sufficient for short piles. In most cases, for piles 50 ft long and longer, two jets, one at each side of the pile, are used. Two jets help to keep the pile from drifting. Obviously, in cohesive soils which do not yield to jetting, other methods have to be employed. Preexcavation may be used in clays where jetting is ineffective. Where piles must reach a minimum elevation and neither jetting nor preexcavation is feasible, precast concrete piles should not be specified.

There are certain soil stratifications encountered occasionally through which prestressed concrete piles should not be driven without continuous jetting. An example is provided where a layer 10 ft or more in thickness of sand overlays a soft deposit of organic silt or clay of sufficient depth so that when more than half the length of pile has penetrated the sand layer, the pile tip has not reached any resistance. The friction of the sand layer can be high enough so that the blow delivered by the pile hammer will cause the lower part of the pile to try to move ahead, but is held back by the middle section which is gripped by the sand. Tension is induced in the pile. If the tension should exceed the compression stress of the pile, it will rupture. In such cases, the tip of the pile may appear to separate from the rest of the pile. The broken pile must be pulled and discarded. Continuous jetting is essential under such conditions to avoid such breakage.

In general, pile driving formulas are *not* applicable to the determination of bearing capacities of precast concrete piles. If a formula is used, it must consider the affect of the weight of the pile. Static analysis plus judgment, verified with load tests, are the best basis for estimating the pile supporting capacity.

Precast concrete piles are at a special disadvantage under difficult driving conditions, such as boulders and obstructions, because they cannot be overdriven. However, their greatest handicap is cut-off waste. The allowance for waste which should be included in cost is considerably higher than for most other pile types.

20.5 Prestressed Cylinder Piles

These piles are very large in diameter, usually on the order of 54 in. They are used for bridges and other large projects. Since they are so specialized, they are not discussed herein.

20.6 Summary

Pile Type	Advantages	Disadvantages
Timber	Low cost, easy to drive.	Readily broken by overdriving and obstructions. High cut-off waste.
Timber composite	Low cost. Often cheaper than creosoted piles.	Connections problems. Can be difficult to drive.
H-beams	Easy to drive. Ability to secure penetration.	Splicing costly. Bottom seating problems. Corrosion a consideration.
Pipe piles	Readily available and economical. Easy to drive. Can inspect bottom. Can be driven in short sections.	Unless splices are welded, can be wet. Friction piles require careful analysis.
Cast-in-place, mandrel driven	Economical. Interior can be inspected. Adaptable to wide length variations. Tapered types beneficial for friction piles.	Heavy specialized equipment needed. Collapse, torn casing, wet pile problems cause numerous rejects.
Cast-in-place, without mandrel	Easy to drive. Readily spliced. Light equipment. Seldom torn or wet.	Limited ability to take hard driving.
Uncased (drilled)	Low cost. Fast. No vibration	Problems in water bearing and caving soils. Load tests costly.

Grout injected	No vibration.	Cannot be inspected. Extensive load tests needed.
Enlarged base	Densification of loose granular soils. High bearing capacity.	Cannot be inspected. Casing needed through compressible soils.
Precast	Permanence. High capacity strong in bending	High cut-off waste. Hard to handle. Jetting needed to assist driving. Easily broken.
Prestressed	Permanence. Resists corrosion, High capacity. Strong in bending. Can take hard driving.	Vibration during hard driving. Careful handling. Heavy equipment. Needs jetting costly cut-off waste.

21

Caisson Foundations

21.1 Introduction

The word "caisson" is of French derivation and means "big box."
In the classical application, it is a structure with watertight sides,
with bottom edges which form a cutting edge. The top and bottom
are open to permit excavation to proceed without dewatering and
sufficient weight is built into the sides so that the caisson will sink as
excavation proceeds. Such caissons are used frequently as the substructure for bridge piers. The same construction also has been used
on land.

As applied to building foundations, caissons are almost always
circular with a minimum diameter of 30 in.; diameters range up to
6 ft or larger. Such caissons are discussed in this chapter. Bridge-type
caissons are not discussed in this book.

The feasibility of a caisson foundation depends on the magnitude
of the column loads, the existence of a bearing stratum to which the
loads may be transmitted, and the soil and water conditions.

Caissons may be constructed with permanent casing or with remov-
able casing. When excavated to hard rock, they are usually of constant diameter. When they are to bear on soil or on soft rock, they
are belled out on the supporting stratum to provide a suitable bearing area and bearing pressure.

Caissons are excavated by hand, by mechanical means, or by some combination of both.

Where soil conditions are favorable, caisson foundations are often economical. If one caisson can support a heavy column load, large footings or pile caps are eliminated. Caisson work avoids vibration and can be conducted on a three-shift basis without causing the noise of pile driving. Heave and lateral movements of soil are avoided.

The installation of caisson foundations can be risky. A thorough analysis of the soil and water conditions, as well as the bearing stratum, is essential. Difficulties should be anticipated, and the method selected should be adoptable to handling such difficulties. One type of difficulty seldom planned for is gas in the bottom of the caisson.

21.1.1 Evaluation of Contract Documents and Applicable Building Codes

A careful review of the general provisions is of equal importance both to the caisson subcontractor and to the general contractor, since the subcontractor will assume by contract all the liabilities placed on the general contractor.

The insurance requirements for public liability and property damage require particular consideration as both risks can be very real in caisson work. Prudence may warrant limits of property damage insurance substantially higher than that called for under the provisions of the general contract. Extended coverage for damage not observed until after completion of the work should usually be carried.

Where structures are located within the influence zone of the work, an examination should be made to detect any structural defects. Any cracking or signs of strain should be recorded with certified photographs filed with the appropriate party to the contract before work starts.

Building codes and other standards, such as industrial safety ordinances, should be reviewed as they may contain provisions which go beyond the requirements of the specifications. For example, where gas or sulphur water may be encountered, requirements of safety laws may be expensive and difficult to comply with. Areas where gas or sulphur water have been found included Boston, Chicago, Cleveland, Detroit, Los Angeles. Inspection of caissons may be the responsibility of the engineer, but is subject also to the approval of the local building department. Such arrangements should be understood to avoid delays.

The section of the specifications relating to the caissons, and the figures in the section, describe and illustrate the type of caisson to be installed, the range of sizes of both shafts and bells, the elevations of the caisson tops, the bottom grades on which the estimate and contract is based, and the construction at the top of the caisson, whether a cap with anchor bolts or simple dowels. The methods by which the caissons are to be installed are usually left entirely to the contractor. However, the specifications may direct that when the bells are excavated mechanically, the final leveling of the bottom and trimming prior to inspection shall be performed by hand labor and that at all times when personnel are in the caisson, the shaft shall be lined from top to bottom with steel casing providing sufficient support to the sides of the shaft to prevent caving or sloughing of the walls. There are usually provisions for the methods to be used in depositing the concrete.

The foundation test borings and the report of the soils engineer are included with the contract documents or may be offered separately. It is important to determine whether the contract documents disclaim responsibility for the accuracy of the soils data. Such disclaimers may seriously weaken claims based on misrepresentations of soil conditions.

The specifications establish tolerances within which the caissons are to be installed. Allowable deviation from the vertical of 1:60 is usual and can be met with normal care in keeping drilling equipment plumb. More rigid tolerances such as 1:100 can be difficult to meet. It is often necessary to interrupt operations to survey for plumbness at two or three points in the drilling of each hole, with the possibility of backfilling, tamping, and redrilling to meet the requirements. In any case, boulders, obstructions, and hard layers may cause drilling equipment to drift off line. The requirements as to minimum shaft diameter and area seldom present difficulties.

The contract documents, including the soils report should be reviewed to determine:

1. Whether there are any provisions which are not feasible or will add materially to the time and cost of normal caisson methods.

2. Whether the soil investigation is adequate for the scope of the work to be performed, both as to the area of the site and to soil, water, and rock characteristics.

21.1.2   Selection of Method

The choice of methods and equipment depend on the soil conditions. The data accompanying the plans and specifications are, of course, the main source of information. Previous experience in the vicinity with other caisson work, deep excavations, or cuts, and the geology of the area should be studied. The ground water, its source, and its hydrostatic head should receive intensive investigation. For example, in the Great Lakes area borings seldom reveal the presence of pockets of sand full of water under pressure; yet they exist throughout the deep beds of clay. In some areas, the hydrostatic head is above the sidewalk levels.

Where the soils are cohesive, drilling by open methods is fast and economical (for more discussion of drilled caissons see Section 21.2.1). Casing is set temporarily for protection of personnel. Where loose wet granular soil predominates, rotary drilling with drilling mud and the use of casing to seal the shaft excavation against the inflow of soil and water will be necessary. In between these conditions, combinations of the soil conditions dictate combinations of the methods of construction.

21.1.3   Submission of Quotations

The usual procedure is to submit a price, or "principal sum," for the number of caissons called for on the drawings. This applies to the minimum size of caps, shafts, and bells, and extends from the elevations shown for the tops to the bottom grades stipulated for each caisson. Adjustments to the principal sum for authorized changes are made by unit prices for additions to or deductions from the basic quantities. Units quoted for deductions are usually one-half to two-thirds of the value of units for additions. Unit prices may be quoted per lineal foot and per cubic foot.

21.2   Belled Caissons

For belled caissons to be feasible, a stratum of soil must exist in which the bell may be formed without risk of collapse. Such a stratum must be sufficiently thick so that the height of the largest bell, with 1 or 2 ft to spare, will fall within it. The soil must also be free from any inflow of water and stiff enough so that the bell roof will not collapse during excavation. The slope of the bell is usually 60 degrees from the horizontal or alternately two vertical to one horizontal (see Fig. 21.1). The horizontal distance from the outside of the shaft to the outside edge of the bell is called the horizontal undercut. For soft clays where the standard penetration test shows three to four blows per foot, the safe limit of the horizontal undercut is about 18 in. Where the blow count is ten, an undercut of about 4 ft can be made. These limits assume tightly fitting casing to support the sides of the shaft just above the top of the bell.

In uncased holes, the bells are constructed by a "belling bucket." Typical machine-cut bell excavations are shown in Fig. 14.3. The tools used to dig and to bell the caissons are shown in Figs. 4.1 and 21.2. Caissons also are constructed by pressure injection, as described in Chapter 19, Section 19.6.2.

21.2.1   Shaft Excavation and Lining

For cohesive soil formations, the caisson shaft may be drilled with a rotary rig equipped either with a bucket or an auger. If telescoping casing is to be used, a bucket with adjustable reamers is more efficient than an auger. For dry granular soils, an auger is the tool to use.

Where the overburden above the layer in which the bell is to be excavated contains granular soils below the ground water level, the shaft has to be drilled by rotary methods employing drilling mud as the circulating fluid to support the sides of the hole. Following that method, casing can be set and driven to a seal. (Fig. 21.3).

For caissons of moderate depth (about 30 ft to the surface of a cohesive layer), an auger can be used to loosen the granular soil. By the addition of bentonite or aquagel, a slurry can be created through

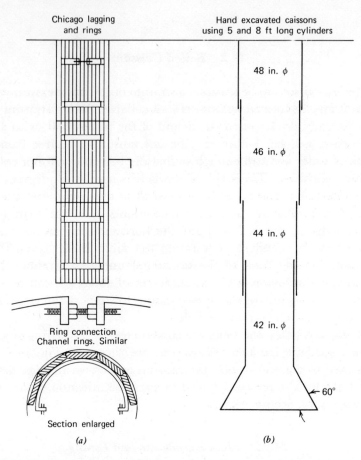

Chicago lagging
and rings

Hand excavated caissons
using 5 and 8 ft long cylinders

48 in. ϕ

46 in. ϕ

44 in. ϕ

42 in. ϕ

Ring connection
Channel rings. Similar

Section enlarged

60°

(a)   (b)

Fig. 21.1 Typical caisson construction. (*a*) Timber lagging and rings. (*b*) Telescoping steel cylinders.

which the casing can be lowered and driven to a seal in the under-lying clay. During the drilling operation, the water level in the hole must be maintained somewhat above the ground water level. After the casing is sealed, the slurry can be bailed out and conventional drilling can be conducted in the dry.

By the use of drilling mud circulated through the drill stem, holes of almost any depth may be drilled. Problems arise in withdrawing the casing and in placing concrete in the caisson properly. Since the casing is subject to full hydrostatic pressure, cylinders have to be in

(a)

(b)

Fig. 21.2 Mechanical belling bucket. Photographs courtesy Earth Drill, Inc.

(c)

Fig. 21.2 *Continued.*

one long piece to be watertight. The force required to withdraw a cylinder is the sum of *(a)* the force required to break the seal in the clay, *(b)* the frictional resistance of the soil acting on the outside surface, and *(c)* the friction of wet concrete on the inside. Thus there is a practical limit to the length of shaft lining which can be pulled. Withdrawal of casing as concrete is being deposited involves some risk. There have been instances of "necking down" of the caisson shaft due to soil or water partially cutting off the shaft area.

The development of rotary excavating equipment has largely displaced caisson excavation by hand labor. Yet there are circumstances under which hand methods should be used. These circumstances can be low head room, obstructions, or excavation close to existing foundations.

Hand excavation is done frequently with timber lagging and steel rings. Known generally as "Chicago" type caissons because they have been used in that city since the late 1800s, the shafts are hand excavated in stages of from 4 to 6 ft. The sides of the shaft are lined with 2 by 6 in. wood lagging, the edges of which are beveled radially so that each set will form a timber cylinder. The lagging is held in place by two steel rings. Each ring is composed of two segments with the

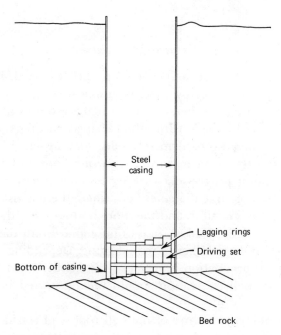

Fig. 21.3 Sealing caisson on rock.

ends turned in to form lugs. The lugs are drilled and fitted with lag bolts and nuts arranged so that rotating the nuts will force the rings out against the lagging and force the lagging against the sides of the excavation. Additionally, wedges may be driven between the rings and the lagging to ensure full bearing against the soil. The timber lining is almost always left in place when the concrete is placed (see Fig. 21.1). Shorter or longer sets of lagging and rings can be used.

Gow type caissons, originated by the late Col. Charles R. Gow, use telescoping steel cylinders from 5 to 8 ft in length as shaft lining as the hand excavation proceeds (see Fig. 21.1). Each succeeding cylinder is 2 in. less in diameter and is set and driven so that there is about a 12-in. lap with the cylinder above. The system requires that the ground water level be lowered by pumping so that it is below the top of the lowest cylinder, assuming that the lowest cylinder is sealed in a cohesive soil. Otherwise, the water level must be kept at the bottom of the excavation, usually by pumping from within the caisson. The cylinders may be withdrawn as the concrete is placed.

21.2.2 Excavation of Caisson Bells

Excavation of the bell can be accomplished by hand, by machine (within certain limits), or by a combination of both.

The undercutting of a bell by hand usually requires the use of air spades or paving breakers with chisel shaped cutting tools. Special "draw knives" may be used in soft soils. For caissons up to 4 ft in diameter, the excavation is started with one bottom man working. As the excavation progresses, working room becomes available for two more men. For large diameter bells where there is risk of collapse of the roof, time is critical, and the more bottom men, the better. In a caisson 100 ft deep it takes time to raise and dump the spoil; this sets the limit on the number of men digging. Depending on the density of the soil, production may vary from about 1.5 to 2.5 yd³ per man per shift. Bell excavation should not be started just before a weekend or other shutdown.

In large undercuts, failure of the bell roof is of constant concern. Quaking of the roof or glistening spots where the moisture is forced to the surface are signals of critical conditions. Shoring a bell roof with timbers and inclined posts is possible in theory, but the time required usually makes it impractical. Reducing the amount of horizontal undercut by enlarging the shaft diameter, while expensive, may be the best solution. The added weight of the larger shaft may, of course, require some increase in bell size. The soil over the area of the bell becomes disturbed during the belling operation. The final cut to the bearing surface should not be made until all other work is completed.

Machine excavation of bells is done by special "belling out" buckets. Because of the economy of this method and competitive nature of the business, there are continual new improvements in belling buckets and techniques.

Bells can be cut with a diameter up to about three times the shaft diameter of a caisson. Thus for a 4-ft-diameter caisson, a bell may be mechanically excavated up to a diameter of about 11 ft, 6 in. Because of the variety of such tools, it is not possible to suggest a limit to the density of the soil which can be excavated. Belling buckets tend to roughen up the bottom area of the bell. Consequently, most specifications require that the final cut to expose the bearing stratum be performed by hand trimming and by cleaning out the bottom of the bell.

Caisson bells work very well in cohesive soils such as clay, silt, and sand containing enough fines so that it will stand when cut. Caissons also cut well in sedimentary soft rocks such as shale, claystone, silt-stone, and sandstone and such. However, caisson bells are not always formed in cohesive soils. In formations consisting of residual rock, the upper 5 or 10 ft may be weathered or disintegrated more than the rock below. Higher bearing capacities may therefore be found (with consequently smaller size bells) by carrying the caissons into the rock. Such work requires air tools and hand excavation. In disintegrated rock, pumping of water from the bell excavation is often necessary. Where disintegration has progressed to the point that the rock has been reduced to sand, the excavation of bells may not be feasible. Core recovery from the borings should be studied carefully. A search of prior experience in the area may help. Frequently in disintegrated rock, there exist nodules, ribs, and large pieces of hard rock unaf-fected by weathering. Where these pieces are as hard as the concrete to be placed in the bell, there is no engineering reason for their removal from the roof or bottom of the bell, and removal should not be arbitrarily required.

Belled caissons supported on soil are designed essentially as deep spread footings. The bearing value of the soil and anticipated settle-ments are estimated using the procedures described in Chapters 14 and 15 (see Ref. 44).

21.2.3 Inspection

The inspection of caisson work includes checking *(a)* the quality of the bearing stratum, *(b)* the dimensions of the caissons as installed and their deviations from the designed dimensions and locations, both vertically and horizontally, and *(c)* the quality of the concrete deposited in the caissons. Inspection may be divided into the follow-ing items:

1. Deviation of the top of the caissons from plan locations.
2. Location of the center of the bottoms of the caissons with refer-

ence to the centers of the tops to establish the deviations from the vertical.

3. Measurements of the diameter of the bell, the slope of the bell roof, and the diameter of the shaft.

4. Verification of the quality of the bearing stratum, including whether it has been cut level or suitably benched.

5. The quality of the concrete as delivered and placed in the caissons, including slump tests, procurement, and storage of concrete cylinders for testing and continuous observation of placing.

In item 1, it is advisable to check the location of all caisson center stakes before spotting the drilling rig. In the absence of obstructions in the soil and with reasonable care to keep the drill stem plumb at all times, most specified tolerances can be met.

In item 2, as the bucket or auger is being lowered into the hole, it should be observed frequently so that where drifting to one side is evident, corrective measures can be taken before it is too late.

In item 3, there should always be one man in the bell excavation crew who is experienced and is given precise instructions as to bell diameter and height.

In item 4, it is usual to drill until the bearing stratum has been reached before starting the bell undercut. It is best to arrange for inspection of the bearing stratum at this stage and before bell excavation is started. It is particularly important if samples for field laboratory testing are required, as it shortens the time when the bell must stand open for final inspection. Bearing strata are not always level. Decisions should be made in advance as to the maximum slope which will be permitted so that where excessive, the bottom can be stepped or benched with a minimum of delay to the bell excavation operation.

In item 5, placing of concrete is discussed under Section 21.6.

21.3   Caissons Bearing on Rock

Where column loads are of the order of 250 tons or higher and ledge rock, having a bearing capacity of 30 tons/ft^2 or more, exists at a reasonable distance below the ground surface, caissons without bells bearing on the rock often provide an economical foundation.

21.3.1   Shaft Excavation and Lining

The choice of excavation methods depends on soil conditions. Where impervious cohesive soils provide a seal against ground water directly over the rock, the excavating methods discussed in Section 21.2.1 will apply. However, where water bearing soils overlie the rock surface, special methods are required. The objective is to seat a casing on or in the rock so that the bottom is sealed against an excessive inflow of water and soil.

If there are irregularities in the surface of the rock, a seal against water and loss of ground cannot be made. It is sometimes possible to place a short set of Chicago lagging held in place with rings inside the bottom of the casing. The individual pieces of lagging can be driven with air tools to close the gaps between the rock surface and the bottom edges of the casing (see Fig. 21.3). Minimum size casing practical for this method is 4-ft-diameter casing. Another limitation is that the reduction in the concrete cross section must be approved by the engineers.

Where drilling to the rock surface is practical, another method for sealing the casing is to fit the casing with a sawtooth cutting edge and rotate it with the drill rig so that it cuts into the rock for the full circumference. Hard granite cannot be drilled in this manner. The method calls for adequate equipment and experience.

Bedrock is covered frequently with a deposit of hardpan or coarse granular soil containing gravel and boulders which prevent drilling to the rock surface. If the granular soil layer is more than approximately 5 to 8 ft thick, caissons to rock may not be economical. It may be possible to sink the casing through the granular soil layer by "dredging," or excavating the material with orange peel, clam shells, or special excavating tools. In this method, the casing is kept full of water. To avoid loss of ground, the excavation must not extend below the cutting edge. Weights are often needed to force the casing to sink. Cleaning of the bottom and inspection has to be done by a diver. Removal of boulders may also require divers. For a diver to operate, the minimum caisson diameter is 4 ft and preferably 4 ft, 6 in. A sloping rock surface cannot be benched underwater but can be made reasonably level by placing sacks of sand and cement on the low side.

Where caissons are carried to rock, there is always the possibility that the bedrock itself will carry water, which flows up through seams and fissures into the caisson. High percentages of core recoveries obtained in core drilling do not entirely eliminate this risk, and all available data, including the structural geology of the rock, should be studied. Waterwell data are particularly valuable.

21.3.2   Inspection

Where caissons are carried to rock, the applicable procedures for the inspection of belled caissons (Section 21.2.2) are similar, provided the bottom can be inspected in the open. When the caissons cannot be dewatered, methods must be improvised to secure the required data.

For testing the quality of the rock, a core drill rig may be set on a platform over the caisson and the rock drilled with a "plug" diamond bit. This is a noncoring bit, but one which will give the same data as that of a jack hammer and drill steel.

The variation from the vertical can be approximately closely by fitting the lower end of a pipe or H-beam with a simple template which will center it at the bottom of the casing and place it to pass through the center at the top. In this way, the slope can be closely determined.

The same pipe or H-beam (without the template) can be used as a spud to sound the bottom to verify that it has been cleaned off sufficiently.

21.4   Dewatering of Caissons

Where the bottom of the waterbearing layer extends no more than 18 ft below the operating level and contains coarse sand and gravel with no more than about 20% fines (by volume), double diaphragm pumps with suction hose, flap valves, and strainers will handle a moderate flow of water. Also, under these circumstances, wellpoints could be used.

The use of sumps located around the site in which large capacity pumps can operate 24 hr/day will reduce the amount of pumping in individual caissons and increase the rate of excavation. On large sites, the sumps may be grouped around six or eight caissons under excavation and moved along as the caisson work progresses.

Where the underside of the permeable layer slopes, permanent sumps or deep wells may be installed at the deep end and pumped continuously to lower the head and partially drain the site. If time allows, pumping should be started several weeks ahead of caisson operations. The effect of dewatering on nearby structures needs careful study.

In deep caissons, where the waterbearing stratum is too deep for surface pumps, caisson sinking pumps are necessary. Open impeller electric powered centrifugal pumps or compressed air operated pumps are commonly used.

21.5   Reinforcing Steel in Caissons

Placing reinforcing steel in the shafts of caissons is a costly, and at times, difficult operation. It adds disproportionately to the cost of the work and introduces problems into the proper placing of concrete.

Reinforcing in a caisson shaft for the full height is not usually required. Irrespective of the L/D ratio, the lateral restraint offered by the surrounding soil usually provides adequate restraint. Reinforcing steel is not too helpful in correcting out-of-plumbness, or dog-legs, in caisson shafts.

However, where eccentric loads or bending moments (as under crane columns) are imposed, reinforcing steel to as much as 30 ft below the top of the caisson may be necessary. Uplift may also call for reinforcing. In seismic resistant designs, caissons frequently are reinforced to full depth.

Where caissons have steel casing left in place, this casing can be designed to perform the same function as reinforcing steel.. It is not practical to pour concrete, and to lift the casing sections out of the caisson at the same time, unless cages are made rigid enough to be free standing. The usual cage which is held together by hoops tied with wire is not strong enough to stand. The cage must be welded and stiffened adequately to be self-supporting.

Where reinforced concrete construction is to rest on the caissons, the reinforcing merely consists of dowels embedded in the top of the caisson, tying them to the concrete above.

If anchor bolts are required, the caisson design usually provides for a caisson cap in which the anchor bolts are set using a template and instruments for accurate positioning. The cap is concreted separately from the caisson and short dowels used, extending through the joint. Normally a sheeted starting pit, larger than the diameter of the top cylinder to be used for casing the shaft, is placed in advance of the caisson work. The anchor bolts are set and the cap concreted after the work on the caisson has been completed.

Costs can be reduced if the caisson and the cap are concreted without interruption. After the concrete has set, holes can be drilled in the concrete, and the anchor bolts can be precision set and secured in place with nonshrinkage grout.

21.6 Placing Concrete in Caissons

Two critical items in specifications for concrete to be deposited in caissons are: (a) slump and (b) height of fall.

Slump is probably the most important. If casing can be withdrawn before pouring concrete, a slump as low as 3 in. can be used. Where concrete has to be placed through elephant truck chutes or into casing before withdrawal, the slump should be not less than 4 in. For underwater concrete placed through a tremie pipe or bottom dump bucket, the slump should be 5 in. minimum. Concrete must have the consistency to flow through chutes and pipes without blocking or arching.

The height of free fall of the concrete permitted by the specifications may be critical. Many specifications consider only the concrete for the superstructure where free fall limits of 6 to 8 ft are normal. Experience has shown that concrete deposited in a hopper centered at the top of a caisson may be permitted to fall free an unlimited distance with excellent results. A slump of 3 in. may be used.

Where there is little or no water entering a caisson at the bottom, concrete may be deposited from the top by pouring it through a hopper fitted with an 8- or 10-in. diameter short pipe directing the flow down the center of the shaft. Many caissons over 100 ft deep have been satisfactorily concreted in this manner.

If the inflow of water at the bottom is too great for concreting in the open, underwater methods must be used. The water head in the casing must balance the external water pressure. Otherwise water will continue to flow upward through fresh concrete until the head is balanced.

The usual practice is to deposit concrete underwater to a height sufficient to counterbalance the water pressure acting on the cross section at the bottom. When it has set, the shaft may be pumped out, and any laitance removed. The balance of the concrete may be poured in the open.

If there is sufficient work to mobilize a modern pumpcrete outfit, an excellent underwater seal can be placed.

The use of a conventional tremie pipe system is somewhat more dependable than the bottom dump bucket and does not involve rental of equipment. However, it is slow and depends greatly on the crane operator. The tremie must never be raised above the concrete already deposited once the pour has started.

It is not advisable to attempt to deposit concrete underwater in a belled caisson, as the bell roof will be weakened by the water and will slough off or collapse with no way to detect the occurrence.

The procedure for concreting a caisson which has been drilled through a saturated granular layer requires careful planning to make sure that as the casing is withdrawn from the waterbearing stratum, the water pressure in the formation will not force soil and water into the caisson shaft and mix with or cut off the fresh concrete. A hypothetical case is illustrated in Fig. 21.4.

The profile of the soil conditions shows that a wet silty sand layer 3 ft thick has to be cased off as the shaft is drilled. The casing can be sealed by driving it into the clay below the sand. Since the diameter of the drilled hole will be slightly larger than the casing, casing needs to extend above the ground water level shown. Obviously, the water and slurry used to drill through the sand will rise outside the casing to the water level. The manner in which the shaft is cased is shown on Fig. 21.4. The short starting cylinder seals off the ground water and stabilizes the loose soil at the surface. After the 50-in. casing is

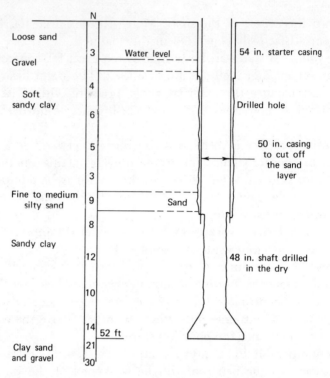

Fig. 21.4   Sinking caisson through water bearing stratum.

sealed, the shaft to the bearing stratum can be drilled dry, the bell inspected, and concrete poured up to the bottom of the 50-in casing. Thereafter, concrete is poured into the 50-in. cylinder as fast as possible up to a level above the water level. The casing cannot be raised above the bottom of the sand layer until then. The head of concrete must counterbalance the head of water and slurry in the annulus between the cylinder and the drilled hole. As the cylinder is withdrawn, the concrete will push out and displace upward all fluid on the outside. After the casing has been removed, the sludge which accumulates in the starting cylinder has to be pumped out. Then the concrete is poured up to grade, and the starting cylinder withdrawn. A supply of concrete without risk of interruption is essential. It must be expected that occasionally a long cylinder will stick, and must be left in place.

21.7   Drilled in Caissons (Socketed in Rock)

21.7.1   Descriptions and Applications

Drilled in caissons are essentially open-end pipe piles driven to rock, cleaned out, and extended into rock by drilling a socket into which an H-beam is grouted; then concrete is poured between the beam and the pipe casing. Probably because of the high loadings for which such units are designed, usage has identified them as caissons. It is feasible to install drilled in caissons from 24 to 48 in. in diameter, but the majority have been 30 in. in diameter. By varying the cross-section of the structural steel beam or "core," a wide range of loads can be supported on caissons of uniform diameter (see Fig. 21.5).

The bearing capacity of a drilled in caisson is determined by applying working stresses to the area of the steel core, the area of the concrete within the casing and the area of the casing. The contribution of the steel casing must take into account the possibility of corrosion. Such caissons may be designed to support loads from about 750 tons to loads in excess of 3000 tons.

The depth that a socket extends into rock is determined by the total load to be carried compared to the bearing value and the bond strength assigned to the rock. Such factors as the soundness of the rock, the existence of seams, and the possibility of the socket being dewatered so that the grout can be placed in the dry have an affect on determining the bond strength. The usual range is from 100 to 250 $lb/in.^2$. The end-bearing strength is usually governed by the applicable building code.

For the load to be distributed between the steel core, the concrete, and the casing, the tops of the core and casing must be milled or ground to an exact plane and a billet grouted in place to bear on all surfaces. For moderate column loads a cage of reinforcing steel may be used in place of the H-beam.

Drilled in caissons are particularly suitable for high column loads. They can be installed where sloping rock makes the use of end-bearing piles difficult and uncertain. Drilled in caissons can be carried to depths of 200 ft or more, which is beyond the reach of most conventional piling. They can be used to resist lateral loads, bending

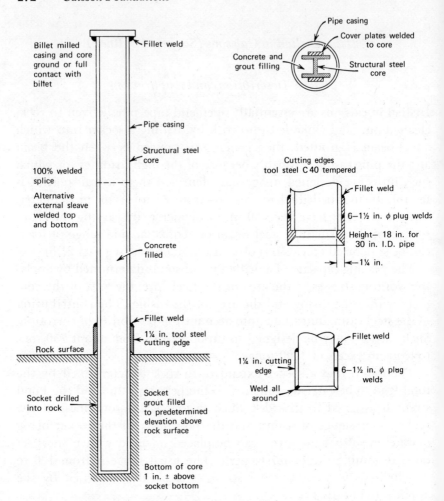

Fig. 21.5 Drilled-in caisson socketed in rock.

moments, and uplift. Boulders and other difficult soil conditions can be overcome by churn drilling and other methods.

21.7.2   Installation Methods and Equipment

The casing pipe must be strong enough to take driving forces without deformation. It is usually ½ in. thick. A tool steel cutting edge of 40/50 carbon steel is welded to the outside at the bottom. The pipe is driven to rock with conventional pile driving hammers. The pipe may be cleaned out by bailing, air and water jets, augers, or cable tools (churn drills). Since it is essential to seat the cutting edge into the rock for its full circumference, alternate operations of drilling ahead of the cutting edge and driving are often necessary.

Controlling within the specified tolerances for location and plumbness demands constant attention. A template of timbers well braced against horizontal movement is used to keep the top of the casing centered. The pile hammer and leads, and the pipe as it is driven, have to be checked with instruments frequently to verify plumbness.

When the pipe has been seated and cleaned out, the socket is drilled with a cable tool drilling rig or a rotary rock drill. Where rock is sound, shot core barrels have been used to remove the rock from the socket in the form of rock cores.

The casing and socket are dewatered, whenever possible, for inspection. Inspection of the walls of the rock socket are valuable to confirm assumptions about the quality of the rock. In most cases, however, dewatering is not possible. The quality of the rock must be judged from careful observation of the rock drilling operation. Underwater television cameras have been employed to scan the rock surface in the sockets.

Cement sand grout is deposited in the socket. Where the steel core can be handled in one piece without risk of interruption, the grout may be placed before the core is in place and the core lowered into position before the grout has a chance to set. Otherwise, the core is placed first, and the grout is pumped into the socket afterwards.

The steel core may be a heavy section made up of an H-beam with plates welded to the web and flanges to provide the required cross section. Guides to center the core in the casing are welded on at intervals. The core must be accurately measured and assembled so that when in final position, the bottom is not less than 1 in. above the bottom of the socket.

After the grout has set, the casing can be pumped or bailed out. Any laitance on top of the grout must be removed by chopping, washing, and bailing. The concrete inside the casing must be placed with great care so that it encases the core completely since it is structural concrete that contributes to the load bearing capacity of the caisson.

21.7.3   Inspection

Inspection of drilled in caissons follows the lines of caisson inspection discussed in Section 21.3.2, with the addition of the inspection of the rock sockets. Specialists are needed whose qualifications apply to the method of inspection, whether by television pictures, by observing drilling operations, or by visual inspection in the dry.

Special precautions are called for when personnel must be lowered into a 30-in. hole below the caisson cutting edge. One method consists of the use of a structural steel cage suspended by a $\frac{1}{2}$-in. cable equipped with a signal rope (or other device). The cage must be 4 or 5 ft longer than the deepest socket. Thus the top of the cage can never pass below the bottom of the casing and get caught under the edge of the casing.

21.7.4   Patents

While the basic patents on the drilled in caisson have expired, later patents were granted for caissons installed on a batter and on certain drilling tools. Any contractor should be informed about existing patents before becoming involved in such work.

21.8   Summary

The primary points in this chapter are as follows:

FACTS: Surveys of structures which could be affected should be made before work starts. Caissons can support heavy loads and may be installed to rock with constant diameter, or belled out for bearing pressures to suit the capacity of the bearing stratum. The soils in which bells are undercut must be sufficiently dense to be free standing. Installing caissons to rock and effectively sealing them can present problems. Where there is an inflow of water into the bottom, or when casing is to be withdrawn as concrete is placed, require special methods of depositing concrete.

WATCH OUT FOR: Water-bearing soils through which the caisson shaft must pass. Saturated fine sands or silts overlying the bearing stratum are dangerous. Saturated sand pockets will cause collapse of bells. Methane gas or sulphur water require special safety precautions. Boulders and other obstructions interface with mechanical excavation. Hydrostatic head of water above caisson cut-offs. Necking-down of caisson shafts due to water or caving.

22

Site Grading

22.1 Site Preparation and Prerolling

The first step in site grading is drainage. If the site is wet, draining immediately is cheaper than working in the mud. If the site is dry, protective ditches, berms, or other facilities may be needed for future rains or possible flooding. The second step is to prepare the existing ground surface. In hillside areas, this may involve removal of trees, brush, grass and weeds, and old mud flows or landslide debris. In lower areas, organic soils, trash and dumped debris, expansive or unsuitable topsoil, or topsoil containing roots and organic material must be removed. Considerable expense may be involved in removing these unsatisfactory materials and finding a suitable place to dispose of them. Therefore, the contractor should have a good knowledge of the site conditions and of the soil below original ground surface.

Basic data, which should be available and which the contractor should obtain and review, include:

1. A profile of the subsurface soil layers.
2. Unfavorable bedding or fracture planes in bedrock formations.
3. A general idea of the firmness and stability of the underlying soils or rocks.
4. The ground water level.
5. Soils that are considered to be unsuitable and require removal.

Specifications generally are vague regarding the amount of organic material which can be contained in soil. Almost all soils contain at least some organic material. In most cases, soils containing a small amount of organic material are acceptable in compacted fills. Organic material becomes objectionable if there are large pieces, roots, or clumps of organic material or vegetation. If the organic material is small and well distributed, it is likely that 2 to 4% of organic material would be accepted in fill soils for most structural fills. In some cases, it may be sufficient to scrape the grass and brush off the surface. The topsoil and roots can mix with the underlying soil and become "lost." By contrast, however, some high quality structural fills, under major structures, may require essentially no organic content. This may require stripping vegetation plus 4 to 6 in. of topsoil off the site and removing it from the site.

If a soil contains some roots, it may be economical to spread the cut soil on surfaces to be filled, and then rake the fill soils to remove the larger roots. A heavy-duty rake is required for this purpose, but may affect a substantial savings in making a particular soil acceptable.

In some cases, chipping machines are used to chop up the sparse brush on a site and spread it uniformly through the borrow soil. So long as the chips are small and well distributed through the fill, this may be an acceptable fill.

The big question is, how much organic material can reasonably be left in fill soil? If a fill is required to be compacted to 90% relative compaction, it would be possible to overcompact the soil to make up for the space occupied by the roots. Assume that the organic material is 3% by weight of the total soil. The roots have a lower density than soil; therefore, 3% by weight would be perhaps 5% by volume of the soil. If the soil were compacted to 95% relative compaction, the roots could decay and disappear, with a resulting drop in relative compaction to 90%. Overcompacting may be cheaper than attempting to get all of the roots and organic material out of the soil. However, it will be necessary for tests to ensure that this procedure will work on the particular soil involved, and also it will be necessary to get approval of the engineer or owner to use this procedure. Ignition tests may be required to evaluate the quantity of organic matter in the soil.

Where large amounts of organic material occur in a soil, and it is not economical to remove a substantial part of the organic material, this soil should be considered for landscaping purposes or for areas in which a high quality structural fill may not be necessary. Such a fill material, after being well compacted, may have satisfactory stability against sliding or erosion, even though it is not satisfactory for support of structures. If adequate information is not available, 1 or 2 days of digging test pits with a backhoe or auger may be a good investment to determine the quantity of soils to be wasted and the amount of usable soil.

Prerolling or proofrolling is a common practice to test a site. Before starting to place fill on a site, or before placing a base course or a floor slab on the soil subgrade, specifications frequently require proofrolling. A loaded dump truck or a compaction roller is used to roll back and forth over the site, followed by an inspector who watches for any soft spots. Frequently soft pipeline backfills or "weaving" plastic soils are found. These soils usually are dug out and replaced with dry sandy soil. Proof-rolling commonly is done on completion of airport runways to confirm adequate compaction of the subgrade.

22.2   Cuts and Fills

Generally, a grading plan is prepared by the engineer to outline the areas of cuts and fills, the depths of cutting and filling, and other details required for the completed rough grading. The grading plan usually is based on balancing the cut and fill. After deducting the volume of any soil which must be wasted, the amount of cut is made to balance the volume of required fill. However, the volume of soil excavated may not exactly equal the volume of compacted fill. One cubic yard of soil excavated may equal only 8/10 yd of fill in compacted embankment. This is described as shrinkage. Shrinkage can consist of several factors such as:

When soil is compacted, it may have a higher density than the natural soil. Therefore, more grains of soil are contained in each cubic yard of fill embankment. This results in reduced volume of the embankment soil.

Calculation of fill volume is based on compacting the soil to the required percent of compaction. If the specifications require that the fill be compacted to 90% (of the specified method of compaction test-ing), but the contractor actually compacts the soil to a density of 93%, there is an additional loss of about 3% of fill volume.

Some soil may be lost by spilling during hauling from the cut area to the fill area.

Fill embankments may be constructed somewhat larger than shown on the plans. For instance, a roadway or canal embankment may be specified as 10 ft wide. However, in construction the embankment turns out to be 10 to 12 ft in width. Unless the contractor goes back and carefully trims the embankment to size, there is additional loss of fill material.

Shrinkage values in many cases are in the range of 10 to 25%, but sometimes are over 30%.

The grading plan usually specifies the required slopes for cut areas and for fill areas. Some typical slope angles are as follows:

Type of Construction	Cuts in Rock	Cuts in Soil	Compacted Fills
Housing subdivisions, uniform building code	2 : 1	2 : 1	2 : 1
Dams			3 : 1
Buttress fills			2 : 1
Canal slopes, medium height	1 : 1	1½ : 1	1½ : 1
Canal slopes, under 6 ft high	½ : 1	1 : 1	1 : 1

Note.   2 : 1 means 2 horizontal to 1 vertical.

Although many building departments list acceptable slope angles for cuts and fills in the building codes, all codes permit variances. The variances depend on careful analysis by a foundation engineer to convince the building department that a slope angle is safe and rea-sonable for a particular site and type of soil.

During construction of fills in hillside areas, it is considered good practice to cut steps into the hillside to bond the fill to the hillside material. This is called benching. The height of risers for each bench may be equal to the height of each lift of fill, or may be higher, say 2 or 3 ft high, depending on which is most convenient to the grading operation.

In the transition from cut to fill, trouble occurs frequently. The fill area tends to settle, while the cut area does not. This unequal movement can crack house foundations and break water mains. Where this condition occurs under house sites, deeper foundation or shifting the house location should be considered. Pipelines should be made more flexible in these locations, by using short lengths of pipe, or pipe designed to bend.

Boulders may be encountered in the excavation. Disposal of boulders can be a serious problem. Also, this results in a loss or shrinkage of available fill material. Sometimes boulders can be used in the embankment fill. This is described in more detail in Chapter 23, Section 23.11.

Site grading also may be required on flat properties to be used for industrial or commercial construction. Specifications frequently require "proof rolling" of the site prior to placing fill. This is especially true for industrial buildings which may have heavy floor slabs, or floors at dock height which will require placing 3 to 4 ft of fill (see Section 22.1).

22.3   Site Drainage

During grading, construction sites are particularly vulnerable to rainy weather. Therefore, good site drainage should be developed as part of the grading plan developed by the contractor. The contractor's grading plan must use the project grading plan as its end result, but the contractor should plan the progress of the various cuts and fills so that he can obtain the most efficient use of his equipment. In addition, the grading plan must be such that the site is not in a vulnerable condition during a rain which would cause the site to become swamped.

In many parts of the country, there is a "rainy season." In some cases, it is almost impossible to run an efficient grading operation during rainy seasons. Therefore, the grading contractor may elect to close down grading operations during this season. In some cases, city codes will force closing down grading operations in hillside residential areas during the rainy season.

When a site is closed down for the rainy season, more attention must be given to good drainage, and to finishing off the surfaces of existing fills and cutting areas to reduce the infiltration of rainwater and to reduce erosion (see Chapter 23, Section 23.10).

22.4 Summary

Primary points in this chapter are as follows:

FACTS: Site stripping and clearing can be an expensive factor of a job. Adequate information is needed to plan the job. Soils shrink between natural and fill conditions.

WATCH OUT FOR: High water or potential flooding of the work site. Large amounts of organic materials. Low density fill soils which will shrink greatly on compaction. Transition from cut soil to fill soil, where differential settlement can crack structure and pipelines.

23

Compaction of Soil

The use of compacted fills and the techniques for construction of compacted fills have developed rapidly over the past 40 years. The development of larger and more powerful excavation and hauling equipment has made grading operations more economical. This has led to the development of many kinds of compaction machines, and the use of compacted soils for many purposes.

This chapter describes the construction of compacted fills *as they are placed* in major earthmoving operations. Compaction of backfill around structures and over pipelines is described in Chapter 13. Compaction of preexisting fills or low-density natural soils "in place" is described later in this chapter.

23.1 Purposes

The major purpose of compacting soil is to make a change in the mechanical characteristics of the soil. These changes include the following:

1. An increase in the strength of the soil—higher bearing value.
2. A decrease in the compressibility (or settlement) of the soil under load.

3. A decrease in the permeability of the soil. This makes certain soils suitable for dam embankments and linings for reservoirs.

4. A soil that is more resistant to erosion.

The uses for compacted soil include the following:

1. Make stable ground on which to place the foundations of structures.

2. Provide better support for footings. The compacted soil has a higher bearing value and settlements are reduced.

3. Provide more uniform support for the floor slabs of structures.

4. Provide firm soils for embankments and approach ramps for highways.

5. For the construction of earth dams.

6. For backfills in streets, after pipes or other utilities are placed, and backfills around footings and around basement walls. It is undesirable for such backfills to settle. Proper compaction prevents settlement.

7. Increase the passive resistance of the soil to resist lateral loads. This may include soils compacted around concrete block anchors, or around foundations subjected to lateral loads.

23.2 Mechanics of Compaction

Compaction increases the weight (dry density) of the soil. This is accomplished by pushing the solid soil particles closer together, and reduces the void spaces in the soil. The void spaces are occupied by air or water, which have no strength.

If the soil particles could be compacted so tightly that all void spaces were eliminated, resulting in a solid mass of soil, the resulting soil would weigh 160 to 170 lb/ft³. This is equivalent to rock. By contrast, soil in its natural condition generally weighs on the order of 80 to 100 lb/ft³. Since the total weight contains some water, it is somewhat greater than 80 to 100 lb.

In Fig. 23.1, a cubic foot of soil is represented. However, the soil particles are all pressed together, resulting in 8 in. of solid soil particles. The remainder of the cubic foot is represented as air. This is a bone-dry soil. The soil weight equals $\frac{2}{3} \times 160 = 106$ lb/ft³.

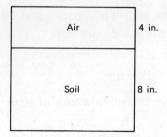

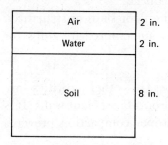

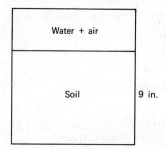

Fig. 23.1   Soil, water, and air relationship in soil mass.

If the soil had been saturated with water, the air is displaced and the top 4 in. of Fig.23.1 would be water. In this case, the weight of the original soil would be as follows:

Soil weight equals ⅔ × 160 lb = 106 lb
Water weight equals ⅓ × 62 lb = 21 lb
Total soil weight equals 127 lb/ft³

This generally is referred to as the wet density.

If the dry density equals 106 lb/ft³, and the water weighs 21 lb, then the moisture content equals

$$\frac{21}{106} = 20\%$$

More commonly, the voids are partially filled with water as represented by the second diagram in Fig. 23.1. The bottom 8 in. consists of solid soil particles. The next 2 in. is water, and the top 2 in. is air. In this case, the soil weight is as follows:

Soil weight equals $\frac{2}{3} \times 160$ lb $= 106$ lb
Water weight equals $\frac{1}{6} \times 62$ lb $= 10$ lb
Total weight equals 116 lb/ft³

Then moisture content equals

$$\frac{10}{106} = 10\%$$

If the soil must be compacted so that it has a dry density of 120 lb/ft³, then the volume of solid soil particles would equal

$$\frac{120}{160} = \frac{3}{4}$$

As shown in the third diagram on Fig. 23.1, the bottom 9 in. could be represented as solid soil particles and the top 3 in. would be water and air. If the soil is saturated, the water content would weigh $\frac{1}{4} \times 62 = 15$ lb. The moisture content equals

$$\frac{15}{120} = 12\%$$

The amount of water in the soil has a strong influence on the compaction of soil. If the soil is dry, the soil particles are too rough to slide easily. Therefore, it is difficult to rearrange the particles and to compact them tighter.

If moisture is added, it acts as a lubricant. The particles can slide easier and they can be pushed into a tighter configuration.

However, if there is too much water in the soil, the void spaces are too full. There is no way to push the particles together except by squeezing out water. Squeezing out water during compaction generally is difficult, except in very porous soils such as clean sands. However, squeezing out water can happen over a long period of time, such as under a structural load.

If the soils become very wet, frequently they are almost plastic. They flow rather than being compressed under the compaction equipment. Therefore, it is very important to control the amount of water in the soil.

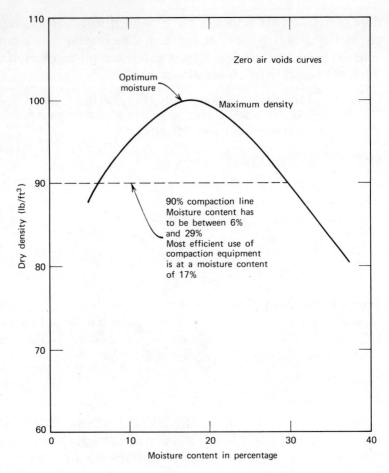

Fig. 23.2   Typical moisture–density relationship or compaction curve.

For any soil, and with a specific compaction effort, samples can be compacted at various moisture contents. If several samples are compacted at various moisture contents, the dry density will be different for each compacted sample. Plotting moisture content of the soil against the dry density results in a curve, shown in Fig. 23.2. This curve indicates the percent of water which results in the highest dry density, and is frequently called a moisture-density curve or a compaction curve.

If test strips are compacted on the job site, using fill soils containing various moisture contents and identical compaction effort, field density tests would result in a similar curve.

The purpose of laboratory compaction tests is to attempt to duplicate the compaction on the job site.

The compaction curve indicates the following:

1. The moisture content at which the least amount of energy is needed to compact the soil (optimum moisture content).

2. Assume that the specifications require that the soil be compacted to 90% (see Chapter 8, Section 8.8). A 90% line can be drawn on the compaction curve. Where the line crosses the curve, it indicates the minimum moisture content and the maximum moisture content at which it is possible to compact the soil using the laboratory compaction equipment. This may also indicate the minimum and maximum moisture contents at which the soil can be compacted using the compaction equipment on the site (see Fig. 23.2). Specifications often define the range of allowable moisture contents in the soil to be compacted.

23.3   Energy of Compaction

For any soil, increasing the compactive effort (size of the roller) results in a higher density. By running a number of tests, a new compaction curve can be drawn. Also, the soil compacts more easily at a lower moisture content. Therefore, it is important to identify the compactive effort used, since the compaction curve changes.

A number of different "laboratory compaction test methods" have been devised. Some of these are indicated in Fig. 8.11. These methods vary considerably. Therefore, when reading the specifications for a job, it is very important to understand the compaction method which will be used by the laboratory in establishing the maximum point on the compaction curve. This point is the maximum dry density and equals 100% compaction. If maximum dry density is 100 lb/ft³, then 90% compaction represents a dry density of 90 lb/ft³.

However, if more energy is used in compacting the soil sample, the maximum density might be 110 lb/ft³. Then 90% compaction equals 100 lb/ft³. Considerably more compactive effort will be required in the field to obtain a density of 100 lb/ft³.

It is interesting that a fill which is too dry could be compacted by using a heavier roller. However, a fill that is too wet could not be compacted with a heavier roller (see Section 23.8.7).

23.4   Selection of Fill Soil

Job specifications may state that soil will be obtained from the following:

1. Excavations on other portions of the site.
2. Specified borrow pits.
3. Sources to be developed by the contractor.

On-site excavation soil usually is the least expensive. However, if the soil is difficult to work with, the completed and accepted fills may cost more than if better imported materials had been used.

In winter months of frequent rains, soils that ordinarily could be compacted in the summer time may become too wet in the winter rains and become impossible to compact. If the soils are scarified to dry, frequently another rain further saturates the soils.

Therefore, selection of the most suitable soil for construction of a compacted fill depends on the following:

1. Weather conditions during placing of the fill.
2. Suitability of the fill soils.
3. Quality required of the completed fill.

Although a borrow area may be designated as "available to the contractor," it is the contractor's responsibility to verify the suitability of the borrow pit. This includes the suitability of the soil, the extent and volume of suitable soil, the uniformity of the soil, or the presence of unsuitable layers within the borrow area.

Construction of a fill is similar frequently to construction of the poured concrete foundations. The fills are required to be constructed to a high quality. These fills will support foundations or floor slabs. Therefore, fills may be referred to as structural compacted fills. For fills of this quality, construction must be done well to pass the rigid requirements of the specifications and careful testing by an inspection laboratory.

Generally, sandy soils, mixtures of clay and sand or silt and sand, decomposed granite, and some clays are good soils to work with. Other soils can be very difficult to compact, such as silt, siltstone, clean round sand, clay, and plastic clay (such as gumbo or adobe).

23.5 *Specifications*

Generally, soils used for fill are required to be recompacted to a higher density than their natural density. Most natural deposits of soil have densities ranging from 60 to 90% of maximum obtained by the standard AASHO compaction method.

If sand fill is compacted to the same density as its original condition, the sand would perform in about the same manner as the original sand. However, clay has some original structure. Excavation and working the clay changes the structure. Some clays are sensitive to reworking and lose some of their strength. Therefore, clays recompacted to their original density may have less strength than the original clay deposit. Usually, most of this strength is regained with time.

However, it is general practice to recompact soils to a higher density than their original natural density. The resulting soils are generally firmer, and consolidate less under load than the adjacent natural soils.

Specifications usually repeat the percentage compaction spelled out in the local building code. In some cases, however, a different percentage compaction may be required to fit a particular purpose. Fills to support heavy footing loads, or to be the liner for a water reservoir, usually are compacted more than the code requires.

In many cases, a site underlain by appreciable depths of loose, compressible soils have been considered unsatisfactory for support of heavy structures. However, these soils have been excavated and replaced into the same excavation as compacted fills. In such recompaction, frequently a 20-ft-deep excavation yields enough soil to backfill the excavation with 15 ft of compacted soil. Additional soil must be imported to complete backfilling the excavation. Many heavy structures are supported on such compacted fills.

Specifications should indicate the following:

1. The soils suitable for use as fills.

2. The percentage compaction required for the compacted fills. Structural fills might be specified as 95%; pavement and other fills outside the building area may be specified as 90%; and yard area fills may be specified as 85%. Occasionally, for airport runways or special conditions, 100% is required.

3. The laboratory compaction test curve which will be used to establish the maximum density considered to be 100% compaction.

4. The agency responsible for making the tests.

5. The specifications will sometimes spell out the equipment to be on the site for compacting the fill soils; however, the selection of equipment usually is up to the contractor, and the requirement is performance. Performance is measured by testing the fill as it is placed.

23.6   Problem Soils

Occasionally a borrow source is specified which contains soil unsuitable for the proposed fill. The contractor might recognize that the material will not perform as required. Proceeding to use the material hurts the job.

Fill soil is not just dirt—it is a construction material. It deserves as much care in its selection as the concrete, wood, and other materials. The contractor bears a substantial part of the responsibility. Several kinds of soils can be considered as problem soils.

In the northern states, proceeding from the New England States through the Middle West and out to Seattle and Portland, good weather for earthwork occurs over a few months of the year. In these months, silty and clayey soils may be used for fills. However, during the major part of the year, silty and clay soils become wet, are difficult to dry, and can become practically impossible to compact. Once a soil layer of silt or clay is "rained on," it may as well be scraped up and taken off the site. It will not dry out. Attempting to scarify and dry this material usually stretches the job out beyond reason. During these wet months, sand is the only steadfast friend of the contractor, even if it is expensive. At least the job can be completed.

Hard silt or shale soils sometimes are excavated and reused as fill. On several such projects, the contractor compacted the soil until it was very hard. Yet, the compaction did *not* come up to the requirement of 90%. Examination revealed that the compacted fill was composed of lumps or "pebbles" of unbroken shale plus a matrix of crushed shale. In the laboratory tests, all the shale was broken down. Recompacted, the density was about 85 lb/ft³ at 90% compaction. However, the original natural shale formation had a density of about 75 lb/ft³, which is about 80% compaction. Therefore, in the fill composed of half lumps and half crushed material, the average compaction was the average of 80 and 90%, or about 85%. Such test results called for rejection. When this condition is realized, the requirements should be reviewed with the engineer or owner. Usually, the specifications can be modified.

Many soils of marginal quality can be upgraded from "subgrade" to "base course" for support of pavements. Frequently this is called soil stabilization. Stabilization can be done by adding certain "clays" to sand, by adding cement to sandy soil, or by adding lime to a fairly wide range of soils. Clay stabilization may involve the addition of lime, or of other chemicals, to improve the strength and drainage characteristics of clay soil. Also, when clay soils are too wet, addition of lime will reduce the apparent water content and make the soil easier to compact (see Ref. 45, Chapter 10).

23.7   Equipment for Construction of Fills

23.7.1   Rollers

A great variety of rollers are manufactured for compaction of soil. These include:

Sheepsfoot rollers.
Wobble wheel rollers.
Straight wheel rollers.
Super compactors.
Flat wheel road rollers.
Grid rollers.

Sheepsfoot rollers come in a variety of sizes. The size usually is indicated by its width and diameter. A 5 by 5 roller is 5 ft in diameter and 5 ft wide. A 4 by 5 foot roller is 4 ft in diameter and 5 ft wide. Common sizes of rollers are 4 by 4 ft, 5 by 5 ft, and 6 by 6 ft.

The drum usually is loaded with water, or with sand and water. The roller is unloaded for transportation between jobs and is loaded for use on the job site. A roller may be used empty or only partly loaded if it is starting out on a moderately soft subgrade.

Feet generally are about 7 to 9 in. in length, and the end of a foot has a bearing area of 5 in.^{2} to 9 in.^{2}. There are several foot shapes.

The pressure on the bottom of each foot is figured by dividing the total load of the roller by the area of all of the feet in one row, assuming only one row of feet is on the ground at one time. Typical foot pressures are in the range of 200 to 400 psi.

Sheepsfoot rollers work well on sand containing silts and clays. They work moderately well in silts, and work satisfactorily in clay as long as the moisture content is at or below optimum. Sheepsfoot rollers may not be too effective in relatively clean or uniformly graded sand.

23.7.2   *Vibrators*

During the past several years, vibrating compactors have become very popular. They include:

Vibrating drum rollers.
Vibrating flat plate rollers.
Vibrating sheepsfoot rollers.

Vibrating sheepsfoot rollers come in sizes similar to conventional sheepsfoot rollers. However, there are some additional sizes available, and also some variations in shapes of feet.

Vibrating rollers have eccentrics driven usually by motors mounted on the roller. On the upstroke of the eccentric, the weight on the ground may approach zero. On the downstroke, the weight on the ground may vary from 2 or 3 tons for smaller rollers up to 25 tons or more for larger rollers.

Soils most suitable for use of vibrating rollers are sand, sand and gravel, or mixtures of sand or gravel containing some silt.

Vibrating sheepsfoot rollers are suitable for compaction of sandy soils, but also are efficient in compacting finer grained soils, such as silts and clays.

Fig. 23.3   (a) Typical compacting equipment.

Vibrating plate compactors are used primarily for compacting granular soils, sands, gravels, and similar materials which may be used for road base or similar purposes.

Photographs of some of the compactors described above are shown on Fig. 23.3.

23.7.3   Hauling Equipment

Hauling equipment sometimes is used to compact fills. Frequently, large hauling units such as scrapers or dump trucks are routed over fills to obtain additional compaction. In this case, the hauling equipment would not follow the same path across the fill each time. Instead, they follow new paths on each trip. These heavy units are efficient in compacting many soils and may be pressed into service as compaction equipment from time to time. On smaller construction jobs, the use of loaded dump trucks as compaction equipment is fairly common.

Bulldozers are sometimes used to compact the soil. Provided the soil is properly moistened and is spread in thin layers, usually 3 to 4

(b)

Fig. 23.3 (*b*) Typical compacting equipment.

in. thick, a bulldozer can in many cases achieve suitable compaction of the soil. The bearing pressure of the bulldozer tracks generally is low, 6 to 10 psi. Therefore, they are not suitable for achieving a high degree of compaction. By contrast, the pressure imposed by the feet of a sheepsfoot roller generally is around 200 to 400 psi.

23.7.4   Tampers

For smaller fills and backfills, space limitations prevent the use of rollers. Tampers are used. Commonly used tampers include:

Barco compactors.
Ingersoll Rand "simplex" air tampers.
Wackers.
Del-Mag thumpers.

For efficient compaction with hand-operated tampers fill layers usually are about 4 in. in thickness. This might be reduced to 3 in. for clay and increased to 5 or 6 in. for sandy soil. Tampers usually are not very efficient in compacting clean sands.

23.8 Compaction of Existing Soil In-Place

The previous sections described construction of compacted fills as they are placed. Sometimes, it is necessary to compact an existing body of soil. This could be a loose fill or loose natural soil.

23.8.1 Vibroflotation

The vibrofloat operates in a manner somewhat similar to a concrete vibrator or "stinger" (see Fig. 23.4).

Vibroflotation is used to compact loose sands. It can compact to depths of 30 to 40 ft. The vibrofloat is inserted into the ground, vibrates back and forth in its hole, and compacts the surrounding soil. As the surrounding soil is pushed sideways, sand is dropped down the hole to make up the lost volume. Water is injected during this process.

The vibrofloat works best in loose, clean sand, or soil that drains rapidly. When the content of silt or clay exceeds about 10%, the process loses its effectiveness. The process works below or above water level.

Under a large mat foundation, the vibrofloat may be inserted in a pattern or spacing of 6 ft apart, or perhaps 8 or even 10 ft apart. Under an individual footing 6 by 6 ft in size, the vibrofloat may be inserted three times on a spacing of 6 ft center-to-center. Generally, sands can be compacted to 90% of modified AASHO.

In bidding on vibroflotation compaction work, it is customary to guarantee that the sand will be compacted to a certain percentage of "relative density." Relative density is different from percentage compaction as normally used in fill work. To illustrate the method of calculating relative density, assume that a particular sand can be compacted to a maximum density of 120 lb/ft^3. Sand in its loosest state

Fig. 23.4   (*a*) Vibroflotation machine.

has a relative density of zero and in the densest state has a relative density of 100%. If the maximum density of the sand is 120 lb/ft³, the actual compacted density in the field is 100 lb/ft³ (and the loosest condition for the sand is 70 lb/ft³, the relative density would be calculated as

$$\frac{120}{100} \times \frac{100\text{-}70}{120\text{-}70} = 72\%$$

It is common to specify relative density values of 70%, up to 80 or 85%.

Sand compacted to a relative density of 70% will support bearing pressures of 6000 lb/ft², while sand at 80% relative density is good for about 8000 lb/ft².

Clean coarse sand responds very well to vibroflotation; an extremely dense and compact fill can be achieved. Marginal results are obtained in fine sand with some silt.

Soil gradation determines the effectiveness and feasibility of this process. Other factors are involved, of course, but gradation appears to be of primary importance. The Vibroflotation Foundation Company usually works as a specialty subcontractor.

23.8.2   Piles

Sometimes piles are driven into loose sandy soil to compact it. Ordinary piles could be used, such as timber piles. However, usually the method used is called "sand piles," because each pile consists of a column of sand. The process usually is as follows:

> Drive a pipe into the ground. There is a plate "loose fitted" on the base of the pipe, so that the pipe remains empty. Fill the pipe with sand. Pull out the pipe, leaving the sand and bottom

Fig. 23.4   (*b*) Vibroflotation machine.

plate behind. These piles may be placed at intervals like 8 ft on centers each way, and sometimes are 40 or 50 ft long.

Such piles also may be used for another purpose, to permit rapid drainage and settlement of soft mud.

Surcharge loading.   Sometimes fill is temporarily stockpiled on a site to consolidate the underlying soil. The increase in relative compaction generally is small (see Chapter 15, Section 15.7.1).

Pressure injection.   See Chapter 30.

23.8.3   Large Vibrators

Large vibrating rollers now are available which can compact granular soils to depths of several feet. Frequently, such compaction equipment is suitable for densifying a deposit of existing soil to a sufficient depth to provide adequate support for spread footings (Fig. 23.3).

In a recent test, it was found that a large vibrating roller, generating a downward impact force of approximately 40 tons, was able to compact a silty fine sand soil in a zone from 3 to 7 ft below grade. The increase was as much as 20% in relative density. At a depth of 7 ft, the relative density was increased as much as 5%. The top 3 ft were not compacted, and a smaller roller was required to compact this zone.

23.8.4   Explosives

A number of sites underlain by loose sandy soil and having a high water level have been compacted by setting off high explosives within the soil (see Ref. 46).

23.8.5   Dewatering

Lowering the ground water level temporarily at a site is used frequently as a means of consolidating loose deposits of hydraulic dredged fill, or other silty or sandy soil. Dewatering can be done by digging perimeter drainage ditches and installing sump pumps, or by installing well points or wells.

Dewatering has two effects on the soil:

1. The water is removed more quickly than by normal drainage.
2. The soil is no longer "buoyed up" by water, and effectively becomes heavier. This greater effective stress in the soil causes more settlement to occur. If the water level is temporarily pulled 10 ft below permanent water level, the temporary increase in effective stress in the soil is about 400 lb/ft². This is equivalent to the weight of most two- or three-story buildings.

23.8.6   Selection of Compaction Equipment

The type of soil proposed for use as fill material will be the primary factor in deciding on compaction methods and compaction equipment. Some specifications require that soils that are excavated be hauled off the site and disposed of, and that selected fill materials be hauled in. However, in most contracts, it is anticipated that soils excavated on portions of the site will be used for fill or backfill in other portions of the site. Usually, these soils will vary with depth and also with location.

From the standpoint of economics of operating the job, the contractor should be sure he knows the construction materials to be used.

The first step in getting compaction is to get the right moisture content into the soil. Wet silt and clay usually are difficult to dry out. Spreading and breaking up the soil is slow and expensive, requiring equipment designed for the purpose such as Pulvi-Mixer type machines. Dry silt and clay soils also are difficult to work moisture into. Presprinkling in the borrow areas can save time. Some silty soils are powdery, and may require mixing along with presprinkling in the borrow area. Rainbirds and similar sprinklers, with temporary quick-connect pipe systems, usually are used.

Sandy soils generally are not a problem for moisture-conditioning and for compaction. They compact well with vibrating rollers and wheel rollers.

Silty and clay soils generally can be compacted efficiently with sheepsfoot rollers. The feet avoid the formation of a surface crust. The feet reach down and compact the lower portion of each lift of soil. In some soils, the sheepsfoot roller will "walk out," meaning that the lower and intermediate portions of the fill lift are compacted and perhaps only the top 2 or 3 in. of soil is still loose. However, in all cases, there is some loose soil on top of each lift.

The ideal method of selecting equipment for a project is to set up a test strip on the site and experiment using various pieces of compaction equipment with various thicknesses of soil layers. Also, try other variations, such as two or three different moisture contents of the soil, so that if optimum is 14%, try 12, 14, and 16%.

23.8.7   Compaction Procedure

Probably the most important factor in compaction of fills is the moisture content of the soil. If the moisture content is at or near the optimum, compaction generally is relatively easy. If the range of moisture content is a few percentages above or below the desired moisture content, compaction still is possible, but more effort is required. When the moisture content is several percentages above or below optimum and is outside the "limiting percentages," compaction will be extremely difficult or perhaps not possible. The concept of limiting percentages of moisture content is shown on Fig. 23.2.

It may seem a waste of time and money to struggle to get the moisture content close to optimum. However, the greater the variance between field moisture and optimum, the greater the compactive effort needed. More passes with equipment also cost time and money, and increase the chances of fill lifts being rejected for inadequate compaction (see Fig. 23.5).

The lifts of fill should be uniform in thickness. The most efficient thickness for the type of compaction equipment being used can be determined by construction of a test fill strip. The most efficient fill thickness may vary from 2-in. lifts where tampers are used, to 6- to 8-in. lifts for sheepsfoot rollers, to 10- to 12-in. lifts for vibrating rollers on sandy soils, to 12- to 14-in. lifts for heavy compactors. Loose lifts 8 to 10 in. thick are fairly common, and compact down 2 or 3 in. to a compacted thickness of 6 to 8 in.

During compaction of fills, it is common practice for the owner to arrange for tests to be made of the completed layers of fill. Where these tests indicate that a layer is not satisfactory (has failed), the contractor should check on the details of the test results. If the moisture content of the soil is too high or too low, the poor results may be

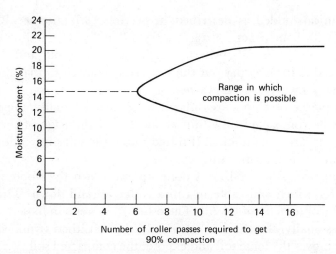

Fig. 23.5 Note that at 22% moisture content compaction to 90% is not possible no matter how many roller passes are made.

attributed to improper moisture content and indicate the corrections to be made. If the soil is at the optimum moisture content, it is possible that not enough passes have been made or that the wrong type of equipment is being used. If the test results are irregular, for no apparent reason, the soil being imported may not be uniform. The soil may change, requiring additional testing of the soil to reestablish a new compaction curve. It is to the contractor's best interests to understand the theory, and the test procedures involved in soil compaction. Test results can be used by the contractor to get the required compaction at minimum cost.

When compaction is difficult, and after many passes the fill still does not quite make 90%, the question is what to do. Frequently, contractors will try a bigger and heavier roller, which may help.

The optimum moisture changes for different rollers, depending on their weight and the energy that they put into the soil on each pass. Generally, for bigger rollers the optimum moisture is lower by perhaps 3%. Thus, if the fill is already on the dry side, a bigger roller will help. If the fill is wet, the bigger roller will not help. In fact, it is even worse. Instead, the smaller roller should be used and the lifts made thinner. If this does not help, then the soil should be dried out or chemicals added as described in Section 23.7 (also see Ref. 45, Chapter 9). Sometimes contractors try a "sandwich" method of constructing with wet soils. Alternating layers of wet soil, and dry soil, are placed. This may dry out the wet layers enough so that they will compact. However, success varies.

Fills placed on slopes are difficult to compact. Usually, the fill layers can be compacted to within about 2 ft of the edge of the slope. The outer 2 ft remain loose. If rolled upon, the soil pushes down the slope rather than compacting.

Frequently, slope rolling is done up and down the slope, using a bulldozer winch and cable to run a roller up and down. This compacts the outer 6 in. of the fill. The other 18 in. remain loose.

Occasionally, the slope is "overbuilt" by 2 ft, then trimmed back. This removes the loose soil and exposes the compacted soil.

23.9   *Filling over Soft Soil*

In many cases of land development, good quality fills are placed over swampy or marshy land. Starting the job can be very important. It is not possible to plunge out onto the soft mud and lay and compact conventional layers of fill soil. The mud may fail, creating mud waves and making the soil even softer.

In almost all cases, it is desirable to maintain the integrity of the underlying soil and take advantage of its limited strength. This may be done by pushing out a first layer which is relatively thick, perhaps 12 to 18 in. thick. This first layer should be pushed out with very small and light equipment. After the first layer is placed, it should be rolled with light equipment. The equipment suitable for such rolling can be determined by experimenting.

Succeeding lifts can be placed with larger equipment, and larger compaction equipment can be brought onto the succeeding lifts to obtain increasingly better compaction as thickness of fill builds up. This method of operation is shown on Fig. 23.6.

In many cases, fills are to be placed in marshy areas with heavy growth of marsh grass or other vegetation. It would be difficult to go into the marshy area with excavating equipment to strip out the grass and vegetation to reach clean soil on which to start the fill. One

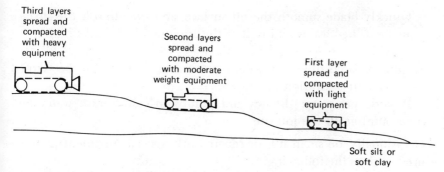

Third layers spread and compacted with heavy equipment

Second layers spread and compacted with moderate weight equipment

First layer spread and compacted with light equipment

Soft silt or soft clay

Fig. 23.6   Procedure for construction of compacted fill on bed of soft soil.

approach is to use light mowing equipment, or even hand labor, to cut off the vegetation close to the ground. Burning also may work in some cases. The remaining stubble provides some strength on which the first layer of fill can be placed. At first there might be some reluctance to leaving some organic material in place. However, a few inches of organic material may be much less compressible than two feet of soft soil churned up and diluted with water.

Another possible method of filling is called mud displacement. Frequently, if the mud is not too deep, the contractor elects to displace the mud. In this case fill is built up to a considerable height. Its weight causes the mud to flow outward. The fill settles down on the firmer soil under the mud. The mud wave must be kept moving; if it "freezes" it has to be dug out or sometimes is blasted to get it to start moving.

23.10   Protection from Weather

23.10.1   Rain

Rain is a problem to almost all compacted fill operations. If the soils used are silt or clay soils, or the work is being done in a cloudy damp season in which evaporation rates are slow, rain can cause delays and may become a disaster.

Some methods used to protect the surface of the fill include the following:

Quickly blade smooth the fill surface, and smooth-roll the surface to make it shed water and reduce the amount which soaks in.

Provide drainage to get the rain water off the compacted fill area as quickly as possible. Also, the borrow area may need to be "closed up" to avoid saturation of the soil.

Provide perimeter ditches and pumps to collect rain water and then pump it off the job site.

Occasionally, on small fills or repair work, special treatments may be used, such as the following:

Sheets of plastic such as polyvinyl-chloride can be bought in wide sheets from builders supply stores. These sheets can be held down by placing sandbags on them at regular intervals.

Sometimes lime is added to the soil and scarified and bladed in to absorb moisture and make the soil more workable. The amount needed varies with soil conditions, but an average is in the range of 4 to 6%.

23.10.2 Freezing

Clay and silt soils are difficult to compact in the winter when freezing occurs. These soils hold moisture, which freezes and becomes hard. This soil cannot compact when it is frozen hard. The next summer, however, when the soil thaws, the frozen layers will still be uncompacted and loose. This results in settlements and soft fills. When freezing occurs, the top layer of frozen soils should be stripped off the site each morning before new fill is placed.

As an alternate, it may be worthwhile to cover the fill area each night with a blanket of soil which would act as a protective surface. This soil would be bladed off the next morning and stockpiled for reuse again that night.

Soils can be compacted in air temperatures below 32 degrees provided the soil itself is not frozen. This requires good planning.

When fills are completed to desired rough grade, they should be covered by a protective layer of soil, or other material such as straw or hay, until other permanent construction can be started. Considerable research in winter construction has been performed by the U.S. Army Corps of Engineers and others (see Ref. 47).

23.10.3   Drying

In dry desert areas, the soils may dry out rapidly, creating a problem in maintaining the desired moisture content. Also, fills left overnight may dry up considerably on top and possibly cause surface shrinkage cracking. It may be necessary to install rain-birds or other sprinkling systems which can be operated by clock to keep the fill surface wet over weekends or to keep completed fills properly moistened prior to pouring of concrete floor slabs.

23.11   Boulders

On projects in which balanced cut and fill quantities have been developed, boulders may be a problem. Hauling the boulders off site is expensive, and it may be difficult to find a proper disposal area. Also, the loss must be made up by importing fill. Therefore, consideration must be given to using the boulders in the proposed fills.

The problems resulting from the use of boulders are as follows:

If the boulders are too close to the final grade, they may interfere with the proper performance of foundations if they are supported partly on soil and partly on boulders.

Boulders may interfere with later trenching for pipelines.

Boulders may interfere with proper compaction of soil, resulting in loose soils in boulder areas and possible future settlement.

It would be desirable to designate areas, such as parking areas, in which no structures would be built or pipelines constructed. Also, a review of grades might indicate areas of deeper fills, where it would be safe to dispose of boulders in the deep portion of the fills.

To compact fill soils around boulders, one method is to place the boulders in rows. Fills can be placed along each side of the row of boulders, with the lifts coming up evenly on both sides.

Some hand tamping work may be necessary in tight spots.

23.12   Inspection and Testing

23.12.1   The Inspector

Almost all compacted fills are inspected and tested during placement by a representative of the owner. The representative, or inspector, may be an employee of the owner or may be a soils engineer or a soils laboratory hired by the owner.

The contractor can obtain information from the soils inspector. When tests indicate the fill is not properly compacted, one should find out why. Is the moisture too far off? What percentage compaction actually was obtained?

In some cases the contract for earthwork requires that the grading contractor hire the soils laboratory for testing. Although the "accepted practice" in some areas, it is not a desirable arrangement, since the soils engineer should act as the representative of the owner. The soils engineer should not work for the person that he is inspecting and checking on.

On most compacted fill projects, the soils engineer will place a field laboratory on the site and have an inspector full-time on the job. On small jobs, the soils inspector may come to the site intermittently, as fill is being placed, and may operate with scales and equipment in the back of his truck. The purpose of inspection is to do the following:

1. Check the soil being used for fill.

2. Observe the compaction operations for complete coverage of each lift of fill.

3. Test the fill layers as they are completed. Notify the contractor whether the tests passed.

4. Review the problem with the contractor if any lifts fail. Indicate whether high moisture content, low moisture content, nonuniformity of compaction, or what other conditions cause the failure. This will permit the contractor to decide best how to correct the situation.

In most cases, a city, county, or federal agency is involved in overall building permit and plan checking, which requires that the soils engineer submit reports to the governmental agency regarding satisfactory completion of the fill.

Fill tests are made by several methods:

1. The sand replacement or "sand cone" test. In this test, a sample of completed fill is dug out. The volume of the resulting hole is measured, using calibrated sand. This test is described in more detail in Section 23.12.2.

2. A balloon testing device. A hole is dug into the fill. The volume of the hole is measured by the balloon apparatus.

3. Nuclear testing. Various nuclear radiation devices have been developed to measure the density of soil and the moisture content of the soil. The manufacturers of such equipment are listed in Ref. 48.

4. A test in the field laboratory of a core of the fill soil obtained by pushing or driving soil samplers into the ground.

5. A probe with a calibrated device, called a penetrometer. One type of penetrometer is the Dutch cone. Resistance to penetration is correlated with previous experience as a basis for estimating the soil compaction.

23.12.2   Sand Replacement Method

The sand replacement method is slow and tedious but is the most commonly used method. The steps in performing this test are as follows:

1. *Calibrating the sand:*   Dry sand of a known density is used to measure the volume of soil removed from the fill. The sand used is "Ottawa" sand or other sand of uniform grain size. When poured at a constant rate or flow from a constant height, the sand will deposit at a uniform density. The density of the sand is determined by carefully pouring it into a compaction cylinder, having a known volume. When the cylinder is full, it is struck off the level and weighed. The weight of the cylinder is then subtracted to obtain the weight of the sand. The weight of sand is divided by the volume of the cylinder to get the density of the sand. A common density for such calibrated sand is 90 lb/ft^3.

2. *Performing the test:*   At each location to be tested, the upper 3 to 6 in. of loose soil is removed. Frequently this is done with the

blade of a bulldozer. A level surface is made on the fill. A metal ring
is placed on the fill. A hole, usually about 5 to 6 in. in diameter, is
dug through the test ring and into the soil. The hole is dug to a depth
of about 5 to 6 in., which will provide approximately 5 to 10 lb of
soil. The soil removed is placed in a can with a tight lid to avoid loss
of moisture. Every crumb of soil is dug out and placed in the can.

The test hole is filled with the calibrated sand. The sand is taken
from a can or jar containing a specific weight of sand. Therefore, the
weight of sand used to fill the hole can be determined by weighing
the jar and remaining sand. During pouring of sand into the hole,
compaction equipment which might cause vibration of the ground
should not be operated close to the test.

3. *Calculating the test results:* The soil removed from the test
hole, and the remaining calibrated sand, are taken to the laboratory.
The soil removed from the hole is weighed. The calibrated sand is
weighed and subtracted from the original weight of sand to determine the amount used to fill the test hole.

The fill soil wet density is calculated as

$$\frac{\text{weight of sand}}{\text{weight of soil}} \times \text{calibrated density of the sand}$$

If the sand calibrated density is 90, then the formula becomes

$$\frac{\text{weight of soil}}{\text{weight of sand}} \times 90$$

This answer is in pounds per cubic foot. Typical soil wet density
values are 100 to 130 lb/ft^3.

    Example: Weight of soil = 10 lb
                Weight of sand used = 8 lb
                Calibrated density of sand = 90 lb/ft^3

Fill soil wet density:

$$\frac{10}{8} \times 90 = 112.5 \text{ lb/ft}^3$$

The dry density of the fill soil is determined by placing all, or a
portion of, the fill soil in an oven and measuring the loss of weight
when the soil is bone dry. In field laboratories, a small electric plate

or gasoline stove can be used with fairly accurate results. A few checks should be made with an oven drying at 105° C. The percentage moisture in the fill soil is calculated as follows:

Step 1: Weight of moisture lost during drying = wet weight of soil minus dry weight of soil.

Step 2: Percent moisture = (this answer is in percent)

$$\frac{\text{weight of moisture lost}}{\text{dry weight of soil}} \times 100$$

Example: Weight of soil = 10 lb
Dry weight of soil = 9 lb
Moisture lost = 1 lb

Percentage moisture:

$$\frac{1}{9} \times 100 = 11.1\%$$

The dry density of the fill soil is calculated as follows:

$$\text{dry density} = \frac{\text{wet density of soil}}{\text{percentage moisture} + 100}$$

Example:

$$\frac{112.5}{11.1\% + 100\%} = \frac{112.5}{1.111} = 101 \text{ lb/ft}^3$$

Testing of fill is not a very accurate procedure. Also, it is possible to sample at an "unrepresentative spot." Statistical methods sometimes are used on larger projects to make logical decisions from test results. On this basis, an occasional failing test can be accepted if the daily averages are consistently above the specified percentage compaction.

23.13 Summary

Primary points in this chapter are as follows:

FACTS: Engineers are tending more and more to consider soil to be a structural material. They write tougher specs and do more testing of compacted fill soils.

WATCH OUT FOR: Soil which is too wet or too dry. Designated borrow pits for which there is no drilling data to verify that the material specified is actually there. Rain is the worst enemy of a fill job.

24

Floor Slabs

24.1 Slabs on Grade

24.1.1 Subgrade

The floor slabs for many large industrial buildings, particularly where large areas are involved, are supported directly on the ground. In many parts of the country, residential housing, schools, and commercial structures also use floor slabs poured on grade.

For such buildings, the underlying soil becomes a structural part of the building. Detailed information regarding the quality of the subgrade soil is necessary.

The subgrade "structural soils" should be prepared properly. This may include removal of topsoil or unsatisfactory soils, and may include proof-rolling of the floor area, as described in Chapter 22, Section 22.1.

For floors that support heavy loads or are subjected to heavy traffic of fork-lift trucks, it is common to place a base course under the floor slab. The base course may consist of crushed rock, sand and gravel, cement stabilized sand, decomposed granite, or other suitable material, which, after compaction, experiences relatively small deflections under load.

24.1.2   Settlement

The columns and walls for such buildings are supported on independent foundations. These may be spread foundations carried down to firmer soils. However, in many cases the foundations are placed only 2 or 3 ft below the floor slab.

The columns may be loaded with 30 or 40 kips per column or to as much as 200 or 300 kips per column. During construction, these foundations will settle as the dead loads of the building are applied. In the case of reinforced concrete industrial structures, a large proportion of the total load may be dead load of the structure.

Usually, settlements of the floor slab are relatively small, compared to the foundation settlements. Therefore, the construction schedule should be such that the structure is essentially completed, and dead loads are on the building columns before pouring of the floor slab. In addition, frequently it is desirable to leave a separation between the floor slab and the columns. Therefore, future settlements can occur with the columns sliding through the holes in the floor slab.

If the floor is used to support heavy storage loads, particularly pallets stacked 15 or 20 ft high with canned goods, tin plate, or other extremely heavy materials, the floor slab loading can be several hundreds, or even thousands, of pounds per square foot. Usually, such storage is placed in islands, with aisles between. Therefore, the soils underlying the floor slab are subjected to heavy stresses. This may cause settlements, differential settlements between storage areas and aisles, and possibly a failure of the soil. Such floors may settle 6 in. or 1 ft.

In many parts of the country, floors for residences or one-story buildings may also serve as the foundations for the structures. In these cases, the floor usually is thickened, or is thickened under the perimeter and interior wall lines. Settlements usually are small because loads are small. The main requirement is that the subgrade soil be stable. Unstable soil may be:

Soft soil or mud.
Expansive soil, gumbo, or adobe.
Collapsing soil.

Loose fill or dumped debris.
Soil loosened by tree removal.

In *all* such cases, the soil must be compacted, "stabilized," or removed before construction. After construction, repairs are expensive and lead to many lawsuits.

In hot, dry weather, soil drying and cracking occurs in many floor excavations which are left open for a long period of time. Drying and cracking of the soil should be prevented. It will not result in settlement, but on the contrary, will cause the floor slab to be uplifted when the soil later regains its moisture. Uplifting may be uneven, causing cracks in the floor. Methods of protection are described in Chapter 11, Section 11.2.1.

24.1.3 Underground Utilities

When the grading contractor prepares the site and completes a fill for the building area which is composed of properly compacted materials, he leaves the site with a feeling of satisfaction of a job well done. However, as soon as the grading contractor leaves, a multitude of other subcontractors enter the site. They bring trenching machines and soon have the site torn up in a maze of trenches, crisscrossing over each other. Sewer lines, water lines, fire lines, gas lines, electrical conduits, steam lines, and a variety of other utilities are placed in the ground. Then these trenches are backfilled. It is this backfill which must support part of the floor slab.

Usually, the plumbing and other subcontracts are separate from the grading contract, and the requirements for compaction may not be similar. In some cases, utility backfills are considered a nuisance to the plumbing contractor, and the backfill reflects this lack of concern.

When the floor slab settles later and cracks, the original grading contractor may be called on to repair his "improper work." While it should be the responsibility of the architect or primary designer of the structure to make sure that utility backfills are as good as the original site grading, it is also to the best interest of the general contractor to make sure that this situation is properly considered.

24.1.4 Heavy Floor Loads

It is fairly common for floor loads to be in the range of 500 to 1000 lb/ft^2 and occasionally to amount to several thousand pounds per square foot. Floor settlements may amount to a few inches up to 6 in. to perhaps 1 ft.

Therefore, the design of the floor slab support becomes as important as the design of the foundations for the building itself. The future settlements of a floor slab can be estimated, using procedures described under Chapter 15, Section 15.2.

24.1.5 Moisture Barriers

Soils underlying floor slabs contain some moisture. The amount of moisture depends on the type of soil, depth to ground water level, site drainage, and rainfall. However, most soils contain at least 10 to 20% moisture. Even in desert areas, soils which appear to be bone dry contain 4 or 5% of water by weight. This represents some 2 or 3 quarts of water per cubic foot of the dry-appearing soil, or 1 or 2 gallons of water for more normal soil. This water may pass through the floor slab either as moisture or as vapor. On reaching the surface of the floor slab, it evaporates. If a fairly substantial amount of water flows up through the floor slab, it may leave behind white salts, commonly called efflorescence.

However, in office areas or in houses with slabs on grade, it is likely that the floors will be covered with tile surfaces, such as vinyl-asbestos tile or plastic tile. These tiles are fastened to the concrete with adhesives or mastic-type glues. Also, some concrete floor slabs are covered by rugs.

The moisture and water vapor moving upward through a concrete floor slab will collect under the asphalt or plastic tiles. (This can be observed whenever old slabs or pavements are removed. The soil underneath is wet.) Once sufficient water has collected, the tiles will loosen or "pop off." Moisture collecting under wool or fabric carpeting may cause the carpets to mildew.

Therefore, moisture barriers are commonly placed under floor slabs to stop the upward flow of moisture and water vapor.

It has been common practice to place a layer of free-draining sand or gravel immediately below the floor slab. This material would have no "capillary rise" and, therefore, would prevent moisture from reaching the bottom of the floor slab.

Studies have indicated that part of the moisture passing up through the floor slab is water vapor. The layer of granular soil or crushed rock apparently will not block the flow of water vapor.

Recently, development of plastic sheets of good quality, strength, and low cost has promoted the use of plastic membranes for moisture barriers. These membranes are placed below the floor slabs. In many cases, the membranes are covered with 2 or 3 in. of sand. The sand covering serves two purposes:

1. It provides protection to the plastic membrane when the wire fabric or reinforcing steel is placed for the slab, and during pouring of the concrete slab.

2. It can absorb excess water from the floor slab developed during curing. This solves the problem of curing of concrete poured on plastic membranes.

By contrast, some feel that the concrete slab *should* be poured directly on the plastic sheets. This avoids the sand "reservoir" below the floor slab. The concrete curing problem is handled by careful control of the concrete mix and curing.

24.1.6 Basement Floors

The ground water level may be very close to the elevation of the basement floor slab. During rainy seasons, the ground water may even rise above the level of the floor slab. Therefore, additional protection is needed.

Underdrains may be placed under the floor slab. Usually, they are perforated plastic pipes or porous concrete pipes, placed in a bed of properly graded sand and leading to a sump in the basement floor. As water flows through the pipes and into the sumps, it is pumped out periodically.

The basement floor slab and walls require waterproofing. The waterproofing usually consists of sheets of asphaltic felt mopped with asphalt or tar, underlying the floor slab.

Occasionally, relief holes or relief valves are placed in a slab if it is anticipated that the ground water level might suddenly rise and develop a hydrostatic uplift pressure on the bottom of the slab.

24.2   Slabs at Railroad Car Height

24.2.1   Subgrade

Many industrial buildings have the floor slab placed at truck-loading height or railroad car height, approximately 3 to 4 ft above outside grade. This requires placing of compacted fill in the building area for support of the floor slab. This fill generally is placed as one of the first operations in the construction sequence. After it is placed, the foundation excavations are dug and poured, and the walls are constructed.

24.2.2   Settlements

The weight of 4 ft of new fill, representing about 500 lb/ft², may cause some settlement to occur over the building area. As a general rule of thumb, settlements are in the range of ½ to 4 in. It is desirable for most of this settlement to occur *before* constructing the foundations and structure.

24.2.3   Retaining Walls

The bottom 4 ft of the perimeter walls must act as retaining walls.

To reduce lateral loads on the walls, it is desirable to tie the floor slab of the building to the perimeter walls. However, it should be remembered that the building foundations and walls will settle differently from the floor slab. Therefore, provisions may need to be built into the floor slab to permit settlement to occur. This might be done by running the reinforcing steel from the perimeter wall into the floor slab, but not pouring concrete in a 2-ft-wide strip around the edge of the floor slab. This 2-ft-wide strip of concrete could be poured later, after building settlements have occurred.

24.3   Slabs in Pile-Supported Structures

24.3.1   Requirements

In areas underlain by soft soils, pile foundations may be required to support the structure. The floor slab may be supported on grade, or on compacted fill. Seldom are such slabs supported on piles.

24.3.2   Grade Beams

It is common practice to place grade beams between pile caps where the soils are soft. The floor slab is above the grade beams.

The weight of the 4-ft-high fill, plus storage loads inside the structure, would cause settlement of the floor slab. However, where grade beams underlie the floor slab, settlement would be prevented. This may cause the floor gradually to take on the appearance of a washboard, with hills over each grade beam and valleys in between. The contractor should be aware that such problems could occur in the future (see Fig. 24.1).

Fig. 24.1   Large differential settlement.

24.3.3   Construction of Floor Slab

To resist lateral loads, it is common for the columns or pile caps to be tied to the floor slab. The floor slab has direct contact with a large area of soil, and therefore provides lateral restraint to the pile caps. This lateral resistance is needed to resist lateral loads due to wind or seismic forces and also to take care of pile eccentricity, particularly in one and two pile groups.

It is common for sliding resistance between the floor slab and soil to be designed for values of 25 to 50 lb/ft^2. These slabs require substantial reinforcing where they are carried into the columns.

24.3.4   Outside Pavements and Underground Utilities

In areas of soft soils, buildings generally are supported on piles. The settlements usually are small. However, the area outside the building may settle, since it is underlain by soft soils. This places the building in the position of "rising out of the ground." Utility lines outside of the buildings will be pulled down, but where they pass through the building walls will be held in position, requiring frequent maintenance. A better solution is to provide adequate flexibility in the transition of utility lines from the building to the outside.

Also, pavements outside of the building will gradually settle. The design must be such that this can be accommodated. It may be preferable for sidewalks, loading areas, and other concrete slabs attached to the outside of the building also to be pile supported.

24.4   Buildings over Old Dumps

Dumps have been created in many areas later proposed for use for industrial or commercial buildings. The floor slabs for such buildings can be expected to experience appreciable settlements, on the order of 1 ft or more. The settlements may be due to the weight of fill brought in to grade the surface of the site and also due to slow decomposition of organic materials in the fill.

In addition to causing settlement, the decomposition of organic materials will liberate gas. This gas would tend normally to accumulate under the floor slab of the building and under pavements outside the building. Therefore, a system should be incorporated in the design to collect the gas, and safely vent it to the atmosphere. Such gas (methane) can be dangerous if it is breathed by workmen. Also, it is explosive.

24.5 Summary

Primary points in this chapter are as follows:

FACTS: Floor slabs frequently settle, and the design and construction must permit the settlement to occur without too much damage. Utility line backfills may be loose, and fail to provide support for floor slabs. Moisture barriers are usually necessary under slabs, if tile or carpet will be placed on the slabs.

WATCH OUT FOR: Placing floor slabs directly on top of grade beams.

25

Landslides

25.1 Types

Landslides occur in slopes composed of all kinds of soil, fills, rock, and mixtures of soil and rock. They may be caused by the following:

Bedding planes.
Planes of weakness in rock or soil.
Undercutting a slope.
Saturation of the ground by rain or water leaks.
Construction of a slope at too steep an angle.
Overloading the top of a slope.
Earthquakes.
Accumulation of rock debris or talus.

Slides may occur as wedges, circular masses of soil, surface flow or mud flows, or downhill creep of wet soil.

25.1.1 Bedding Plane Slides

Many areas are underlain by sedimentary rocks with well-defined bedding planes. This sedimentary material may be tilted. In many areas, tilting of 20 to 40 degrees is common.

An illustration of tilted bedding planes is shown in Fig. 25.1 (also

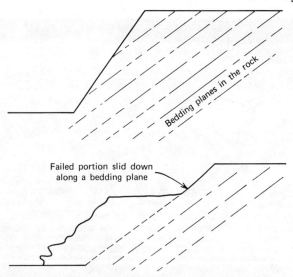

Fig. 25.1 Rockslide along tilted bedding planes.

see Fig. 11.4). Also shown in Fig. 25.1 is a typical landslide along bedding planes.

25.1.2 Fractures and Faults

Many bedrock formations contain fractures or old faults. Faults generally indicate displacement or prior movement, frequently with altered material in the fault zone. A photograph of a fault zone is shown in Fig. 25.2.

Fractures and faults represent weak planes within the rock. Excavation into rocks containing fractures or faults may encounter such a weak plane. If this weakened plane is tilted, the rock sitting above the plane may slide out. Frequently, such slides may occur as pop-outs, or blocks falling out of a slope.

25.1.3 Sand Slides

Sand soil will stand on a slope frequently referred to as the angle of repose. This angle is nearly the same as the angle of internal friction of loose sand determined by laboratory tests (see Fig. 8.5).

Fig. 25.2 Photograph of fault zone.

If an excavation is made into clean sand, the walls of the excavation will slough down to the angle of repose. If the sand contains moisture, it may temporarily stand at a steeper angle, rather than slough down at the angle of repose. Small amounts of clay or silt in the sand also may give it greater strength so that the sand can stand at a steeper angle.

Frequently, excavations can be made in clean sand, which is temporarily held together by moisture. In such cases, it is common to attempt to hold the moisture in the sand so that the temporary strength can be retained. This sometimes is done by covering the slope with plastic or other membrane, spraying the slope with sodium silicate or other chemicals, or by frequently moistening the slope.

25.1.4 Clay Slides

Slides in clay soils generally are characterized by a circular or rotational movement of a large block of material. Such a slide is illustrated in Fig. 25.3. Such slides may be small, or in some cases have involved many acres of land (see Ref. 49).

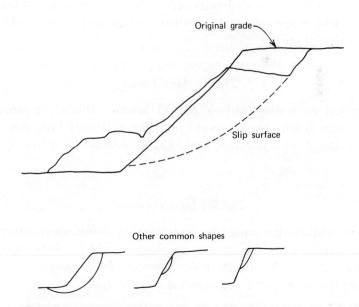

Fig. 25.3 Landslide in clay soil.

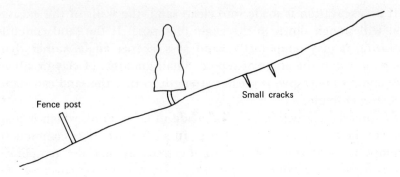

Fig. 25.4   Creep of soil down a hillside.

25.1.5   Creep

The soil on hillsides may be stable during dry weather, but may experience small movements each winter or during heavy rainy seasons. When the soil becomes wet, the soil particles are lubricated. Also, there is a loss of strength. However, a landslide-type failure does not occur. Instead, the soils gradually inch their way down the hillside.

Creep frequently is demonstrated by leaning fence posts, leaning trees, cracks in the soil, and by other signs. Some evidences of creep are illustrated on Fig. 25.4.

25.1.6   Mud Flows

If the soil on a steep hillside should become sufficiently saturated with water, it may tend to move downhill relatively fast, as a fluid. A photograph of a mudflow engulfing a residence is shown in Fig. 25.5.

25.1.7   Undercutting

Many landslides are caused by undercutting slopes which otherwise would remain stable. This may be done to widen roadways, or to extend backyards of houses, or for basement excavations.

Usually city building departments require that undercut slopes be supported by retaining walls or other structures. Temporary undercuts are made frequently to get in footings or other permanent struc-

Fig. 25.5   Mudflow engulfing a residence.

tures. This work should be done in the dry season if possible. Cuts should be opened up in short lengths, or windows, and should be backfilled before adjacent windows are cut. If the factor of safety of the slope is reasonable for a permanent slope, there should be no difficulty in figuring a reasonable length of window to be cut temporarily for construction. These calculations should be done by the soils engineer.

25.2 Investigation

The size of a potential slide can be estimated to a moderate accuracy. Figure 25.6 shows potential slide surfaces for sand soils and also for

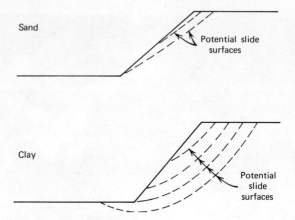

Fig. 25.6   Typical sliding surfaces for sand and clay slopes.

clay soils. Since sliding could occur on any one of several potential slide surfaces, it is necessary to calculate each one.

For each assumed sliding surface, a calculation can be made of the force tending to cause sliding. Also, the strength of the soil is figured, based on laboratory tests of soil samples.

Failure of the soil will occur if the sliding force is greater than the strength of the soil. The resisting strength of the soil compared to the sliding force results in a number called the *factor of safety*. Factor of safety equals resisting strength divided by sliding force. For instance, a factor of safety of 1.0 indicates that the slope is barely stable. Any small change could result in sliding. Such a small change, which causes sliding, is called "triggering" the slide. If the factor of safety is 2.0, the resisting strength is twice as much as the force trying to cause failure. It is common for permanent slopes to be cut at such an angle that the factor of safety is 1.5.

Before a large cut is made into the soil, it is common to estimate the factor of safety for various proposed angles of excavation. Typical slope angles for various types of soils, and various slope heights, are shown in Section 22.4. These are for permanent slopes. Temporary slopes can be cut steeper (see Chapter 11, Section 11.1.1).

A method of calculation of the stability of a slope uses a method called the "Swedish circle" or method of slices. Such a calculation is shown in Fig. 25.7 (also see Ref. 52). There are other methods of

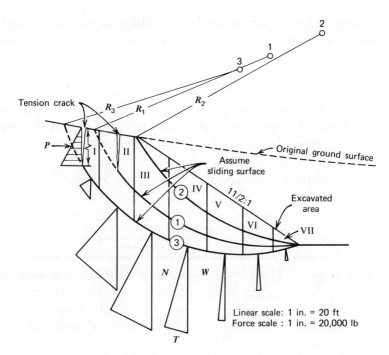

Fig. 25.7 Calculations for slope stability.

CIRCLE 3

Segment No.	W	N	T
I	6,100	3,600	+4,900
II	22,400	17,000	+14,400
III	26,500	23,500	+12,600
IV	23,600	22,800	+6,500
V	17,900	17,900	+1,500
VI	10,000	10,000	−1,100
VII	1,500	1,500	−400
Total		96,500	38,400

$$\text{F.S.} = \frac{\Sigma\,N\,\text{Ton}\,\phi + CL}{\Sigma\,T + ZP}$$

$$\text{F.S.} = \frac{96,500 \times .268 + 400 \times 68}{38,400 + (0.47 \times 3800)} = 1.3$$

calculating and short-cut methods for estimating safe slope angles. Many engineering offices have programs set up in their computers for performing these calculations.

Sometimes loads will be placed at the top of excavations or slopes. These loads may be excavated soil, other material or equipment, or traffic load. It is common to convert these loads into equivalent heights of soil. A slope 20 ft high might be calculated as though it is 26 ft high, or some such number. Then the calculation becomes the same as for any other stability analysis, except that the top load does not have any internal strength (see Chapter 11, Section 11.1.5).

25.2.1   Other Factors

A number of additional factors must be considered. Of primary importance is water. Many slopes are stable until the first sustained rainy season. During wet winter seasons, many cities experience a multitude of landslides. In the winter of 1962, the City of Los Angeles experienced approximately 1700 landslides or mudflows which damaged residential properties. The average cost of damage to each house was $3500.

Measurement wells (also called piezometers) consisting of perforated pipes placed in holes in the ground can be used to observe the water level in a slope. If the water level builds up in the slope, the soil must act as a dam to hold back this hydrostatic pressure. In addition, the water tends to lubricate the soil and also to soften it. These factors act together to encourage a landslide (see Section 25.3.4).

25.2.2   Soil Layers

Usually soils are not a simple uniform homogeneous mass throughout the height of a proposed excavation. Instead, they occur in layers. Layers can complicate the investigation of stability of a proposed excavated slope.

Each layer has its own individual strength. Softer layers are a likely zone for a slip plane. In addition, various soils develop their maximum strength at different amounts of deflection. Therefore, a brittle soil combined with a soft soil would not mobilize the total shearing resistance of both soils. The soft soil would develop only part of its strength at the time the brittle soil had reached full stress. The brittle soil would break and lose most of its strength before the soft soil would develop its full resisting strength.

25.3   Stabilizing of Potential Landslides

25.3.1   Buttresses

Slopes that are potentially hazardous can be stabilized. Some methods include the following:

Compacted buttress fills.
Cribs, consisting of structural frameworks, filled with soil or rock.
Structural walls.
Structural frames.

Each of the methods of buttressing above are illustrated in Fig. 25.8. Usually this work is done in the dry season when the slope is less hazardous.

25.3.2   Removal

Frequently, it is possible to remove an area of potential sliding. This may involve a major change in the site grading plan. As an alternate, the slope area can be dug out, and then reconstructed of compacted fill.

25.3.3   Burial

Occasionally, it is possible to bury a potential landslide. This can be done in special circumstances, such as a steep slope on one side of a gully. By placing a storm drain in the gully, it can be backfilled. The backfill then serves as a buttress to both sides of the gully.

In occasional circumstances, a landslide can be buried by placing a mass of soil on the toe of the slide. This new compacted fill over the lower portion of the unstable slope increases resistance to sliding.

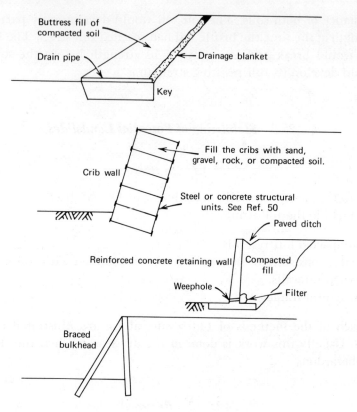

Fig. 25.8 Methods for retaining banks and slopes.

25.3.4 Drains

Water is the enemy of slopes. Therefore, good drainage is essential for any earth or rock slope. Good drainage includes top drainage. Water should be intercepted at the top. The water should be drained back from the slope or around the slope.

An appreciable amount of water can accumulate on the slopes. Therefore, interceptor drains or slope drains should be placed at various intervals of the face of a slope. Such drains are illustrated on Fig. 25.9. The drains can be constructed of asphalt, concrete, or other stable surface. They need to be cleaned out after each heavy rain, and before the start of each rainy season.

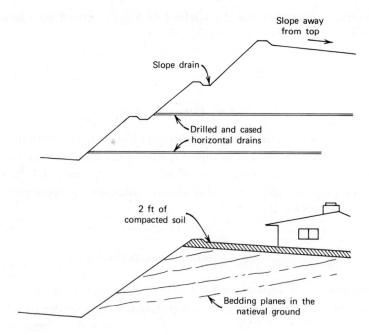

Fig. 25.9   Slope drainage methods.

Interior drains may be required to prevent the buildup of water within soil mass. If the slope has been constructed, drainage devices can be built into the slope. However, if a cut slope must be drained, or other existing slope, drains must be inserted into the slope. One method commonly used is to drill horizontal holes back into the slope and to case the holes with perforated pipe. Such an installation is shown on Fig. 25.9. Usually, such holes are 3 to 6 in. in diameter, and are lined with plastic or metal pipe. Such horizontal drains usually slope upward approximately 5 degrees to flow freely. Such drains frequently are installed to depths of 100 to as much as 300 ft back into the slope. The drains are spaced horizontally at intervals on the order of 25 to 50 ft, center to center. Grading to provide a flat surface may have sliced off topsoil and exposed inclined bedding planes in a rock formation. If these bedding planes are tilted, water may get in from sprinkling or from rainfall. In such cases, it is desirable to cover the bedrock. A layer of compacted soil can act as such a cover (see Fig. 25.9).

Erosion protection for the surface of slopes should be placed as early as possible during construction.

Finally, avoid cess pools, leaching fields, or other sources of water on all sloping or hillside sites.

25.3.5   Other Methods

Other methods of correction may include lowering the height of the slope or flattening the slope angle by giving up some flat land at the top of the level area. Also, some small slides have been stabilized by pins through the slide zone and also by injection of chemicals into the slide zone (see Ref. 51).

25.4   Active Landslides

Frequently, it is important to develop temporary protection when some signs of sliding start to develop. Usually, this occurs in a heavy rain. Large sheets of PVC can be used to cover a slope temporarily. Sandbags can be placed on the PVC to keep it from blowing away. Number 2 reinforcing bars 3 ft long can be stabbed through the sandbags, PVC, and into the ground to help hold the PVC.

Water running over the top of a slope should be diverted away with temporary curbs of sandbags.

Any cracks or fissures developing in the ground should be filled with silty or clay soil or covered over with PVC or asphalt.

After the rains stop, the conditions should be investigated by a soils engineer. His work may include borings, laboratory tests, and calculations. Also, he may set special casings in the borings to find the slip surface, if slippage is occurring (see Ref. 18, p. 1042, and Fig. 10.7).

25.5   Summary

Primary points in this chapter are as follows:

> FACTS: Landslides can result from many inconspicuous actions of man.Frequently, a slope may be barely

stable. A small act is enough change to "trigger" a slide.

WATCH OUT FOR: Water draining out of slopes; cess pools at the top of a slope; leaking swimming pool at the top of a slope; breaks in utility lines for no apparent reason. Cracks or fractures in the soil; separation of curbs, sidewalks, walls, indicating stretching.

26

Retaining Structures

26.1 Types

Retaining structures may come in many sizes and styles, according to the ingenuity of man. Some retaining structures are well-designed and are functional. Others may have the appearance of strength but may be more a showpiece. Retaining structures may also be used in combinations.

Some common types are as follows:

Vertical concrete cantilever walls.
Vertical concrete buttress walls.
Soldier piles with lagging, and frames of vertical and battered piles.
Soldier piles, free-standing.
Soldier piles with tie-backs or sheet piles with tie-backs.
Rock gravity walls.
Buttresses of compacted soil.
Bin-type wall.

The various types of walls described above are illustrated in Fig. 26.1 (also see Chapter 12).

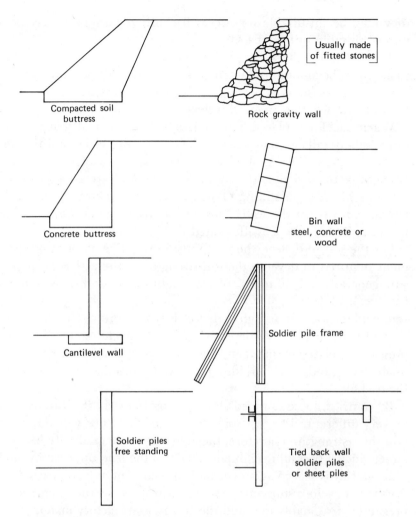

Compacted soil
buttress

Usually made
of fitted stones

Rock gravity wall

Concrete buttress

Bin wall
steel, concrete or
wood

Cantilevel wall

Soldier pile frame

Soldier piles
free standing

Tied back wall
soldier piles
or sheet piles

Fig. 26.1   Examples of retaining structures.

26.2   *Retaining Structures*

Retaining structures usually are constructed first, and the backfill is placed between the wall and the excavated slope.

The backfill soil should be selected from the available on-site materials. If the on-site materials are wet soils or expansive clays, they may be unsuitable for use as backfill; it may be necessary to import suitable soil for backfill.

The backfill soil will impose a lateral pressure on the retaining structure. The amount of lateral earth pressure will depend on many factors, such as the type of soil, the degree of compaction, dry or wet backfill, and whether the wall is flexible or rigidly braced.

When backfill is placed behind a wall, it is assumed that the wall can bend laterally a small amount. The block of soil behind the wall starts to deflect. This mobilizes the shear strength of the soil. The strength of the soil plus the strength of the wall are enough to prevent the block from sliding. This soil strength thereby reduces the lateral pressure on the wall. This frequently is called the active soil pressure. This concept is illustrated in Fig. 26.2.

For the soil to deflect, the wall must move. The amount of movement required to develop the soil strength for the active earth pressure generally is 1/10 to 1% of the height of the wall. It is common for a wall of 10 ft high to deflect ½ in. or more at the top of the wall, and for walls 20 ft high to deflect 1 in. or more.

Sand generally is considered to be good backfill soil. The active pressure is relatively small, and the required deflection of the wall is small. Also, sand drains rapidly if rain water or other water gets into the backfill.

By contrast, loose dumped clay soils, particularly if saturated, can be very different. The wet soils creep, and therefore will not maintain their strength. Therefore, the active pressure gradually becomes larger. Such a backfill may impose 300% of the load imposed by sand.

If the clay is placed at proper moisture content as a compacted fill, it usually develops substantial strength. In this case, the lateral active pressure is reasonably low, and the clay is a satisfactory material.

Some clay soils are expansive. They swell when they become saturated. Such soils would be extremely undesirable for backfill, since they would swell when they get wet and impose very large lateral pressures on the wall.

Occasionally, an excavation can be cut neat to the outside wall dimensions. In this case, a form can be placed for the inside of the wall and the concrete can be poured directly against the soil. Since no backfill is placed, the lateral pressure on the wall theoretically is zero. In such cases, it is general practice to design for a lateral earth

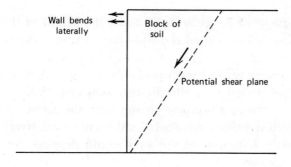

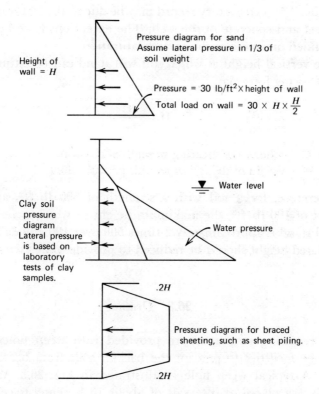

Wall bends laterally

Block of soil

Potential shear plane

Height of wall = H

Pressure diagram for sand
Assume lateral pressure in 1/3 of soil weight

Pressure = 30 lb/ft² × height of wall

Total load on wall = $30 \times H \times \dfrac{H}{2}$

Water level

Clay soil pressure diagram
Lateral pressure is based on laboratory tests of clay samples.

Water pressure

.2H

Pressure diagram for braced sheeting, such as sheet piling.

.2H

Fig. 26.2 Active soil pressure on retaining structures.

pressure in the range of 25 to 30 lb/ft² times the height of the wall. This number is sometimes called the equivalent "fluid pressure"; the pressure would be the same as for a fluid weighing 30 lb/ft³.

The lateral pressure behind walls probably is larger than generally is assumed in the design of walls. In compacting backfills behind walls, the soil must be at a pressure greater than the active pressure. However, it is believed that a compacted soil becomes relatively rigid. Therefore, a small deflection of the wall would develop the active pressure within the soil.

Also, it has generally been found that walls designed and constructed for lateral pressures of 30 to 35 lb/ft² have performed satisfactorily. This satisfactory record may be due to the factor of safety in the steel and concrete of the wall. The exceptions have been due to unplanned pressures, such as water saturation.

The vertical height at which soil will stand can be estimated from the following formula:

$$H = \frac{2C}{W}$$

where $C =$ cohesion or shearing strength of clay soils.
$W =$ weight of the soil in pounds per cubic foot.

Therefore, for a soil with a strength of 500 lb/ft², and with a weight of 100 lb/ft³, the maximum height to which a vertical bank would stand is approximately 2 times 500 over 100 equals 10 ft. This calculated height should be reduced to provide some factor of safety.

26.3   Drainage

Most retaining structures are provided with weep holes or other drainage facilities to prevent the backfill soils from becoming saturated. A typical weep hole is illustrated in Fig. 26.3. Weep holes usually are placed at intervals of about 10 ft center-to-center along walls. Weep holes are a nuisance to build, and contractors have trouble doing them right. If the gravel is coarse, the soil backfill works into the gravel and clogs it up. This requires that a graded filter be

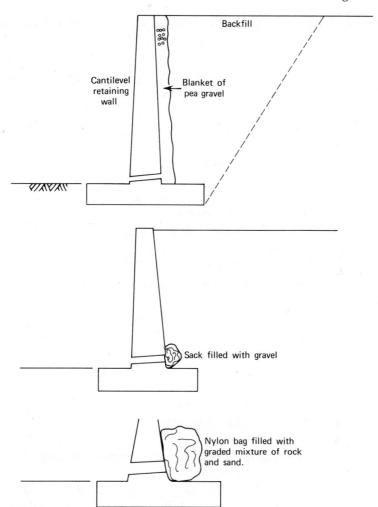

Fig. 26.3 Retaining wall drainage systems.

used between the soil and the weep hole. Certain commercially available mixtures of sand and rock are better for this use. The sand keeps soil from clogging the gravel. Just at the back end of the weep hole, the sand will wash out, but will leave the gravel.

Where lawn watering, heavy rains, or other large sources of water drain into the backfill behind a retaining wall, it is necessary to beef up the weep hole and drainage design. Of most importance is to run a gravel blanket up the full height of the wall (see Fig. 26.3). In addition, continued saturation of the fill will cause greater lateral pressures on the wall. Also, continued saturation of the soils supporting the foundation of the wall may weaken the foundation soils, resulting in greater tilting of the wall.

26.4   Attachment to Other Structures

Retaining walls must be expected to move or tilt slightly during construction and also after construction.

If such structures are doweled or otherwise fastened to buildings, the lateral deflections will cause cracking at the intersection of the wall with the adjacent building.

At right angle external corners of walls, vertical cracks occur frequently.

Retaining walls should be designed so that they can tilt slightly; $\frac{1}{4}$ to $\frac{1}{2}$ in. is common. Joints may be cut in the wall to permit this flexibility. The joints may be filled with joint compound and can be backed up with metal or permanent flashing-type material.

26.5   Foundations

The foundations of cantilever walls will have two primary forces— overturning and sliding as shown in Fig. 26.4.

Overturning will cause pressures at one edge of the footing to be much larger. This edge pressure cannot exceed the soil bearing value. Sometimes the bearing pressure is assumed to act over only a part of the footing area, as shown in *b*. The back part of the footing is considered to be not acting.

Sliding or skidding of the footing is resisted by"passive resistance" in front of the footing. Typical values for passive resistance are in the range of 200 to 500 lb/ft^2 times depth in feet. In addition, there is sliding resistance on the bottom of the footing. This resistance usually is in the range of 100 to 500 lb/ft^2.

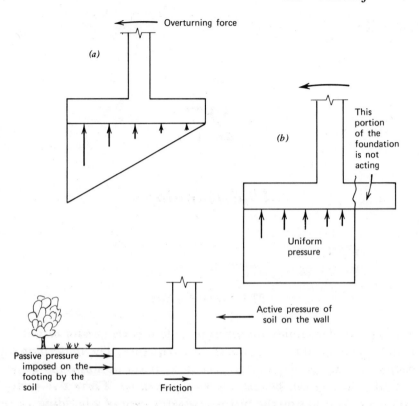

Fig. 26.4   Pressure distribution on retaining wall footings.

26.6   Summary

Primary points in this chapter are as follows:

FACTS: The kind of soil used for backfill behind a retaining wall has much to do with the pressure on the wall. Retaining walls move or bend outward when the backfill is placed behind them. Weep holes and drainage of the backfill are important.

WATCH OUT FOR: Using different backfill from that planned for. Future saturation of the backfill behind the wall. The wrong kind of "gravel" behind weep holes.

27

Underpinning

27.1 Introduction

The term underpinning means to provide new temporary or permanent support for the vertical loads of a structure. The underpinning device may also be required to provide restraint of horizontal forces.

Underpinning can be corrective or preventive. Corrective underpinning is used to stop the progressive settlement of a building, or of a few columns causing differential settlement within a building. Where settlements take place at an accelerating rate, emergency measures may be called for. In such cases, temporary relief of the loads on columns and walls may be provided by transferring the loads to improvised foundations to avert disaster.

Common devices include "needle beams" to pick up column loads (see Fig. 27.2). By these means time is made available to determine the cause of the settlement and plan corrective measures. In other cases, the rate of settlement may be so slow or so uniform throughout the structure that settlement can be tolerated for extended periods of time. An extreme example may be cited of a building constructed in 1917 which, by 1942, had developed differential settlements between the interior columns and the walls of about 20 in. The columns were then underpinned to prevent further settlement.

Corrective underpinning is largely an art calling for judgment and broad experience. By its nature it should never be part of a subsurface construction contract. Only foundation engineers and specialty contractors with experience in this field should be entrusted with such work.

Preventive underpinning is designed to protect existing structures from damage from the construction of adjacent structures or from modifications therein. Such work is frequently a part of the subsurface construction included in the general construction contract. Obviously, where the excavation for a new structure is to be carried below an adjacent building, subway, or structure, settlement of the existing structure must be prevented. While underpinning is employed frequently to solve such problems, it is by no means the only solution. Site and soil conditions, and the weight and value of the adjacent structures need to be analyzed to determine the most economical and adequate procedure. There have been times when the best plan was to buy the adjacent building and demolish it.

27.2 Obligations Imposed by the Contract Documents

Generally the contractor accepts responsibility for design of underpinning, including method of installation, coordination with other work, satisfactory performance, and consequential damage. The actual design and preparation of underpinning plans are done by registered engineers employed by, or retained by, the contractor.

Specifications and plans sometimes outline some form of underpinning. Usually, however, this is only schematic, and the contractor is required to prepare plans and to outline methods of installation. These must be submitted for review and approval. Such approval does not relieve the contractor of the responsibility for the adequacy of the design nor the performance of the work.

With respect to insurance for property damage, contracts usually stipulate the minimum coverage. It is up to the contractor to evaluate the real risk and to cover himself. Adequate coverage may need to be much greater than the contract minimum requirements.

The contractor may subcontract the underpinning work to a specialist in this work. In this case, the subcontractor for underpinning work assumes the responsibilities of the general contractor.

This includes having the underpinning design performed by registered engineers.

The engineering phase includes (a) review of the soil and water conditions, (b) study of the local building code, (c) surveys and weight calculations of the building to be underpinned, and sometimes (d) excavations of test pits to verify the "as built" depth and dimensions of the foundations. Cracks or signs of structural strain not only in the building to be underpinned but also in all structures close enough to be affected by the operations should be measured and recorded by dated, certified photographs filed with the general contractor. A series of periodic level readings should be made on all structures. The survey should be tied to two reference points located outside of the influence of subsurface construction (see Ref. 52).

27.3   Continuous Pit Underpinning

The most commonly employed form of underpinning consists simply of extending the footing carrying the wall of a building vertically with a continuous concrete footing to an elevation just below the level of the basement excavation of the new building. To accomplish the purpose, sheeted pits are excavated to the desired level, filled with concrete to within about 2 in. of the underside of the existing footing. When the concrete has set, very dry grout is rammed into the 2-in. space. This "dry pack" procedure causes a prestress, or transfer, of the load onto the new concrete piers. The pit is then backfilled. Several pits may be sunk at a time so long as no two pits are adjacent to one another. Usually, no more than one-third of the wall is unsupported at any one time. Underpinning of this type is shown in Fig. 27.1. Certain conditions are required for such underpinning to be feasible. The soil on which the underpinning bears must be as good or better than the soil under the existing wall footing. The ground water level must be below the bottom of the pits, or it must be drawn down by a reliable dewatering system. The existing wall footing should have enough strength as a beam to span a pit opening of at least 3 ft, 6 in. Where the mortar used to bond stone rubble footings has disintegrated, steel plates or channels have to be grouted against the underside to support the wall over pit openings.

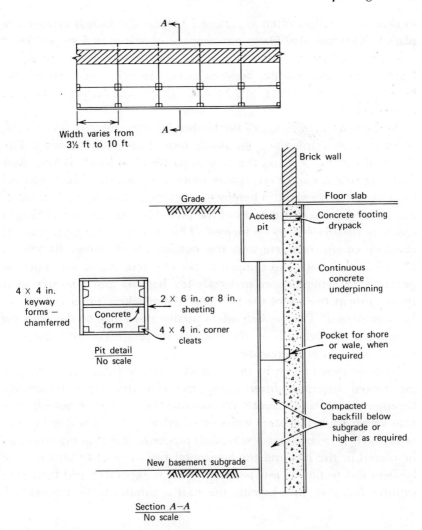

Fig. 27.1   Continuous pit underpinning.

The width of pits varies from 3 ft, 6 in. to 10 ft, depending on the stability of the soil. A man cannot dig and place timber in any space smaller than 4 ft, 6 in. by 3 ft, 6 in. The deflection of 2-in. sheeting can become excessive in deep pits over 5 ft wide. Deflection of the sheeting permits soil to move outward resulting in settlement of the floor slab of the building. Loss of ground must be prevented, otherwise the floor or wall will settle. In loose, granular soils that tend to cave or run, hay often is rammed behind the boards as they are placed. The hay also filters any seepage of water and stops loss of soil. The load per running foot on the wall footing has to be calculated so that the spacing between open pits will not increase the bearing pressure between pits by more than some factor, usually no more than 50%.

As the work progresses, all the timber between the pits is removed, leaving the sheeting along the inside face of the underpinning. The eventual rotting of wood sheeting must be considered. Where floor loads are substantial or create vibrations, the resulting loss of ground might cause settlement. Therefore, concrete panels or steel channels can be used to sheet the backs of the pits. The outside face of the pit concrete usually has to be formed. This results in a space between the face of the concrete and the outside pit sheeting. Backfill is placed in the space and tamped as the concrete is poured. The importance of using proper materials for backfill and compacting it thoroughly at the toe of the wall and higher where necessary cannot be overstressed. The backfill offers passive resistance to the outward movement of the wall as the excavation progresses and the wall comes under lateral pressure.

Keyways may be cast in the sides of alternate pits so that the pits are locked together. Interlocking the pits also prevents seepage through the wall. Horizontal recesses may be cast in the outside face into which timber or steel wales or rakers may be set where bracing of the wall is necessary as excavation proceeds. Reinforcing steel can be placed in the pits and the horizontal ties so placed that they can be bent out to tie the pits together. This is expensive and time consuming, however, and bracing the wall is usually more economical.

27.4   Column Underpinning

Columns supported on individual spread footings often are underpinned by installing two or more concrete piers under the footing by the same methods as pit underpinning. It usually is necessary to relieve the footing of most of the column load. Otherwise, during the excavation of a pit the loading increase may be too great and also may become eccentric. To unload the footing, shores can be

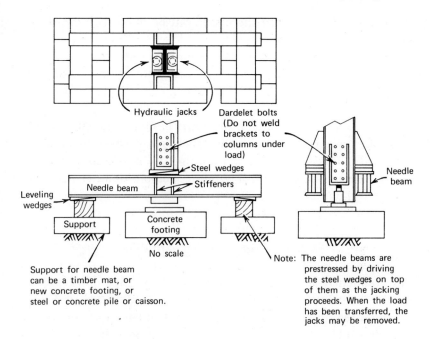

Fig. 27.2   Needle beams for temporary column support (see Chapter 27).

placed and wedged against the column at the ceiling where beams intersect the column, or horizontal "needle" beams may be placed on each side of the column. The beams are supported on temporary footings and the load transferred to the needles by jacking or wedging against brackets fastened to the column (see Fig. 27.2).

27.5   Pier and Lintel Underpinning

In this type of underpinning, separate independent pits are excavated to the new bearing stratum. Steel or concrete beams are placed under the wall to span between the pits. The spacing of the pits depends on the maximum length of opening under the wall which is safe to open up for placing the lintel beam. Also, the soil must have adequate capacity to carry the new piers. While steel lintels are more convenient to install than reinforced concrete beams, the problem of encasing them in concrete is difficult. The space between the flanges and the web in the inside can be filled with grout under low pressure.

As excavation for the new basement proceeds, the soil between the piers is sheeted where necessary with horizontal lagging. The piers also must be restrained with rakers, or cross beams or tie-back anchors.

In sandy soils, the ground water must be drawn down completely below the lowest level, otherwise such pit excavation cannot be made without loss of ground. Pumping from within the pit will increase the loss of ground. Therefore, remote dewatering, such as wells or well points, is necessary.

27.6   Underpinning with Piles

Piles frequently are used for underpinning. Pipe piles are most generally used, although H-beam piles can be also used under some circumstances. Piles may be driven closed-end in short or long sections, depending on the head room, or they may be jacked down, usually open-end, using the weight of the existing structure as the reaction. Physical limitations influence the decision as to type and loading of underpinning piles as well as the soil conditions. For example, where a lightly loaded wall has to be underpinned because of adjacent excavation, pipe piles in short sections may be driven from the bottom of continuous underpinning pits to furnish a staggered line of pile supports designed for 25 to 30 tons, depending on the size hammer which can be slung in the pits. On the other hand, if the wall is heavily loaded, it might be more economical to jack 12- or 14-in. pipe piles open-end to a bearing of possibly 80T or higher, depending on the reaction of the wall which can be mobilized. When open-end piles are used, they are cleaned out with a small orange-peel-type bucket and concreted. Where efforts to clean out the pile to the bottom cause loss of ground, it is better to leave the lower part unexcavated.

Where H-beams can be jacked to the same stratum and for the same loadings as pipes, they will compete with open-end piles in spite of the high cost of welded splices. Corrosion is a consideration.

The walls of a structure at right angles to the one to be underpinned are always underpinned for a short distance along each wall. Where soil conditions dictate the use of piles for the underpinning, the short return wall sections often can be picked up by driving pipe piles or H-beams in pairs, inside and outside, and by placing needle beams under the wall footing. The needles can be prestressed by using jacks or by driving steel wedges.

There are several ways to rig a pile hammer to drive under a wall. A head frame can be erected in the pit from which a hammer may be hung. The hammer is operated with a hoist outside on the ground surface. Where there is enough space on the ground surface for a crane driver to operate, the driver may be rigged as follows: A set of long extensions is inserted in the leaders and fitted with sheaves so that the hammer line can raise and lower the extensions. The hammer is attached to a bracket which is bolted to the lower end and in front of the extensions so that the center of the hammer is about 24 in. out from the center of the extensions. Rigged this way, the hammer can be lowered into the access pit and then moved forward by the crane to the location of the pile under the wall. No head room is lost other than the hammer length. Hammers used for such work are usually double-acting of the McKiernan-Terry type, either 7B or 9B3. It is advisable to operate the hammer with compressed air.

When piles are to be jacked down, reacting against the wall footing, a thick steel plate is grouted and supported against the footing. A section of pipe is set vertically and braced. A hydraulic jack is set on a plate on top of the pile. Where jacking is easy, a moderate capacity long-throw jack is used, and short sections of pipe are added as needed. When several short sections have been added and jacked, they may be removed so that a longer section can be inserted and the short sections reused. As the resistance builds up, higher capacity hydraulic jacks are used. Piles are usually jacked down until the force required to move the pile is 50% greater than the design load. After reaching a resistance of 150% of design load, it is wise to recycle the loading and unloading to make sure that the pile will not move on reloading.

The design loads for underpinning piles should consider two factors: (a) in low head room, only hammers with low energy can be used; and (*b*) in many cases there is no practical way to load-test the pile to 200% of design load. Driven underpinning piles usually are limited to 30- to 50-ton capacity. Piles jacked open-end to dense formations can be designed for high loads, provided the structure being underpinned offers sufficient reaction.

27.7   Special Underpinning Systems

When circumstances are right, special methods of underpinning may be used which result in substantial economy. Two such systems are as follows:

The first method consists of driving soldier beams alongside the wall footing of the existing building. Brackets are welded to the piles (see Fig. 27.3). The brackets extend under the wall footing and the load of the wall is transferred to the brackets by driving steel wedges. As the excavation for the new basement proceeds, horizontal lagging is tucked behind the flanges of the soldier beams. When the basement wall is poured, the soldier beams will be embedded in it. The access pits dug to install the brackets may be filled with concrete to encase the brackets. For this method to be feasible, the building wall must be fairly light, say not more than 9000 lb per lineal foot. This will permit driving the beams on 6- or 7-ft centers and limit the load on the brackets to not over 30 tons. Closer spacing can be used to limit the load per bracket. The depth of the excavation should be moderate, say 12 to 14 ft. These factors determine the section of soldier beam to drive.

The second method consists of installing two or more piles down through concrete footings. This method is applicable to the underpinning of spread footings and continuous footings and also to concrete pile caps. To be feasible, it must be possible to clear the floor around the columns and to have at least 12 ft of head room. First, 12-in.-diameter holes are drilled through the footing. Drill rigs using core barrels and steel shot have been used successfully. Line drilling may also be used. Then, a 10-in. closed-end pipe is driven in sections through the holes. After reaching bearing, the pipes are concreted to within 2 in. of the underside of the footing. The pipes are cut off level with the bottom of the footing. The top of the pile and the hole

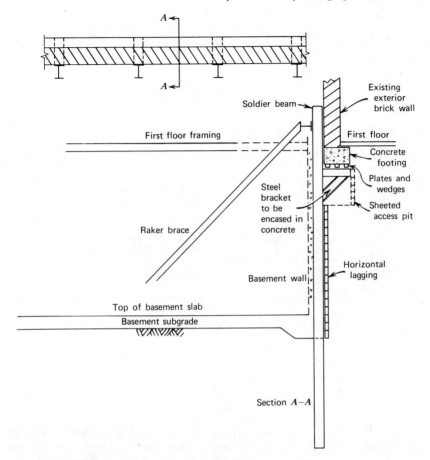

Fig. 27.3   Underpinning soldier beams and brackets. No scale.
Note: Bracing system shown in schematic only. Refer to Chapter 27.

through the footing are filled with zero slump concrete containing additives to prevent shrinkage. These plugs permit transfer of footing load to the piles. Holes are located as close to the column as possible, to reduce or eliminate tension in the footing. This is required, since drilling of the holes will cut off the reinforcing bars. The loads for which the piles may be designed depend on soil conditions, the size of hammer, and the bond strength between the plug and the footing. Experience indicates that bond strengths of 150 lb/in.² is conservative. Forty-five-ton piles have been used successfully

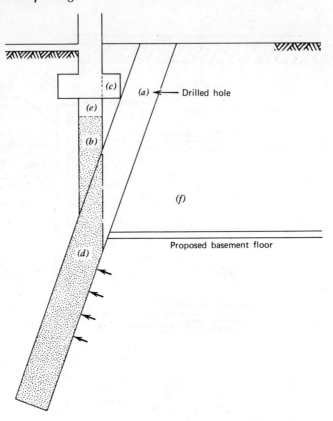

Drilled hole

Proposed basement floor

Fig. 27.4 Work procedure: (*a*) Drill the hole at an angle. (*b*) Excavate under footing by hand. (*c*) Remove projecting part of the footing. (*d*) Place re-bars and pour concrete in drilled hole, and up the vertical hand dug part (*b*). (*e*) Prestress with jacks, then dry pack. (*f*) Excavate and brace.

under 24-in. thick footings. A concrete plug in a 4-ft 6-in. footing carried a load of 250 tons for 24 hrs without any sign of movement.

27.8   *Inclined Piles*

In areas where drilled holes will stand open, and cast-in-place concrete piles can be constructed, it is economical to use slant piles for underpinning existing footings. This scheme is shown in Fig. 27.4. These "dog leg" piles rely on adequate lateral strength of the soil to prevent lateral bending of the piles, and loss of support.

27.9 Methods of Load Transfer

Every type of underpinning requires that the load of the existing foundation be positively transferred on to the new foundation. The usual expression is "pinning off." The following are the common methods used:

Dry pack: Where concrete piers are used for underpinning, the space between the underside of the old footing and the top of the pier (usually about 2 in.) is filled with a no slump sand-cement grout, proportioned 1:1 with just enough water to slake the cement. The sand-cement grout is rammed into place so as to compact it between the two surfaces. A similar procedure is used where steel beams or plates are the contact between the old and new work.

Plates and wedges: Plates and wedges may be used by themselves or in conjunction with other forms of pinning-off. Plates and wedges are sometimes driven on concrete piers to ensure that the piers are stressed before dry-pack is placed. Plates and wedges are used to stress shoring and to pick up the loads on needle beams, steel brackets, and such. There is no set standard as to taper, length, or width of wedges. A typical pair measures 1½ in. wide, 12 in. long tapering from ⅛ to ¾ in. Where they are to remain permanently in place, wedges are often tack-welded after they have been "married" (driven home).

Stub columns: Where heavy loads are involved and in the case of highly loaded underpinning piles, a more controlled pinning-off method is used. For such work, a stub H-beam is embedded in the concrete of the new foundation. When the concrete has set, hydraulic jacks in pairs are placed close to the stub (sometimes between the flanges) and a predetermined pressure applied to the footing or beam. Plates and wedges are then inserted between the stub and the structure and the wedges are driven until the pressure gauge shows that the load on the jacks is falling off, thus indicating transfer to the pile or concrete pier.

Screw jacks: Manually operated screw jacks, 10- to 25-ton capacity, are used for stressing shoring raker braces and such. They are also used for pinning-off of underpinning. Where dry-pack cannot be depended on to transfer load, screw jacks may be employed and concreted permanently in place.

27.10   Inspection

So many steps and much careful work is required in underpinning that inspection by the contractor is essential for his own protection. Inspection is required before bidding, before starting to work and during the work. Although the city building department or other agency may inspect the work occasionally, it is the contractor, or underpinning subcontractor, who is responsible (see Section 27.2).

In some cases, the underpinning devices to be used on a job are designed by a structural engineer, foundation engineer, or others. The contractor still is responsible, and the design should not be accepted by the contractor unless he agrees with it and accepts the responsibility for it.

27.11   Summary

Primary points in this chapter are as follows:

FACTS: Lagging or sheeting of access pits must be placed to bear uniformly against the soil. Any voids behind the sheeting must be rammed full of hay, oakum, or other free draining material. Each unit of underpinning requires prestressing by drypack, wedges, or jacks to avoid any settlement of the structure. Backfilling of access pits requires compaction of the backfill, preferably with mechanical tampers.

WATCH OUT FOR: Overjacking of light structures which may cause cracking. Loss of ground either between the sheets or from deflection of the pit sheeting. Flow of water from broken or leaking water lines. Ground water above the bottom of the pit excavation, which may cause a "boil" and serious loss of ground. Heavily loaded floors near walls or columns to be underpinned. Wedges becoming loose as work progresses. Widening of cracks or other signs of structural damage.

28

Linings and Membranes

28.1 Uses

Reservoirs, canals, storage ponds, evaporation ponds, artificial lakes, oil storage reservoirs, and ditches may be lined to prevent loss of water or other fluid.

28.2 Soil Linings

The most common lining material is soil. Soil linings generally are referred to as clay linings. Such linings may be constructed of clay, or mixtures of sand, silt, and clay.

Bentonite, a very plastic clay, is mined in several parts of the United States, and is sold in sacks or in bulk. Bentonite frequently is used for lining. Usually it is mixed with the native soil.

In areas where clay is not easily available reasonably good linings have been constructed of mixtures of available soil. On one reservoir, a mixture of fine sand and silt was used. With the proper moisture content and good compaction, a relatively tight lining resulted.

Soil liners usually are 2 to 3 ft thick and are placed in layers 6 in. thick. Each layer is compacted with larger rollers. On slopes which are 2 horizontal to 1 vertical, or flatter, the soil layers can be placed conforming to the slope. Compaction usually is performed with sheepsfoot rollers, or other compaction equipment, operating up and down the slope. Usually the liners consist of at least three layers, and more commonly are four layers thick. The soils should be at optimum moisture content, or slightly wetter. Soils compacted slightly on the wet side tend to have a lower permeability. Also, they are more plastic and do not tend to develop vertical cracking during the compaction process.

Deformations in completed reservoirs lined with clay indicate that soil can accommodate some movement without cracking. This is a very desirable asset. It is difficult to compact the soil on steeper slopes. This could be done by placing the soil in horizontal layers the width of the rolling equipment and then trimming off the outside 2 or 3 ft of soil after compaction is completed.

Compacted fills usually are compacted to densities of at least 90% of the modified AASHO method of testing. It is desirable to keep the soil lining wet. If it is allowed to dry out, it may shrink and then crack, and become less watertight.

28.3   Concrete Linings

Concrete linings are used in many projects. Usually the concrete is cast in place. Sometimes it is placed as shotcrete (gunite). These linings usually are not reinforced, but the shotcrete lining may contain a minimum amount of mesh, primarily for control of cracking due to shrinkage. Sometimes, however, it may be desirable to reinforce the concrete lining where it is on steep slopes, or where hydrostatic back pressure may develop behind the lining.

Concrete linings encounter difficulties in several circumstances, as follows:

Collapsing soil.   In many arid areas where water canals are constructed, there are "streams" of low density soil crossing the path of the canal. Generally these low density soils can be recognized only by testing. Settlements of 1 ft occur frequently, and sometimes settlements are several feet where a canal crosses such soil.

Expansive soil.   Expansion of adobe or gumbo-type soils can cause cracking of a concrete lining, particularly at transitions with structures.

Loose backfill. Pipes, culverts, and other structures may cross under a canal or reservoir lining. When the reservoir has been full for some time, it must be expected that some water will leak through the lining and get into the subgrade soil. The backfill may not be as stiff as the natural soil and may settle, cracking the concrete and causing more leakage. Reports of such damage appear in ENR and the newspapers (see below).

Rapid drawdown. See Section 28.6.

Water Saturation Blamed for Break in Southland Aqueduct

SACRAMENTO ((AP)) The break in a state aqueduct about five days after the first water began flowing from Northern California apparently was the result of water saturating the surrounding soil, not sabotage or earthquake damage, the California water chief said Friday.

William R. Gianelli, director of the state Department of Water Resources, said the difficulty in pinpointing the cause is that "the evidence was almost completely eliminated by the break itself."

The concrete canal in the Antelope Valley broke three months ago, causing an estimated $130,000 damage. The location is between Los Angeles and Bakersfield.

In a report to the state Water Commission on the results of an investigation, Giannelli said "the actual cause of the break can only be postulated."

"It does appear that the alluvium became saturated from water originating in the canal section itself, or from a water spring in the area, and that such water caused a differential settlement and a piping of embankment material which finally resulted in erosion and collapse at the culvert," Gianelli said.

"The analysis was able to conclude that no evidence of sabotage could be found, and that it was improbable that the San Fernando earthquake of Feb. 9 was of sufficient magnitude in the vicinity of the break to have weakened the aqueduct or to have been a contributing factor," he added.

Gianelli said the canal had been repaired and returned to service and a monitoring program had been established on the system in an attempt to avoid similar problems until the canal becomes well stabilized.

28.4   Commercial Linings and Membranes

Many commercial lining materials are manufactured. These include many types of plastic. Sheets of polyvinyl chloride are available in various thicknesses and at reasonable cost. Some common plastics are reinforced with fiberglass or other materials to increase their strength. Butyl rubber and other materials are also commercially available as linings.

Linings also are constructed in sheets or panels. These panels may be constructed of asphalt, asphalt-soaked fibers, or precast concrete.

Plastic sheets require a carefully prepared and smooth bed. Rocks and other sharp objects are not permitted in the supporting bed. Frequently sand is used to prepare a suitable bed.

The plastic sheets usually come in rolls and can be unrolled and cut into panels in place. Where each joint occurs, the panels usually are overlapped, and can be joined by heating irons which weld the sheets together. Usually, the joints are overlapped, and two passes are made with the irons to result in double bonding of sheets.

Because the plastic sheets are sensitive to weather and deterioration by sunlight, and also to damage from being poked—causing holes—it is common to cover the plastic with a layer of sand or gravel or other protective soil. Usually the soil thickness is 6 to 12 in. The spreading operation takes hand manual labor, with some mechanical assistance, to prevent damage to the plastic.

Rolled asphaltic concrete linings generally are 3 to 6 in. thick. They are placed and rolled following procedures common to roadway paving. Usually the asphalt is spread with mechanical equipment, and two layers of asphalt are placed. The pattern of placing and rolling is perpendicular to the underlying layer.

The placing of gunite concrete or poured-in-place concrete involves the use of low water content concrete, particularly in slope lining. Low water content also is necessary to limit shrinking and cracking of the concrete which would result in leaking. Concrete linings usually are 4 in. thick. Expansion joints usually are placed 20 to 30 ft, center-to-center. Where canals are lined, they usually are lined with a machine especially designed for placing and finishing the concrete.

Fig. 28.1 "Fabriform" concrete canal lining as furnished by Intrusion-Prepakt (Contech).

Concrete sometimes is placed by special forming techniques. One such technique is the "fabriform" sold by Intrusion-Prepakt (Contech). This is a nylon cloth form placed in the desired location on a slope or channel bottom. It can be placed on a dry surface or underwater. When the form is in the desired location, concrete is pumped into it, causing it to expand and resemble a mattress in appearance. This method is indicated in Fig. 28.1 (see Ref. 53).

28.5 *Permeable Protective Linings*

In some cases, permeable linings are desirable to provide stability to slopes and resistance to erosion, and yet free drainage to avoid built-up of hydrostatic back pressures. Gravel is used frequently, as well as manufactured porous concrete planks and similar devices.

28.6   Underdrains

Some reservoirs or canals must be emptied or the water lowered considerably, in short periods of time. This is called rapid "drawdown." In spite of all care in the use of materials and good construction techniques, it must be expected that linings will leak to some degree. Therefore, the soil embankment behind the lining must be assumed to be saturated.

If the embankment walls are fairly steep, the water in the soil tries to flow back into the reservoir. This water pressure pushes against the back side of the concrete lining.

Hydrostatic uplift occurs only during rapid lowering of the water in the reservoir. The hydrostatic pressure in the soil embankment causes the concrete slab to lift or deflect slightly. This reduces the hydrostatic pressure. Then water flows to this low pressure area and causes the slab to deflect again. Therefore, this type of failure is progressive. Failure may not occur during one emptying; however, with several occurrences, the slab could be continually deflected more and more, until it breaks.

Some soils may be sufficiently strong to remain stable in the condition of rapid drawdown of the reservoir water level. Also, concrete liners sometimes can be made sufficiently strong to resist hydrostatic uplift. However, in many cases it is necessary to relieve the water pressure in the slope. This is done by constructing "underdrains" in the embankments, or relief holes in the lining.

Underdrains may consist of: (a) blankets of sand, (b) trenches at intervals of 10 or 15 ft on centers filled with sand, (c) porous concrete or porous wall pipe, and (d) perforated or slotted pipe, with sand or suitable filter material surrounding the pipes. These drains must be designed as filters, so that soil cannot wash into the drains and clog them. The design of filters (graded filters) requires a knowledge of the grain sizes of the soil in the embankment. Such designs should be made by an engineer experienced in this work (see Ref. 9, p. 66).

Damage of concrete lining slabs is due to deflection of the slab. Deflection is due to the sustained flow of water into the thin space between the embankment and the concrete slab. If the concrete slab

Fig. 28.2   Uplifting of concrete lining slab.

is sufficiently heavy, the water pressure in back of the slab is not sufficient to raise the slab. Also, if the rate of emptying the reservoir is slow enough so that water will drain out of the embankment, the slab will not be uplifted.

A photograph of slab uplifting is shown in Fig. 28.2. Generally, such movements are more likely to occur on steep slopes. Flatter slopes involve longer flow paths, and the weight of concrete is more effective in resisting uplift (see Fig. 28.3).

The worst conditions for uplift are as follows:

(1) Steep slopes, such as 1 to 1.
(2) Silty soils.
(3) Rapid drawdown.

28.7   *Blowouts*

Blowouts are very similar to the condition described under Section 28.6. When a reservoir is emptied quickly, the hydrostatic pressures

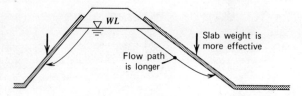

Fig. 28.3   Flowpath at drainage under canal lining.

under the bottom slab may be sufficient to cause the slab to raise and to break the slab or cause a blowout. Generally, this is relieved by placing a drainage blanket or other drainage collection devices under the bottom slab. They may connect to a drainpipe leading away from the reservoir. As an alternate, there may be pop-up valves, relief wells, or other devices that permit the temporary excess water pressure under the slab to drain upward through the slab.

28.8   Maintenance

Liners generally require periodic maintenance. Original construction should be done anticipating that future repairs and maintenance will be necessary. Large washouts occur from time to time. Usually, they can be traced back to sustained leakage through the lining, causing softening of the soil, then erosion of the soil.

28.9   Summary

Primary points in this chapter are as follows:

FACTS: Clay or silty soil makes a good lining for canals and reservoirs. The best linings are compacted when the soil moisture content is a few percent above optimum, resulting in a "plastic" soil. "Plastic" linings can accommodate some movement without cracking. Concrete linings are brittle and must receive good uniform support from the subgrade to avoid cracks.

WATCH OUT FOR: Trenches cut in the supporting subgrade and backfilled with soil not as stiff as the surrounding natural soil. Areas of expansive soil, or any indication that soft or compressible soils have been found in previous work in the area.

29

Potential Damage

29.1 General

Construction operations frequently cause damage to adjacent property. It is the duty of the contractor to do his work in a careful manner, planning each phase of his work, to avoid damage to adjacent property. It is also the duty of the adjacent property owner to notify the contractor of any indication that damage is starting, and that additional protective measures should be taken. The adjacent property owner must take all steps necessary to protect his property from damage, even though he intends to sue the contractor.

The most dangerous phases of construction include demolishing old structures, excavating for basements, blasting rock, site dewatering, setting and stressing anchors or braces to shore up the sides of the excavation, and driving pile foundations. Damage may occur to adjacent structures, or to underground utilities, streets, or sidewalks.

After construction is completed, there is the potential of damage to the completed work. Such damage may include high water levels with wet floors and seepage into basements, foundation settlements, cracked floor slabs, corrosion, vibration due to machinery operation, and slope erosion.

29.2   Excavation

A general discussion of excavation and bracing is presented in Chapters 11 and 12. Although excavations may stand up satisfactorily, and the bracing system may prevent cave-ins, frequently the adjacent streets settle and crack, utility lines settle, break, and flood out excavations, or cut off service in a neighborhood, and the foundations and sidewalks of adjacent structures stretch, settle, and crack. Bracing generally is required for vertical or steep excavations exceeding depths of 6 ft. Sometimes deeper vertical excavations are permitted where the soils are proven to be sufficiently strong to stand vertically. Building codes usually specify shoring and bracing, but give no guidelines. State industrial safety codes may give some specific requirements.

The design of shoring and bracing systems is almost always left to the contractor. The contractor may have his own forces do the design or may hire an engineer to design a system. He may pass on to a specialty subcontractor the responsibilities to design and install the shoring system.

Occasionally, damage is due to serious underdesign of the shoring system and actual failure during excavation. Much more often however, the bracing and shoring system remains intact. However, the shoring deforms and yields small amounts as excavation proceeds. Another possibility is that the job superintendent wants the excavation to proceed rapidly, and he may not take the time to be sure all of the bracing system is in place and completed in all respects before making the next stage of the excavation.

To limit the amount of lateral yielding of the excavations, the bracing system must be preloaded or prestressed as it is constructed; otherwise, the steel, concrete, and wood must deform in order to develop its design stress.

In addition, shoring systems frequently are based on the active pressure of the soil. The active pressure develops only after the soil has deformed. Sufficient deformation to develop active pressure may be on the order of 1% of the depth of the excavation. Therefore, for an excavation 20 ft deep, properly shored and braced, measurements on many projects have shown that lateral movements of the top of the ground may be 2 to 3 in. For soft soils, the movements may be greater, and for firm soils they may be less. However, a movement of 2 to 3 in. laterally can be enough to substantially damage utilities and adjacent structures.

If the excavation is 40 ft deep, lateral movements become in the range of 4 to 6 in., with much greater resulting damage to adjacent structures.

The greatest stretching of the ground is close to the edge of the excavation, but stretching may extend back from the excavation a distance equal to the depth of the excavation, or even greater distances such as twice the depth of the excavation. Therefore, for an excavation 40 ft deep, buildings or utilities within 40 ft can be expected to stretch and develop some cracks. On softer soils, buildings 80 ft away may be affected. In sandy soils, the movements usually are much smaller and are much less likely to be a problem, except saturated sands which can be difficult to work with and prevent loss of ground.

In design of the shoring system, the usual procedure is to make the shoring system as light and low-cost as possible. The lateral soil pressures are assumed to develop into the fully active case, resulting in the least possible lateral pressure on the shoring system. As mentioned previously, substantial soil deformation is required to develop the full active case. Therefore, lateral deformation of the soil must be expected.

It may be possible to reduce lateral deformation by using a stiffer, stronger bracing system. Such a design can be developed assuming that the fully active case does not develop. Lateral pressures then would more likely be somewhere between "at rest" and "active." One should ask the soils engineer whether it is safe to use the active pressure and how much deformation may result.

In making surveys of adjacent buildings, it is good to have some guide as to when to become concerned with the measured settlements. In most buildings, column spacings are 20 to 25 ft on centers. As a rough guide, it is desirable to limit differential settlement between columns to the range of 1/4 to 1/2 in. If differential settlement reaches 1 in., some cracking will become apparent. At 2 in. it is expected that cracking will be serious, and there may be structural damage. Therefore, when survey readings show that a column has dropped, even as little as 1/16 in., some action should be taken. If settlements progress to as much as 1 in. with respect to the adjacent column, it is time to take definite corrective action.

29.3 Methods of Detection

It is important that the contractor inspect regularly the street and adjacent buildings for indications of movement. One of the most common and best systems is a well-planned grid of survey points. Elevation monuments should be established at several locations in each adjacent building, and on the street and sidewalks. The monuments should be surveyed regularly. Two or more reference bench marks should be established at a distance far enough away from the site to be free of disturbance from excavation and construction activities.

Where deep excavations must be dug, or where the site is underlain by soft soils, it may be desirable to take horizontal measurements between elevation monuments, and also to set up separate survey points to measure lateral stretching of the ground. Frequently lateral movement is detected by observing new cracks, and measuring cracks on a regular basis. However, survey points measured regularly by tape can provide better information.

Also, vertical holes can be drilled outside of the perimeter of the proposed excavation, and casings can be set in these holes to measure lateral movements of the ground as the excavation proceeds (see Chapter 11, Section 11.1.6). Special casing is installed in such holes, and a precise inclinometer device can be used to record gradual deformations of the ground near the excavation.

In addition to measurements, good quality photographs before and during construction can be very helpful to indicate changes, which otherwise may occur so slowly that the job superintendent is not aware of them except by referring back to previous photographs.

29.4 Additions to Existing Buildings

Frequently new additions are constructed which tie into an existing building. The old building has experienced its settlement;

however, the new building will settle during construction, and perhaps for some time after construction. The amount of cracking at the joint between the old building and new building can be reduced if some separation is left between the two buildings as long as possible before they are joined.

Permanent embankments of soil several feet thick may be placed for industrial warehouses with the floor slab at dock loading height. Such fills weigh several hundred pounds per square foot and can be expected to settle perhaps several inches. Therefore, the embankments should be placed as early as possible, long before foundations are placed in or near these embankments. Settlement readings can be taken to chart the progress of settlement of the embankments.

It may be desirable to stockpile soil on the site for backfilling purposes. Frequently the stockpile is placed at the edge of the site, adjacent to an existing structure. The weight of the stockpile may be expected to cause some settlement of the ground and may drag down the foundations of the adjacent building.

29.5   Site Dewatering During Construction

Substantially lowering the normal ground water level in the construction area can have a profound influence on adjacent structures.

In many cases, adjacent buildings are supported on untreated wood piles. As long as the wood piles are saturated completely, they will not rot or deteriorate. However, if they are dried out, they are susceptible to rapid rotting and decay. Several cases of serious damage to pile foundations of existing buildings have been due to temporary lowering of the ground water level.

If the lowering of ground water levels lasts only for a short period of time, and then the ground water conditions are established at their previous level, there may not be time for any substantial damage to the piles. Generally, serious damage occurs when dewatering is extended over many months or years of time.

In some cases, the ground water level under adjacent structures has been kept high by recirculating water back to the structures and recharging it into the ground (see Refs. 21 and 22). The design of injection wells for this purpose requires the services of someone experienced in this field.

Lowering of the ground water level for a long period of time also causes consolidation and settlement of the soil. When the water level is high, the soil particles are buoyed up by the water, and in effect are lighter. When the ground water level drops, these soil particles become heavier. Therefore, if the water level is dropped 10 ft, the soil weight is increased roughly 400 lb/ft². If the water level is dropped 20 ft, the effective increase in soil weight is 800 lb/ft². This increase in weight can cause compressible layers of soil to settle several inches. The zone affected may extend several hundred feet away from the edge of the dewatered area.

The most common method of dewatering is sump pumping. Usually, one or more pits or sumps are dug in or adjacent to the excavation, extending a few feet below the bottom of the general site excavation. Rim trenches lead water to the sump. A submersible or suction pump is used to pump water from the sump. Occasionally, an excavation is dug as deep as possible before installation of any dewatering system. The ground water level tends to flow up into the bottom of the excavation, creating a soft condition, and in some cases, even a quick condition. In one such case the writers are familiar with, the bottom became so unstable the contractor could not operate equipment on the bottom. The contractor claimed that this "quicksand" condition made it impossible to support the building on spread foundations, and that piles would be required. Fortunately, the contractor was persuaded to put in a drainage system; within 3 days the bottom was stable and the contractor then proceeded to form and pour the foundations.

In some cases, sump pumping is not sufficient to adequately dewater a site. Either the bottom continues to stay soft, or boils form causing loss of ground in the subgrade. In these cases, a deeper dewatering system is required. The most common system is well points. Well points are shallow wells and are usually installed around the perimeter of the site. The well point system can pull the ground water level down approximately 15 ft. If deeper dewatering is required, it is necessary to put a second stage of well points at a lower elevation.

Another system for deep dewatering is to install several wells around the perimeter of the site. Wells permit dewatering to any depth desired.

It is very important in any kind of dewatering system that the water pumped out runs clean. If soil is pumped out with the water, it indicates removal of material which could lead to the formation of cavities or areas of soft subgrade. The contractor should check frequently the discharge and take samples of water in large glass jars. The jars should be allowed to stand to see if any sediment settles out, or if soil particles can be observed in the water.

29.6   *Driving of Pile Foundations*

The act of driving piles can cause problems, such as heaving of the ground surface (see Chapter 16, Section 16.8). Pile driving also can cause lateral movement of the soil. This is a great hazard when driving into cohesive soils, adjacent to a deep excavation (see Chapter 16, Section 16.8). If the soils in the area are loose sands, the vibration may result in some compaction of the soil, causing settlement of nearby buildings.

In addition to possible damage to buildings, utility lines buried in the ground also are susceptible to damage due to vibration, or to ground heaving, lateral displacements, or settlement.

Frequently it becomes necessary to drive piles in such locations. Various methods are used to accomplish pile driving without creating damage. Some such methods are as follows:

1. Pilot-jet a hole to be followed by a pile and pile driving.

2. Jet the pile down, with a jet system which goes down with the pile.

3. Predrill a hole at the location of each pile. Usually, predrilled holes are slightly smaller in diameter than the size of the pile (see Chapter 16, Section 16.8).

4. Use a pipe pile, driven open-end, and clean out the pile as driving progresses.

5. Use a heavier, slower acting hammer with more cushion blocks. Heavier, slow acting hammers tend to develop less shock, and somewhat more push on the pile.

29.7   Shock and Vibration

Large pile driving rigs put a large amount of shock energy into the ground each time the hammer strikes the top of the pile. These shock forces travel rapidly through the ground to adjacent structures, and often can be felt by people in the adjacent buildings. Vibration of the building due to the shock forces can in some cases be damaging to adjacent structures. This is not very common. Vibrations strong enough to cause structural damage generally are very upsetting to people. Therefore, complaints from the neighbors usually are sufficient to stop pile driving operations before structural damage actually occurs.

Very often, a recording seismograph is used to measure ground motion vibrations during pile driving, blasting, or other construction operations causing shock impacts on the soil. This includes operation of pavement breakers, operaton of large pumps or compressors, and operation of heavy truck traffic.

A seismograph is shown in Fig. 29.1. Generally, accelerations or displacements are measured on the ground surface, or on floor slabs in the adjacent buildings. The measurements are made of vertical vibrations, and horizontal vibrations in two directions. The ground motion is amplified and printed on paper or film. These records are reviewed by someone experienced in this work, and the results are used to reach opinions regarding possible damage to adjacent structures.

Figure 29.2 shows a plot of amplitude of vibration measured at three locations away from the point of the blast. A series of curves indicating the effect of vibrations on people and on structures are also shown in Fig. 29.2. Assuming that blasting is being done 360 ft from an adjacent building, the amplitude of motion is 0.008 in. at a frequency of 18 Hz. This point is shown plotted in Fig. 29.2. This indicates that the level of vibration is severe to persons but safe with regard to damage to the structure. Since human beings are very sensitive to vibrations, readings of this kind are very important to show that construction operations can proceed without structural damage to adjacent structures. Such data frequently are used in court (see Ref. 54).

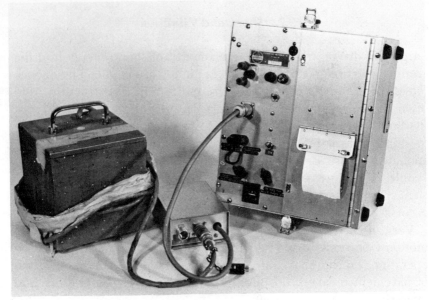

Fig. 29.1   Recording seismograph.

29.8   Damage After Construction

Water leaks through basement walls or floors can be due to holes in the waterproofing system. Also, many basements are designed with a drainage system to relieve the pressure around the basement walls. Drainage systems are difficult to build, and to prevent from clogging. Therefore, the drainage system should be constructed in such a way that maintenance is not too difficult. If the system does not work, the contractor will usually be called back to correct the problem and get the system into a working condition. Frequently, soil will wash through the gravel pack around drainpipes and will settle out inside the drainpipe. Therefore, drainpipes must be laid out so that they are easy to clean out.

29.8.1   Settlements

A new building frequently will experience some settlement during construction and after completion. This settlement may cause some

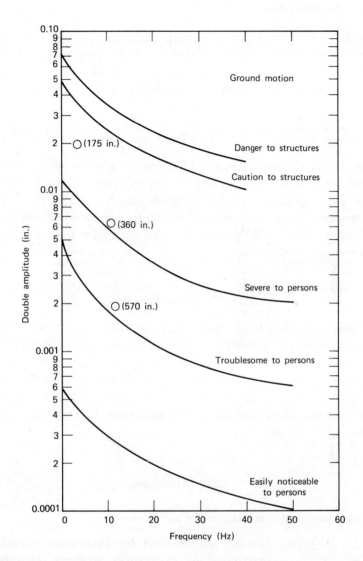

Fig. 29.2 The amplitude and frequency of vibrations with consequent effect on structures and persons.

downdrag of the foundations of adjacent structures. In the bidding stage, make sure that this possibility has been adequately considered by the structural engineer and soils engineer. Damage due to this cause should not become the responsibility of the contractor.

29.8.2   *Cracked Floor Slabs*

Floor slab settlements and cracking can be a result of poorly compacted backfills in trenches cut for utility lines, or occasionally are due to swelling and heaving of subgrade soils. Generally, slabs should be separated from columns and walls, to permit some differential movements. The cracks should be filled with joint material, such as Thiokol.

29.8.3   *Slope Erosion*

In many cases, new landscaping vegetation has not become well established when the project is ready to turn over to the owner. Heavy rains can cause erosion of slopes, resulting in disagreements between the contractor and owner. Repair of eroded slopes is a tedious, difficult, and expensive process. The contractor should make sure he has some understanding with the owner concerning this type of potential damage.

29.9   *Summary*

Primary points in this chapter are as follows:

FACTS: Bracing and shoring for excavations should be prestressed as excavation proceeds. Dewatering of a site requires careful consideration, and should be done by experienced people. Problems with dewatering have been the source of many lawsuits. Pile driving can be a serious source of annoyance to neighbors. Under some circumstances vibration due to blasting or pile driving can cause structural damage to adjacent buildings.

WATCH OUT FOR: Excavating too fast, without adequate shoring; driving piles on slopes; driving piles adjacent to open excavations or channels; driving piles in saturated clay soils; stockpiling soil adjacent to existing structures. Also, proper backfilling where steel sheeting is to be withdrawn.

30

Grouting and Chemical Injection

30.1 General Applications

Several kinds of grout, and chemicals for chemical stabilization of soil, are commonly used in the construction industry.

Grouting may be done to fill voids in the soil, or to fill voids or cracks in rocks. Also, grout curtains act as a barrier for the flow of water. Some grouts are installed to displace earth, and to compact it in place.

Chemical grouts generally flow into a coarser-grained sand or gravel soil, and are used to cement the soil together. Chemical grouts also may be used to stop the flow of water through the ground.

30.2 Cement Grout

Cement grout may be a mixture of cement and water, or sand, cement, and water.

On many construction projects, it is necessary to fill voids in the ground. Soft soil or peat, which are compressible, must be stabilized to limit future consolidation and settlement. This type of intrusion grouting is sometimes described as consolidation grouting, and is briefly discussed herein. Grouting for curtain walls and to reduce seepage around dams, which is a highly specialized grouting technique, is not discussed in this book. Several companies have the equipment and trained personnel for this work. Two projects indicating the usefulness of this method are described as follows:

The site of a proposed structure in Florida was found to be underlain by large cavities formed by the solution of limestone bedrock. These cavities were estimated to be at least 30,000 cu yd in volume. The solution cavities started about 50 ft below ground surface, and extended to a depth of as much as 100 ft. Borings indicated that the top few feet of the cavities were filled with water, and below that the cavities contained extremely soft soil of low density in the range of 50 to 60 lb/ft^3. The drill stem on a drill rig dropped through the soil with no resistance. The initial grouting into the cavity was sand and water. The sand was pumped in through pipes extending down into the cavities. Also, relief pipes were installed to permit excess water to drain out. Over 3000 yd of sand was placed in the cavities, followed by 700 yd of a grout mixture of sand, cement, and water. Later borings showed that the cavities had been filled, and that there was a substantial increase in the strength of the soft soils in the cavities. Soil density changed from a range of 50 to 60 lb/ft^3 to 70 to 90 lb/ft^3. The purpose of filling was primarily to prevent future sinkhole-type collapse of the overlying soil which had been "bridging over" the cavities.

On a second project, a building was constructed over an area which had once been a peat bog. The foundations extended down to firm soil. The floor slab was supported directly on an earthfill dumped on top of the peat bog material. Settlements of the floor slab varied, and were as much as 1 ft. A mixture of sand, cement, and water was pumped into the peat bog material, starting at the bottom of the soft soil. By pumping up the bottom, and then gradually raising the pipes and pumping at higher elevations, the grout was forced into the peat bog material, tending to compress and compact it. Approximately 2000 yd of material were pumped into the peat bog material, representing an addition of approximately 45 lb of material to 1 ft^3 of the peat bog soil. On completion, the floor slab was lifted substantially. It should be noted, however, that it is frequently necessary to return and grout a second time when dealing with soft compressible clay or peat soils.

30.3   Soil-Cement Displacement Grouting

The injection of soil-cement to displace and compact soils has become a relatively important part of soil stabilization. It is done most frequently to repair buildings damaged by settlement. This work is done by specialty subcontractors.

If the soils underlying the site are relatively low density, settlements of footings or floor slabs may be substantial. If the soils are compared to the compacted soil density, the resulting degree of compaction of the existing soils may be only 60 to 70%.

The characteristics resulting from low density are as follows:

1. Low bearing value.
2. Settlement under load.
3. Additional settlement with substantial increase in moisture content.
4. Additional settlement if the soil is vibrated or subjected to shock loading, such as by an earthquake.
5. The potential for liquefaction and soil instability in cases of extreme earthquake shocks applied to low density saturated sand.

Assume that a building is supported on footings resting on low-density soil, and many of the footings have settled. The solutions possible include: (a) underpinning each footing, one at a time, with new and wider footings or pile foundations, or (b) increasing the strength of the underlying supporting soil, and raising the old footings.

Usually, increasing the strength of the soil is most desirable because it would cause the least interference with operation of the structure.

Compaction can be accomplished by injecting material into the ground. This forces the soil to compress sideways and vertically. The soil would occupy less space and therefore would be more compacted.

The material must be injected in such a way that the ground surface will not be moved or heave upward. Foundations must be raised slowly, in several steps, and in unison. The material injected is a low-moisture content, nonplastic, soil-cement. This material usually is installed at a number of select locations. This material does not "flow." It is confined to the place injected. It must be controllable.

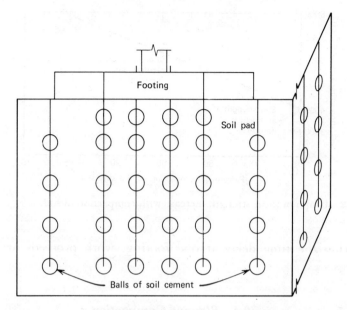

Fig. 30.1   Sketch of pattern of intrusion of balls of soil-cemenι.

A pump at the ground surface takes a specific volume of soil-cement and pumps it down a grout pipe to a specific depth below the ground surface. At this point, a ball of soil cement is formed. Because it is dry and nonplastic, this ball stays at the desired location. A definite known volume of material is contained in the ball. For instance, the ball might contain 2 or 3 ft³ of soil-cement, and be on the order of 18 in. in diameter.

The soil surrounding the ball would be squeezed and would compact. If the soil is sand, it will compact quickly. If the soil is silt, compaction is slower. After inserting a ball of soil-cement, the water pressure in the soil pores increases. A time delay is necessary for this excess water to drain away.

During the time delay, a second ball can be placed at ·another location through another pipe. Later the grout pipes are raised a few feet above the previous balls, and additional soil-cement balls are inserted into the earth.

This is repeated until the full volume of the soil "pad" underlying the footing has filled with properly spaced balls of soil-cement. This is indicated in Fig. 30.1.

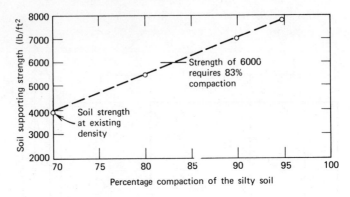

Fig. 30.2   Graph of shear strength increase with compaction of soil.

During the time delay at one footing, work proceeds at other footings.

30.4   Planned Compaction

Laboratory tests can be performed to estimate the required degree of compaction to achieve a desired bearing capacity of the soil. Samples of the natural soils are compacted at various higher densities, and shear tests are performed to measure the new strength. An example graph of a series of such tests is shown in Fig. 30.2.

This graph indicates the shear strength of the soil at its natural density is 70% relative compaction. The graph also indicates the increase in strength at higher densities.

As an example, assume that a bearing value of 4000 lb/ft² exists, and it is desired to raise it to 6000. The bearing value graph on the previous page indicates that approximately 83% compaction is required in order to obtain the desired strength.

In compacting the soil from 70 to 83%, there would be a loss in the volume of the soil. Assume that the soil mat to be compacted is 20 by 20 ft in plan dimensions and is 20 ft thick. This is about 300 yd³. This soil when recompacted would occupy 85% of the total previous volume, or about 255 yd³.

This would require adding 45 yd³ to the volume of the soil mat. This would be done with soil-cement. This amounts to about 18 lb of soil-cement added to each cubic foot of soil. Obviously, the numbers given here are for illustration purposes only.

Levels must be set up, and ground surface elevations must be read frequently during injection to make sure that lifting of the footings is done in small steps.

The soil-cement usually is 7 or 8% cement and 92 or 93% soil. The moisture content is kept as low as possible.

The soil is a graded sand, with some fines, such that the void spaces between larger particles will be filled with appropriate size smaller particles. The subcontractor should select the material to be used.

Grouting, mud jacking, and pressure injection have been used for a number of years. In many cases the results have been good, although occasionally they were not. Probably the most important consideration is that skill and specific experience in this work are essential to doing a good job.

30.5   *Chemical Grouting*

Chemical grouting generally is done in sandy soils or soils that are permeable. The chemicals are in a liquid form, frequently with a consistency not much thicker than water. The chemicals must be very fluid, because they must flow through the soil. The purpose of this kind of grouting is not to displace soil. Instead, these chemicals flow around the soil grains. These chemicals harden or set up and cling to the soil grains. They tend to cement the soil together. Some chemicals after setup are hard. Others are like firm gelatin. Also, the chemicals fill the small void spaces between grains of soil and make the soil less pervious. Water cut-offs can be developed with chemical grouts.

The primary problem is to decide whether the soil will "take" the chemicals. Sand usually is suitable as long as it does not contain too much fine material. Some silt in the sand generally is acceptable. However, silt and clay soils generally are not possible to stabilize by chemical grouting. Occasionally, chemicals can penetrate moderately well into fairly silty soils, but some laboratory testing is necessary to determine this.

Commonly used chemicals include the following:

1. *Sodium silicate.* This was originally developed as the "Joosten" process. There are several modifications of this process, operating under a number of names, including Siroc, Hunts process, and others.

2. *Chrome lignum.* This is a process that uses byproducts from the paper pulp industry.

3. *AM9.* This material is like a stiff gelatin when it sets.

Generally, chemicals are mixed in large tanks, and then are fed through a manifold system to a pump which forces the fluid into the ground. Pumping pressures are frequently on the order of 20 lb/in.²

Specialty contractors work with these chemicals. Considerable experience is needed for successful operation. Since hardening of the chemicals is based on a chemical reaction, it is possible that the chemical characteristics of the soils, or ground water, or even of the mixing water, can have an adverse effect on the reaction of the chemicals in the ground. The reaction time must be delayed so that the chemicals can penetrate into the soils before starting to set up.

The resulting strength of stabilized sand is generally good for silicate-type grout (Joosten process). Generally, compressive strengths are greater than 100 lb/in.² Frequently they are 300 to 400 lb/in.²

This process is used for underpinning of foundations, stabilizing slopes of excavations, and stabilizing the soils above the arch in tunneling through sandy soil. In addition, the chemical can be sprayed on slopes to reduce erosion from wind or rainfall.

Inspection of grouting operations is very difficult. By probing it is possible to fairly well outline the extent of cemented material. It is difficult to get core samples of stabilized soil for laboratory testing. Instead, laboratory samples are prepared using predetermined amounts of the chemical, for laboratory testing.

30.6   Soil Stabilization for Pavement Base Course

Since crushed rock or gravel sometimes is very expensive, a substitute is to upgrade available soil. Sometimes a clay binder added to sand can increase its strength and stability. Also, cement is frequently used to add strength to on-site soil. The amount of cement used varies with the type of soil, and with the strength desired. However, the amount of cement usually is 5 to 10% of the soil used. The resulting strength usually is in the range of 300 to 800 lb/in.² The soil-cement mixture is compacted at optimum moisture just like compacting any fill soil (see Ref. 55).

Frequently lime is used to improve the characteristics of clay soils. Clay soils usually are a poor and unstable subgrade to support the base course for pavements. They are plastic and have a high plastic index (see Chapter 8, Section 8.4).

The addition of lime reduces the plastic index, and the strength of the compacted clay may be doubled. Lime also tends to "dry out" the soil if the clay is too wet for compaction.

31

Legal Aspects of Construction Operation

31.1 General

A number of attorneys specialize in the construction field exclusively. Many others become involved to a considerable extent in construction work. Why? At least partly because underground work involves some unknown conditions. Never can an engineer have perfect knowledge of the soil, rock, and water conditions underlying a site. The owner of a large construction firm once said, "We never lost any money above ground."

This subject of the legal aspects of soils and foundation conditions on construction operations is discussed in much greater detail in Ref. 56. Therefore, only a few comments are made in this book.

31.2 Available Information

Many contractors feel that it is not their responsibility to know anything about the soil conditions at a site. This is a problem of the owner and of the architect or design engineer. By contrast, many owners feel that it is not their responsibility to know anything about the soil conditions at the site, and this information must be developed and used by the contractor. Some owners are reluctant to submit soils data to the contractor, even if submitted on the basis of "information only."

Therefore, obtaining sufficient data on a site sometimes is a problem. In general, however, the trend is more and more toward the owner obtaining information, and making it available to the contractor. Therefore, both become informed concerning the site conditions and both recognize that there are limits in the amount of information available. This probably is better than some existing conditions in which contractors prefer to bid "blind" on soil conditions, and assume that all other contractors will bid "blind." All such bids then contain contingencies concerning the unknown soil conditions. In a way, providing data to the contractor requires that he make more specific estimates of construction procedures based on these data. This takes time. Contractors do not like to spend this amount of time in preparing bids. They can do this if they get the job.

31.3 Changed Conditions

Usually, contractors have only 30 days to prepare a bid for a job. Therefore, they rely to a considerable extent on information given to them.

Some changes will occur on almost all projects. Usually if there are truly greatly different conditions than anticipated, contractors are able to get awards for extras. After all, the project would have been designed differently if the different condition had been known from the beginning. However, the owner should be told ahead of time that he *may* have to pay more if the conditions do change.

Generally, the law does not expect the drawings to be perfect. However, the law does require good practice and reasonable care on the part of the designer. Also, the designer or owner is expected to act reasonably when something unexpected does show up, requiring a change in the drawings.

For a contractor to claim "changed" or latent conditions, he is required to demonstrate that he evaluated correctly the soil conditions as represented, and that he visited the site to study the terrain and learn what he could from nearby outcrops, cuts, or excavations.

For additional information also see Refs. 57 through 60.

32

Construction Specifications

32.1 Purpose

Construction specifications add to and supplement the contract drawings. They should spell out the quality of the materials to be used, the work which the contractor is to perform, the time schedule for the contract, the basis for compensation, and the procedure for authorized changes to the contract price.

Construction specifications, as a rule, leave the contractor freedom to select his own methods of doing the work, including excavation, design and installation of temporary shoring or bracing, foundation construction, and backfilling.

The specifications spell out the responsibilities of the contractor for performance and for providing protection to the workmen and the public. The owner, engineers, and others are to be protected against claims arising from the contractor's acts (negligent or otherwise) and property damage.

Provision is made for evaluation of claims for delays, authorized changes, and claims for extra work. Several methods may be included such as unit prices, agreed-upon prices, time and material, and—in the event of no agreement—arbitration. Many specifications nominate the engineer as the arbiter of disputes and the interpreter of the intent of the contract documents.

Alternative forms of construction considered by the engineers as potentially economical are included frequently on the drawings and in the specifications. However, specifications seldom make provision for alternates proposed by contractors.

Information concerning soil, water, and rock conditions may be included on the drawings, in other contract documents, or may be included in the specifications.

Where a foundation includes caissons or piles, specifications set forth in detail the basis for pricing that part of the work. The types of piles that may be used, the lengths and resistance to which they shall be driven, permissible tolerances, type of hammer, the class of concrete (if required), methods of depositing concrete, and the criteria for acceptance of the driven piles are presented. Also, if test piles or pile load tests are required, the test program is described.

The specifications should tell the contractor what he is expected to do, the responsibilities he will assume, and the services that the owner will provide. The specifications also try to protect the owner from the contractor's acts and from unreasonable claims.

32.2   Disclosure of Information

It is the professional (and legal) obligation of the engineers to furnish contractors with all the information they have concerning site and soil conditions. Since this information is the property of the owner, the owner must direct the engineer to give all such information to the contractor.

With reference to the soil information, this means all information available in field notes and boring logs must be included. Notes which report, for example, "Lost all water at 26 ft," must not be passed over. Furthermore, if the engineer has reclassified the soil samples to better describe the soils, that fact should be recorded. In addition, the samples and field logs must be preserved and be available for inspection by the contractors.

In many areas of the country, certain general conditions exist which are known to local engineers and contractors, but not necessarily to others. Such latent conditions might be expansive surface soils; caliche or hardpan; an artesian head of water extending several feet above the street level; the probability of encountering gas; two water levels as the result of perched water above the true ground water; or buried shallow peat deposits or old swamps that have been filled over. This kind of information is easily overlooked in writing specifications.

In the case of buildings adjacent to a proposed excavation, all information concerning the depths and dimensions of the building foundations must be furnished. Otherwise, the absence of such information should be plainly stated.

The contractors, however, must make every reasonable investigation themselves of site and soil conditions, and be able to prove that they did investigate them.

Some specifications state that soils information and reports may be inspected at the office of the engineer, or the owner. Frequently jobs are bid and won by contractors who did not come in to look at this information.

The technical sections of specifications may require that the contractor review soil mechanics literature to determine the significance of the soil data presented. For example, where dewatering of a site is required or compaction of soil is necessary, the percentage of fines in the soil, or the shape of the grain size curves helps to assess the feasibility of the work. Also, the specifications should be compared with the appropriate sections of the local building code (where applicable).

The contractor may feel that some provision of the specifications cannot be accomplished without extraordinary methods and expense. He should explain his concern to the engineer and request an interpretation. A more difficult alternate (if he gets the contract) is to demonstrate in the field the difficulties of meeting the specified requirement, and securing a modification.

The last resort in the face of an impossible requirement is to submit a qualified bid. If the bid is low and the engineers can agree legally to consider it, a change may be negotiated.

32.3   Shortcomings in Specifications

It is an unfortunate fact that specification writing is an unpopular chore in most design offices. Some specifications seen by the writers were so inappropriate that one could wonder if the wrong book was sent along with the plans. Usually the specifications are prepared by "borrowing" paragraphs or even chapters from other specifications—prepared years before for other jobs. With scissors and Scotch tape a specification for the job at hand is pasted together. Therefore, many specifications contain contradictions and vague wording, and sometimes important features are not included.

32.4   Conflicts or Impossible Requirements

Specifications sometimes require that piles be driven "to refusal." Without definition, "refusal" is an impossible requirement. Even when defined—such as "until the hammer bounces"—this applies only to single-acting hammers and is insufficient. Refusal must be defined as a specific resistance to penetration, such as "10 blows per inch for at least 6 in. of penetration, using a McKiernan-Terry 10-B-3 hammer operating at the rated speed of 105 blows per minute."

An example of an impossible requirement was an underpinning job involving jacking and cleaning out open-end pipe piles to hard rock, which was overlain by from 8 to 12 in. of broken, somewhat weathered rock. In the cramped quarters there was no practical way to be sure that the weathered rock could be penetrated by the pipes and cleaned out to hard rock. The contractor who undertook the work failed in many cases to meet the requirement; however, the work was accepted, since there was nothing else to do.

In another case, the specifications called for the piles to be driven through a layer of sand and into "hardpan." The driving resistance in hardpan was specified as "50 blows of a 19,500 ft/lb hammer for the last 6 in. of penetration." The successive driving of piles in a group so compacted the sand that the specified driving resistance was reached in many cases before the piles reached hardpan. Jetting was considered impractical because of a 50-ft clay layer above the sand layer. The use of a heavier hammer helped, but caused damage to the piles. It should be noted that wet rotary preexcavation had not been developed at the time the work was done.

To protect a bridge pier from the effects of dredging rock in front of it, a cellular cofferdam fender was designed. Two of the outboard cells were to be sunk about 6 ft into the rock to assure anchorage. (The rock was sandstone, called locally "red shale." Core recoveries were 75% or better.) The specifications stated, "If the steel sheeting cannot be driven to the required grades, the rock is to be excavated, preferably in the dry, and then the sheets are to be driven to grade." Permeable soil over the rock interconnected with the nearby river made excavation in the dry impractical. The cost of bracing the cells, drilling and shooting under water, and excavation—in part by divers —of the broken rock would have cost as much as the rest of the project. The contractor attempted to drill overlapping holes from ground surface to create a slot into which to drive the sheets, but did not go about it the right way. The project ended up in the courts. From a legal point of view, the specifications could have been satisfied, but at a cost which could not be justified.

32.5 Summary

Primary points in this chapter are as follows:

FACTS: Specifications should set forth all the requirements of the work to be performed. They should
also include terms of payment, time allowed for
completion, and provisions for adjustment for
changes in the work and for unanticipated (latent)
soil and water conditions. Sometimes information
essential to the performance of the work may be
omitted. The contractor has an obligation to
undertake a reasonable investigation into soil,
rock, and ground water level conditions beyond
that furnished with the contract documents. The
investigation should extend to structures and
utilities within range of the work. Architects,
engineers, designers, and planners make mistakes
just like anyone else. Contractors should not hesi-
tate to discuss the work with them to gain a complete meeting of the minds as to what is intended.
Any provision impossible to meet or impractical
to perform should be challenged.

WATCH OUT FOR: Specifications, parts of which appear to be "cut out and pasted" from other jobs. Conflicts between the specifications, city building codes, or other ordinances.

References

1. D. R. Lueder, *Aerial Photographic Interpretation*, McGraw-Hill, New York, 1959.
2. *Handbook of Ocean Engineering*, McGraw-Hill, New York, 1949.
3. Gordon Fletcher, "The Standard Penetration Test—Its Uses and Abuses," *Journal of the Soil Mechanics and Foundations Division*, ASCE, Paper 4935, July 1965.
4. K. Terzaghi and R. B. Peck, *Soil Mechanics in Engineering Practice*, 2nd ed., Wiley, New York, 1967.
5. T. R. Dames, "Practical Shear Tests for Foundation Design," *Civil Engineering*, December 1940.
6. RQD stands for rock quality designation and is described in the following publications: (a) Deere, "Technical Description of Rock Cores for Engineering Purposes," *Rock Mechanics and Engineering Geology*, Vol. 1, No. 1, p. 17, 1964. (b) Fairhurst, *Failure and Breakage of Rock*, Port City Press, 1967, p. 249.
7. J. J. Jakosky, *Exploration Geophysics*, Trija, Los Angeles, Calif., 1950.
8. Schultz and Cleaves, *Geology in Engineering*, Wiley, New York, 1955, also Crimins, Samuels, and Monahan, *Construction Rock Work Guide*, Wiley, New York, 1972.
9. Peck, Hanson, and Thornburn, *Foundation Engineering*, Wiley, New York, 1953.
10. D. Taylor, *Soil Mechanics*, Wiley, New York, 1948.
11. Cedeargren, *Seepage, Drainage and Flow Nets*, Wiley, New York, 1967.
12. *Special Procedures for Testing Soil and Rock for Engineering Purposes*, Special Test Publication 479, Committee D-18, ASTM, 1970.
13. *Earth Manual*, United States Department of the Interior, Bureau of Reclamation, 1963.
14. *General Catalog*, Soil Test, Inc., Evanston, Ill.
15. *ASTM Test Designation D1143, American Society for Testing and Materials*, Philadelphia, Pa.

16. *Uniform Building Code,* International Conference of Building Officials, Whittier, Calif., Chap. 29.

17. Wayne C. Teng, *Foundation Design,* Prentice-Hall, Englewood Cliffs, N.J., 1962.

18. G. Leonards, *Foundation Engineering,* McGraw-Hill, New York, 1962.

19. Aerospray 52 Binder is a commercially sold spray-on protection for slopes and faces of excavations. It is sold by American Cynamid Company, Bound Brook, N.J.

20. Peurifoy, *Construction Planning, Equipment and Methods,* 2nd ed., McGraw-Hill, New York, 1970.

21. Byron Prugh, *Construction Dewatering Guide,* in preparation.

22. James D. Parsons, "Foundation Installation Requiring Recharging of Ground Water," *ASCE Construction Journal,* September 1959.

23. Weldon S. Booth, "Tiebacks in Soil," *Civil Engineering,* September 1966.

24. Norman Liver, "Tension Piles and Diagonal Tiebacks," *ASCE Construction Journal,* July 1969.

25. Mansur and Alizaden, *Journal of Soil Mechanics and Foundations Division, ASCE,* March 1970, p. 495.

26. "References on Slurry Trench Excavation," *Western Construction Magazine,* October 1968.

27. Manufacturers of narrow vibrating rollers are Essick Manufacturing Company, Los Angeles, Calif., Vibro plus Products, Inc., Stanhope, N.J., plus others.

28. *Handbook of Drainage and Construction Products, ARMCO Manual,* Middletown, Ohio, 1955, also, *Handbook of Steel Drainage and Highway Construction Products,* American Iron and Steel Institute, New York, 1971.

29. Spangler, *Soil Engineering,* International Textbook Company, Scranton, Pa., 1969.

30. "Compacted Earth Fill for a Power Plant Foundation," *Civil Engineering,* August 1961.

31. "The Distribution of Sulphates in Clay Soils and Groundwater," The Institution of Civil Engineers, Paper 5883, London, England, 1953.

32. Jacob Feld, *Construction Failure,* Wiley, New York, 1968.

33. J. McWhorter and J. Burrage, *Construction Contract Law,* in preparation.

34. William W. Moore, "Experiences with Predetermining Pile Lengths," *ASCE Transactions,* 1949.

35. Robert D. Chellis, *Pile Foundations,* McGraw-Hill, New York, 1961.

36. J. D. Parsons, "Difficulties in the New York Area," *Proceedings ASCE Journal of the Soil Mechanics and Foundation Division,* Vol. 92, pp. 43–64. Nai C. Yang, "Relaxation of Piles in Sand and Organic Silt," *Journal of the Soil Mechanics and Foundation Division,* ASCE, Vol. 96, No. SM21, Proceedings Paper 8123, March 1970, pp. 395–409.

37. *Steel Sheet Piling Design Manual*, U. S. Steel Corporation, Pittsburgh, Pa.

38. M. Romonoff, "Corrosion of Steel Piling in Soils," *Materials Protection*, National Bureau of Standards Monograph 58, Washington, D.C., October 1963.

39. Catalog, *Associated Pile and Fitting Corporation*, Clifton, N.J.

40. J. D. Parsons and Stanley D. Wilson, "Safe Loads on Dog-Leg Piles," *Transactions, ASCE,* Paper 2816, Vol. 121, 1956, p. 695.

41. Catalog No. 92 on Monotube, Union Metal piles, Canton, Ohio.

42. Michael W. O'Neill and Lyman C. Reese, *Journal of the Soil Mechanics and Foundation Division,* ASCE, "Behavior of Bored Piles in Beaumont Clay," Paper 8741, February, 1972.

43. G. G. Meyerhoff, *The Design of Franki Piles,* Symposium on the Design of Pile Foundations, Stockholm, 1960, pp. 105–123; "Compaction of Sands and Bearing Capacity of Piles," *Soil Mechanics and Foundation Division,* ASCE, Vol. 85, SMJ, 1959.

44. Woodward, Gardner, and Greer, *Drilled Pier Foundations,* McGraw-Hill, New York, 1972.

45. E. J. Yoder, *Principles of Pavement Design,* Wiley, New York, 1967.

46. Byron J. Prugh, "Densification of Soils by Explosive Vibrations," *ASCE Construction Journal,* March 1963.

47. D. D. Yoakum, "Winter Construction of Earthwork and Foundations," *Civil Engineering,* August 1967, p. 50.

48. Manufacturers of nuclear soil density testing equipment include: (a) Seaman-Nuclear Corp., Milwaukee; (b) Hydrodensimeter, Middlesex, U.K.; (c) Soil Test, Inc., 2205 Lee Street, Evanston, Ill. 60212.

49. "Landslides and Engineering Practice," Highway Research Board, National Academy of Science, Washington, D.C., Special Report 29, Publication 544, 1958.

50. *ARMCO Manual,* Middletown, Ohio, Chap. 47.

51. Handy and Williams, "Chemical Stabilization of an Active Landslide," *Civil Engineering,* August 1967, p. 62.

52. Prentis and White, *"Underpinning: Practice & Application,"* 2nd rev. ed., Columbia University Press, New York, 1950.

53. Bruce A. Lamberton, "Revetment Construction by Fabriform Process," *ASCE Construction Journal,* July 1969.

54. *Foundation Facts,* Raymond Concrete Pile Division, Houston, Tex., No. 2, 1967; D. J. D'Appolonia, "Effects of Foundation Construction on Nearby Structures," Fourth Pan American Conference.

55. *Soil-Cement Construction Handbook,* Portland Cement Association, New York.

56. See Ref. 33.

57. "Who Pays for the Unexpected in Construction?" *Construction Journal,* ASCE, Committee on Contract Administration, September 1963.

58. William W. Moore, "Who Pays for Unforeseen Subsoil Conditions?" *Civil Engineering.*

59. Prentis and White, "Underpinning," Appendix B, *Legal Aspect of Underpinning and Foundation Work,* out of print. Consult engineernig libraries.

60. G. F. Sowers, "Changed Soil and Rock Conditions in Construction," *ASCE Construction Journal,* November 1971.

List of Illustrations

Subject Index